The FOURTH BOOK of GOOD BOATS

Roger C. Taylor

INTERNATIONAL MARINE PUBLISHING COMPANY
Camden, Maine

Typeset by Journal Publications, Camden, Maine
Printed in the United States

Published by International Marine Publishing Company
21 Elm Street, Camden, Maine 04843
(207) 236-4342

Library of Congress Cataloging in Publication Data

Taylor, Roger C.
Fourth book of good boats.

Includes index.
1. Sailboats. 2. Sailing Ships. I. Title.
II. Title: 4th book of good boats.
VM331.T386 1984 623.8'22 83-18335
ISBN 0-87742-171-4

This book is dedicated to the genius of
Nathanael Greene Herreshoff

On November 16, 1904, he wrote to the Committee responsible for selecting his design for the New York Yacht Club thirty-footers: "They will have a good lot of ballast and I believe, plenty of stability and will be mighty good boats."

Contents

Preface

Here is yet another book of plans of good boats. As you can tell by the title, it is the fourth in a series. The titles of the other three are — and I say "are" advisedly (the advice coming from my publisher), for all three are still in print — *Good Boats, More Good Boats,* and *Still More Good Boats.* These books — and the fourth one is no exception — are made up of articles about good boats that I have written for a number of magazines, and that means I get a certain amount of mail about them from the magazines' readers. That's a nice reward for digging out these good old designs, dusting them off, and presenting them: sailors from all over the place see them, appreciate them, and write me about them.

Sometimes my correspondents correct a statement of fact I have made about a boat (if they correct me in time, before the article sees print in a book, the readers of the book benefit). Sometimes they disagree with an opinion I have expressed about a boat (you'll find I am forever expressing opinions about boats). And sometimes — bless 'em — they simply encourage me to keep going with my little crusade to urge designers, builders, and sailors to involve themselves with good — as opposed to lousy — boats.

A few of my correspondents have tried to help me escape from the corner I painted myself into with the titles of the first three books; I have received several excellent title suggestions for a sequel to *Still More Good Boats.* I apologize to their originators for reverting to a mere numbering system, but at least we have achieved a certain orderliness should my crusade for good boats continue.

In each of the first three books, you were supposed to get 36 good boats; I miscounted in *Still More Good Boats,* and you only got 35. So in Number 4, I cleared the files right out and you get 41.

In case you should be a stranger to my concept of what makes a boat good — and the crusade has yet to reach every corner of the globe — I have included in this volume, as an Introduction, a little essay on the subject providing a fuller definition of a good boat than has heretofore appeared. Doubtless you will see that there are three designs included within these pages that do not fully qualify. The trimaran *Scrimshaw,* the J-24, and the Boston Whaler have been allowed into this select society because, though they are not beautiful or handsome — a prime requisite for the good boat — they are innovative, functional designs that well achieve their purpose. They need no apology, just an explanation.

We writers stick our necks out when we write about a subject like good boats. Readers ask me, "What kind of boat do *you* have?" And, of course, any answer is judged as are the shoes of a cobbler. A reader was once told that a certain tin canoe with orange-pink Styrofoam stuffing and manila fendering on metal outriggers (see Chapter 3) lying at a float in the harbor at Camden, Maine, belonged to me. I heard later that the reader gasped at the news. Yet the tin canoe has the lovely traditional canoe shape, her flotation makes her relatively safe to operate in cold water, and the manila muffles my float neighbors' complaints. And the vessel is nonchalant about snow, neglect, ice, rocky shores, and rough driftwood. Since Chapter 3 was written, she has even brought home a small trawl door salvaged from a wrecked dragger. I wouldn't even be explaining her but for a reader's quite understandable gasp.

I said, back a page or so, that readers benefit from corrections of fact that arrive before book publication. I got hold of a fact just recently, though, well after the publication of *More Good Boats,* that is too important to trust to a possible reprint of that title at some future date. In that book I wrote of the great French pilot cutter *Jolie Brise* and perpetuated the oft-repeated statement that she was modeled, as well as built, by M. Paumelle. Recently Jay Paris, the naval architect of Brunswick, Maine, returned from England, where he had seen the *Jolie Brise* and gammed with her people. He brought the news that the *Jolie Brise* was indeed built by Paumelle, but that she was designed by one Alexandre Pâris. This intelligence drove me skeptically to a newly acquired French book on the pilot boats, *Pilotes: Les Hirondelles de la Manche; Pilotes du Havre* by Pierre-Henri Marin, published in 1981. The following words jumped off one of its pages: "Une bonne partie des dix bateaux-pilotes lancés entre 1893 et 1914 furent dessinés par Émile Galodée, architecte naval notoire, qui forma Alexandre Pâris, le créateur de *Jolie Brise.*" And I learned that the mysterious M. Paumelle did indeed have a first name: Albert. It's satisfying to learn stuff like this, but frustrating to have gotten it wrong in the first place.

A new way of looking at good boats appears in this fourth book: the vicarious voyage. Having for years visualized how various boats would handle and behave at sea by sailing them — in my mind's eye — all over the place in all kinds of weather, I thought why not share some of these sails? So I tried one on the editors of the *National Fisherman* right upstairs, taking the staysail schooner *Quicksilver II* out for a sail on Penobscot Bay. Instead of screaming bloody murder, they printed the thing. I had so much fun writing it, I tried another, this despite a letter from a reader who hadn't caught that the sail was imaginary and wrote how glad he was to learn that the *Quicksilver II* was back on the east coast and being well cared for. Then I got all carried away and wrote about a good boat from the viewpoint of an albatross who chanced upon her in mid-ocean. This was too much for the *National Fisherman* editors, who, after conferring, quite properly came to the conclusion that if they printed *that* one, a lot of commercial fishermen would think they (the editors) had lost it and would cancel their subscriptions. So I took out the albatross. For some reason we expect you book readers — commercial fishermen or not — to be tolerant of such whimsy, so in Chapter 20 the big Winslow schooner has again picked up her following albatross.

Imaginary sailing is not only fun, but also useful, if backed by enough sea experience to make it realistic. I urge you to take imaginary sails in any boats that interest you. Maybe the boat exists only on paper and you are thinking of building her. Sail her first. Maybe the boat exists in three dimensions and you are tempted to buy her or go voyaging in her. If you can "really" sail her, by all means do so (there are some "real" sails in this book too), but if not, take her out on trials in your mind's eye. It's a good chance to see how she likes heavy weather.

By far the greatest reward I get for writing about good boats — and it is, I think, an unusual reward for a mere writer — is to learn of good boats being built to the designs I have dusted off. Jim Crawford of Easton, Maryland, gave me tremendous satisfaction when he wrote that the Hand double-ended schooner in *Still More Good Boats* had caught his eye and he just had to have her built. She has been launched as the *Simplicity* and Jim is pleased with her. Last summer I saw a new *Fundulus,* from *Good Boats,* another Hand design, anchored in a Maine harbor looking just grand. Just the other day I received the accompanying invitation to the launching at Freiburg on the Elbe River of the *Johann Ehlers,* built to Fenwick Williams' design of the *Gloucesterman,* which her owner, Dr. Detlef Zschoche, had spotted on the pages of *More Good Boats.*

There have been several starts on building the 50-foot Cogge ketch, the first good boat I wrote about for the now-defunct *Skipper* magazine in 1968, and the vessel in Chapter 1 of *Good Boats.* All save one seem to have been abortive, but the Cogge ketch taking shape in the Pacific Northwest seems to be really becoming a vessel and will probably be finished and launched. Now *that* will be something. The Cogge ketch is my favorite, romantic design, the one I'd choose above all the rest.

I want to say thank you to a number of people who have made this book possible. First, of course, thanks to the designers whose plans grace these pages. Thanks to the builders who fashioned good boats from many of

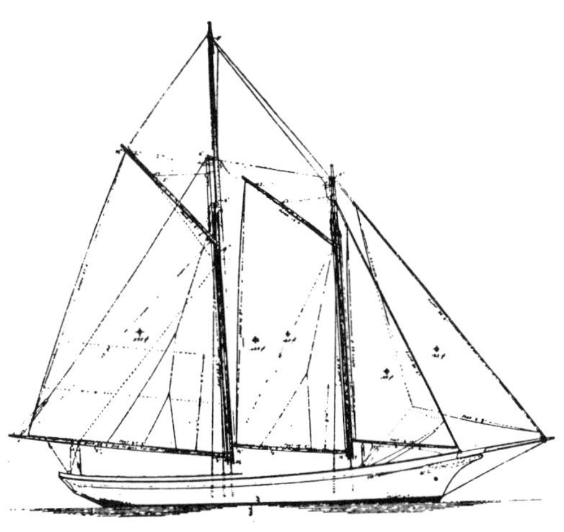

Johann Ehlers

Taufe und Stapellauf am 11. Juni 1983

Bau-Nr. 3051 der Schiffswerft Heinrich Hatecke & Sohn, Freiburg/Elbe

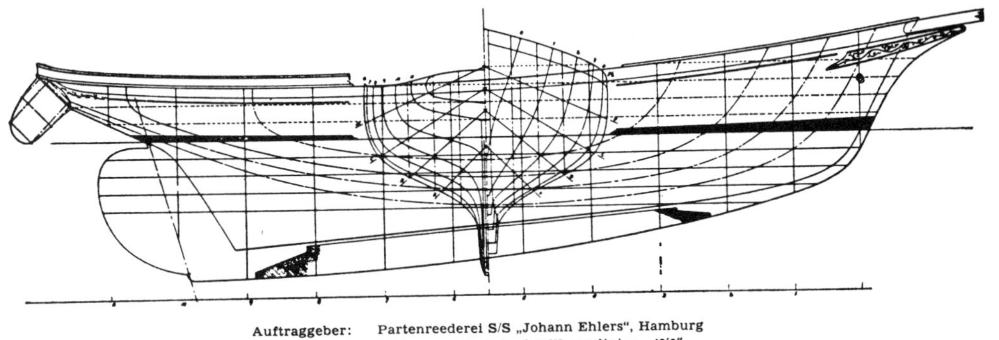

Auftraggeber:	Partenreederei S/S „Johann Ehlers“, Hamburg		
Länge an Deck:	51′6″	Länge in der Wasserlinie:	42′6″
Größte Breite:	14′0″	Größter Tiefgang:	8′0″
Verdrängung:	31,5 ts	Außenballast:	7,5 ts
Segelfläche:	1.721 sq.ft.	(Groß: 595 sq.ft./Schonersegel: 365 sq.ft./ Baumfock: 168 sq.ft./Außenklüver: 192 sq.ft./ Groß-Top-Segel: 155 sq.ft./Fisherman-Stagsegel: 246 sq.ft.)	
Hilfsmaschine:	M.A.N.-6-Zylinder-Dieselmotor, 110 PS/2.800 rpm		
Klasse:	Germanischer Lloyd + 100 A4 Große Küstenfahrt		

Die Schiffswerft Heinrich Hatecke & Sohn

Inh. Jürgen Hatecke

und

die Brüder Ekkehart & Detlef Zschoche

freuen sich

Mr. Roger C. Taylor

zu dem am Sonnabend, dem 11. Juni 1983 stattfindenden Stapellauf

des unter der Bau-Nr. 3051 gebauten Segelschiffes

„JOHANN EHLERS“

einzuladen.

Die Taufe findet statt um 15.30 Uhr auf der Werft in Freiburg, Am Bassin 1.

the plans. Thanks to owners who let me sail their boats. Thanks to interested readers who corrected or added to the magazine articles. Thanks to the editors of the *National Fisherman, The Small Boat Journal, WoodenBoat,* and *Nautical Quarterly* for printing the articles. Thanks to Pat Feener for listening to all the dictation and typing it. Thanks to Barbara Castle Johnson for keeping my prose from being *too* idiomatic. Thanks to everyone who loaned plans and photographs. Thanks to Nan Kulikauskas for making the most of them.

Many designs for good boats still wait to be dusted off, brought out, admired, built to, and sailed. Let's keep dredging them out of the libraries and museums. Let's make good boats drive out lousy boats.

Roger C. Taylor
Camden, Maine

The FOURTH BOOK of GOOD BOATS

Introduction — What is a Good Boat?

A good boat is *handsome* and *able*. Old words. Words you seldom see used in magazine advertisements for new boats. What do they mean?

The aesthetics of boat design are subjective, of course, beauty being in the eye of the beholder. Yet some boats never fail to attract admiring glances while others go unnoticed. A general sense of harmony about a vessel seems to be much more responsible for good looks than is any particular shape. There are handsome boats whose hulls are full of curves and handsome boats with straight stems and hard chines, but there never was a handsome boat with a ponderous bow and dainty stern, or vice versa. High freeboard is almost as quick a way to rob a boat of her good looks as is a flat sheer. Bow profile and transom shape are critical.

You know beauty when you see it. Accept only the genuine article.

An able boat can carry out the mission for which she was designed. She may be suited just for local conditions of sea and wind, or she may be ready to put to sea and try her luck against whatever Old Ocean has in store for her.

If a vessel is to go offshore, seaworthiness, easy motion in rough weather, weatherliness (the ability to make something to windward in frightful conditions when she closes with a coast), and carrying capacity will be important. If she is to cruise coastwise, speed under sail — especially to windward — becomes important.

An easy motion in rough water is the hallmark of a good boat. If it weren't for the joy of a boat's motion in the waves, there would be little point in going afloat for pleasure; might as well watch them from the safety of the shore. But that joy can be turned quickly to sorrow by pounding or a quick snap at the end of a roll. When judging the lines of a boat, visualize her motion at all reasonable angles of heel. And think of her in a big following sea; will she be pooped easily? Is her bow buoyant enough so she won't root? Is it sea-fendy enough to cope with a big head sea?

A good boat is steady on her helm. She steers like a well-trained thoroughbred, not like a just-broken range pony.

A good boat should seem fast to her owner. Be the captain's expectations of speed great or small, if speed is disappointing, then the boat is not good. I like to think in terms of the average lifetime speed of a boat. Most boats seem to do quite well off the wind in a fresh breeze and flat sea. When judging the speed of a boat, also visualize her struggling to windward in a light air and leftover bobble of a seaway.

Any hull material that will keep out water is all right by me. Wood has its spirit, its texture — and its seams.

Fiberglass has it wholeness, its smoothness — and its sterility. Steel has its strength, its simplicity — and its drips.

A good boat is appropriately rigged. She may have one sail or twelve, but the rig must not be wrong for the hull or for the vessel's purpose. Rigs should be as generous as the crew can handle, divided no more than necessary toward the same objective, and be as long and low as expectations of beating to windward will allow. It's good to be able to set plenty of sail, have no sail quite big enough to take charge of the crew, and enjoy the many advantages of the low, long rig commensurate with patience in working to windward. The running rigging in a good boat can be worked reasonably easily by human beings of mediocre strength.

Good boats don't have to have bowsprits, but a bowsprit is a grand contrivance in a boat.

Good boats don't have to be engineless, but the pace of life in an engineless boat is a wonderful thing. If a good boat does have an engine, it must be accessible.

A good boat ought to have a comfortable cockpit. You can sleep and eat in the darnedest places, but the cockpit is where you stand watch.

A good boat has good visibility in all directions from the helm and plenty of deck space from which to work the vessel. Since she has a pleasing shape and a nice motion, it's fine if from the helm you can see the rail all the way round the vessel without any obstruction from superstructure, so you can enjoy these good things to the fullest.

Down below, a good boat ought to have a place to sit to leeward on either tack, some secluded bunks for the watch below during the day, and a galley that is not too far forward. Deckhouses, chart tables, and great cabins in the stern are just fine.

So there are many features that a good boat ought to have. Combining these features into a harmonious structure is the yacht designer's great challenge. If he can create a structure whose looks will turn heads and perhaps trigger the word handsome and whose reaction to wave and wind may earn her a reputation for being able, then he will have designed a good boat.

1/ The Skiff

October 15, 1961, happened to be the day when I found out what sort of a little sailing skiff I had on my hands. It was near the end of my second season with her. I thought she was quite quick in coming to the point.

The message the little boat gave me that day was, "The unreasonable I can handle, but don't expect the impossible." It was blowing a small gale from the northwest, straight down the South River on the western shore of Chesapeake Bay. I rowed out of our fully protected cove and, as usual, tied up at the outside dock at the mouth of Little Aberdeen Creek. We were still well under the lee of Ferry Point. Tied the reef in the sail and sailed out into the strength of the wind. Reached across the river to Glebe Creek, leaning out over the weather rail and getting an occasional tailful of cold water. Made the shelter of the creek all right, beat up to its head in fluky going, and ran back down. Found that the wind had increased plenty more on the river as I put her up full and by on the port tack to fetch back across to my dock. (I later heard it was blowing around 50 along about then.) She didn't get quite overpowered, but a lot of times when she dove into a trough a couple of bucketfuls of water would wash in over the lee coaming. I was afraid that if I let the sheet run and stopped to bail I'd never get her going again without tipping her over when I started filling the sail again without steerageway.

There seemed to be nothing for it but to hang on and hope for the best. A third of the way across the river she was half full of water. This mathematical relationship gradually forced its way into my numb brain, and I realized I had to do something different to avoid swamping. With my heart in my mouth, I put her about. Managed to get her going and heading off a bit on the other tack to reach back into the protection of Glebe Creek. Took in sail and thought to row to the windward side of the creek to bail out and take stock. Could make nothing to windward. Saw that the shoal off Cedar Point on the leeward side of the creek was being kept calm by its thick Sargasso Sea of weeds. Rowed gratefully down to this lee shore (!) and put her right into the grasp of the weeds, which held her quietly. Bailed out and got generally reorganized.

With the boat dry, I found I could just row her to windward. Worked across Glebe Creek and fought up along the South River shore far enough to make it a beam reach back to Little Aberdeen. Then she went scalding home, and I was mighty proud of her, even if she couldn't sail to windward that day. Some powerful, able little vessel, I thought, for an 11-footer.

I am ashamed to admit that I don't know any other dimensions of my little skiff. I never even measured her, much less took off her lines. I always meant to do this,

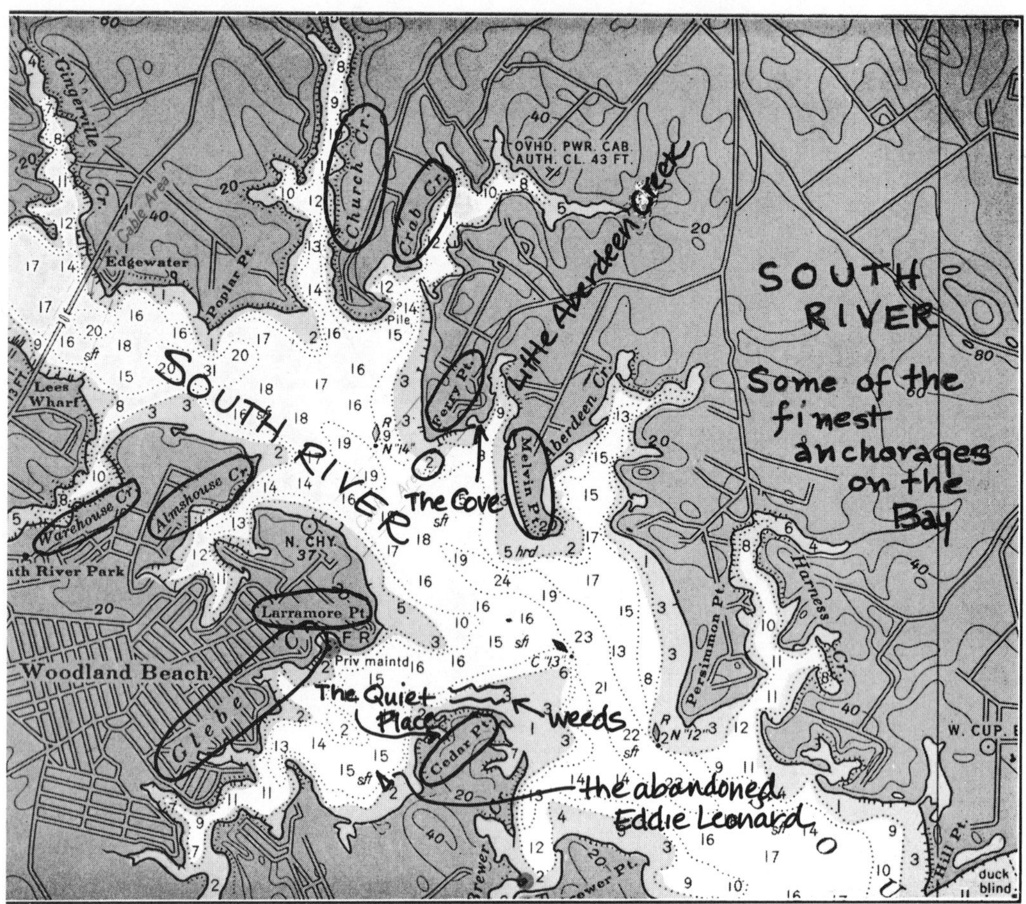

The "cruising grounds" of my nice little sailing skiff. (A Cruising Guide to the Chesapeake *by William T. Stone and Fessenden S. Blanchard)*

but kept procrastinating, and then, after I'd had her ten years, she was sold quite suddenly in a deal with a bigger boat.

I got the skiff at the Eastport Marina in . . . I almost said Annapolis, but of course it was in Eastport. In Annapolis, they say "you-all," but across the bridge in Eastport they say, "all-of-you," and you'd better not confuse the two places.

The Eastport Marina should have been photographed before bulldozers leveled it to make way for "progress." It was the most ramshackle, down-at-the-heels, fascinating boatyard I was ever in. I wish I had an inventory of the place on any given day. It would make a great book.

Part of the inventory, on most days, would include Big John and Little Eddie. Big John seemed to run the place — at least he was always holding forth in the shop. He had a Ph.D. in physics, but it was people that fascinated him. He'd talk all day with you about boats, on which subject he was always eager to learn; or about anything else, on which subject he was always eager to teach.

Little Eddie did most of what work got done around the place. He was so relaxed he once fell asleep in a bosun's chair while working aloft. There was nobody to yell at him, so he survived.

Anyway, one day I was prowling around this emporium, looking for a small boat. I saw a forlorn little skiff hauled up on the shore, sandwiched in amongst all manner of useful marine artifacts. The more I walked round this little skiff, staring at her, the more I liked her shape.

I went up to the shop to see what was what. It took Big John about an hour to tell me that she wasn't for sale, but that her sistership was. Big John said they were building her sistership right in the next shed, and, sure enough, there was Little Eddie working away on a duplicate. She wasn't far from finished. It took me a lot less than an hour to arrange to be the person for whom this new little skiff was being built.

The original boat was named the *Tardy*. She had a sailing rig to her. She was supposed to be fifty years old. She had been left behind by the owner of a big motor-sailer "from up north" in part payment for a yard bill. I was glad the guy had run out of money.

Big John had ambitions for Little Eddie to build a whole class of these nice little skiffs; he was already talking about the fun everybody was going to have racing them on the creek. Little Eddie did start another one, but he never finished her.

I liked this skiff's design, for it looked to me like a good compromise for both rowing and sailing. She seemed to have enough rocker at the stern so she'd row well, but not so much as to lose too much bearing aft for sailing. Her rather high, flaring sides (for such a little skiff) I thought would make her stiff and able for sailing, yet were not so high as to make her hard to row to windward or cranky to maneuver under oars in a breeze. Whatever else I thought of her, I knew I was in love with her springy sheerline.

The skiff had a wide plank outside keel and the normal skeg. The construction of the bottom worried me. It was fashioned from a single sheet of Beaverboard, to be sure, finished hard on both sides. It took Big John another hour to muster enough physics and engineering terminology to explain that the stuff was not soluble in water. (At least I think that was the gist of it.) I was younger then, and figured nobody with a Ph.D. in physics would allow to be built, right under his nose, a skiff with a bottom that didn't agree with salt water. The stuff was only quarter-inch, but it certainly seemed strong enough. Big John thought it was the greatest. (After ten years, this bottom material was good as new. The skiff never leaked a drop.)

Her sides were thick pine with a single lap. She had narrow, one-plank side decks and a short foredeck with a single beam just abaft the mast hole. This little decking didn't close her in too much, yet it was just enough to keep the water out when she was sailing rail down. It also gave the boat a much more finished look than that of a totally open skiff.

The decking was edged with a tiny strip of coaming. It was too tiny. It was always splitting and breaking off, and I got so I kept a pretty fair run of coaming-size stock on hand so I could nail on a new piece every other thing. Never did get around to replacing this coaming with something bigger. It looked to be the right scale, but it just couldn't survive accidental kicks and oar bangs.

She had a nice, big stern seat, a midships thwart, and a short trunk for a daggerboard. There were two big floorboard gratings with an opening between them under the midships thwart so you could dry her out with a rag.

We used the boat under oars during her first summer, as much as a swimming tender as anything else. We did take one good, long sail in her (out into the bay, around an anchored and obviously suspicious USS *Hanks,* DD-702, and back), using for the occasion the borrowed rig of the *Tardy*. It seemed just about right for her, so I planned to duplicate it closely.

Years before, we had changed rigs in a 15-foot knockabout, and it was the old rig from that boat that I cut down for a mast and boom for the skiff. I didn't really think it was going to work, but that was all I had.

Running off, pre-sailing board, thus cramped and uncomfortable in the bottom of the boat instead of comfortably ensconced on a movable seat. (David Q. Scott)

The skiff ready to tend the skipjack. (Robert de Gast)

The mast was solid, and, I thought, much too heavy for the little boat. Not at all. I was amazed at how stiff she was with that big, heavy stick right up in the eyes of her.

The only standing rigging was a wire headstay set up to the stemhead with a rope tail.

When ordering the sail, I said I wanted a single fairly deep reef in it. The sailmaker thought a reef in such a tiny sail was ridiculous. Somehow, we ended up in an absurd compromise: he would put the reef in the sail, but would make it a shallow one.

For running rigging, I used the smallest Dacron I thought I could hang onto and ran it through some nice big (for this little boat) wooden blocks. The destroyer in which I had served once called at Genoa. The port has a great waterfront to explore. In a chandlery, I saw four fine wooden blocks. The only metal on them was the pins. At eight lire apiece, I couldn't resist and I smuggled them into my locker on board ship so as to avoid any derisive comments from midwestern shipmates. I knew, of course, that seven years later I would need those blocks to rig up this little skiff. I used two for the mainsheet, one at the masthead for the halyard, and one at the foot of the mast to lead the halyard aft, so I could reach it without going forward.

To belay the mainsheet, I cut a broomstick-size hole through the fore-and-aft support under the center of the midships thwart, the hole being near the after side of this vertical piece. With about seven inches of broomstick driven in there, I had a nice hefty place to belay the sheet when under oars with the sail stowed or when the boat was tied up. It was also very satisfactory to take one turn with the sheet around the lee end of the broomstick, making just enough friction so the sheet was easy to hold in a breeze, yet could be eased quickly. Another broomstick driven through the after edge of the midships thwart over next to the port side of the boat made a handy place to belay the halyard and hang the coil.

I held the luff of the sail to the mast with a nice little set of wooden hoops saved from a previous generation. All I know is they came out of my father's boathouse. I laced the foot of the sail to the boom. The sail was left bent on all the time and just barely lasted ten years in the hot Maryland sun.

Of course, I rigged a topping lift. It dead-ended at the masthead, led down through a screw eye on the end of the boom, and came in to belay at a cleat on the boom. I'd top the boom way up high out of the way when rowing and would leave it up there when the boat was tied up, so I could jump in and row off without having to fiddle with anything.

I hate booms that bang you on the head in a little boat and so took great glee in putting the gooseneck up where I wanted it. Then I thought I had overdone it a bit — it almost looked silly — so I dropped the gooseneck back down about three inches.

At first she was all out of balance, but the mast hole was plenty big, so I could change the rake of the mast quite a bit. Finally got it just right, cut some permanent oak wedges to hold it there, and even numbered them so that the following spring I could pretend I remembered what I was doing.

During her first summer under sail, the skiff suffered from appendages that were too short. The centerboard didn't have enough depth to make her really hang on going to windward, the rudder needed more depth to assist with lateral plane, and the tiller was too short to be reached from up in the boat when sailing single-handed.

The next year she came out on the river with all these appendages bigger. Now she started to come into her own and proved to be quite a fast sailer. She never was much good at going to windward in a light air if there was much bobble. She'd bob and slap, jump the wind out of her sail, and stop as if to remember what it was she was supposed to be doing. She was fast to windward in a breeze, though. On the Fourth of July that first year with the deep centerboard and rudder, we beat a 25-foot skipjack to windward in a fresh breeze. But then the skipjack couldn't have been very well sailed.

She reached and ran just like a little fool and didn't seem to mind how hard or gently it was blowing once you gave her her head. She could sure scamper off to leeward.

She'd heave-to with great docility by simply letting the sheet run, bringing her up with the wind three or four points on the bow, and gradually putting the helm all the way down as she stopped. Then she'd sit there flapping along, making a tiny bit of headway, and slowly drifting off to leeward. Even in a strong breeze, she was perfectly content and would let you bail her out or pull on a sweater.

She could be overpowered going to windward in a strong breeze. You had to luff so much of the sail to keep her upright that she'd lose almost all her headway. Then you just had to wait till it eased up so you could get her going again.

To trim her properly in light going or when running off, you had to sit down in the bottom of the boat between the stern seat and the midships thwart with your weight a little to leeward. In this position you had nothing to lean back against, and your arm was all cramped up steering. I hate to think how many hours I suffered sailing in this uncomfortable position; this was before I had discovered the sailing board.

I told you all about the sailing board in *Still More Good Boats* (pages 277, 278), and I can't for the life of me understand why you haven't either: (a) Written me hundreds of pointing-and-laughing letters telling me how funny you think it is that I just discovered this device when everybody else in the world has known about it all along; or (b) Formed a committee to award me some sort of prize for coming up with the boating invention of the millennium.

It's all right, though. I've been cramped and uncomfortable sitting in the bottoms of little sailboats for forty years. No more. I now span my sailing board between the seats, adjust it to precisely where I want my weight in the boat, and then take my luxurious ease.

This nice little skiff rowed beautifully. I had some big, heavy, galvanized circular oarlocks for her and a pair of commonplace, heavy, six-foot ash oars, no leathers or anything. They balanced perfectly and she pulled along smoothly and swiftly in calm water. If you really pulled hard for a bit, you could pull up a big, long, smooth stern wave, and felt you were really flying. Going to windward in a slop, she would slap and thrash around a bit, but if you had any distance to go in such conditions, you would make sail. She was one of the most maneuverable boats I have ever known under sail, oar, or oar-used-as-paddle.

Because the boat was kept in a little circular cove protected from river and creek by a narrow strip of beach, this body of water being all of 50 yards from the back door, and because the boat could be gotten underway under oar or sail almost instantly, I used her more than I have used any boat. If there was a breeze when I got home from work, I'd walk in the front door, shed coat and tie on my way through the house, go out the back door, and be underway within five minutes of shutting the car door. In a southerly, I'd row out of the cove, tie up at the outside dock, make sail, and be off, putting her on a fast close reach across the river. She'd usually fetch to about Larrimore Point. I'd keep her going right in to the shore, spin her round onto the other tack at the last second, and broad reach home, admiring the sunset over the stern. Sail into the cove, tie up, furl up, and be on time for supper.

I'd do almost the same thing if the breeze were northerly: sail out of the cove, pick up the breeze, and fetch probably to Almshouse Creek on the starboard tack. Reach home, tie up outside, furl up, and row in.

On a day off, with the wind in the south, I'd beat way down the South River, maybe to Turkey Point, and run back. If the wind were north, I'd work her up to the head of one of the creeks upriver, like Warehouse, Church, or Crab. It was a test of patience to see if you could keep the oars stowed all the way up a long twisty creek from whose high shores the wind might come in any direction or in no direction.

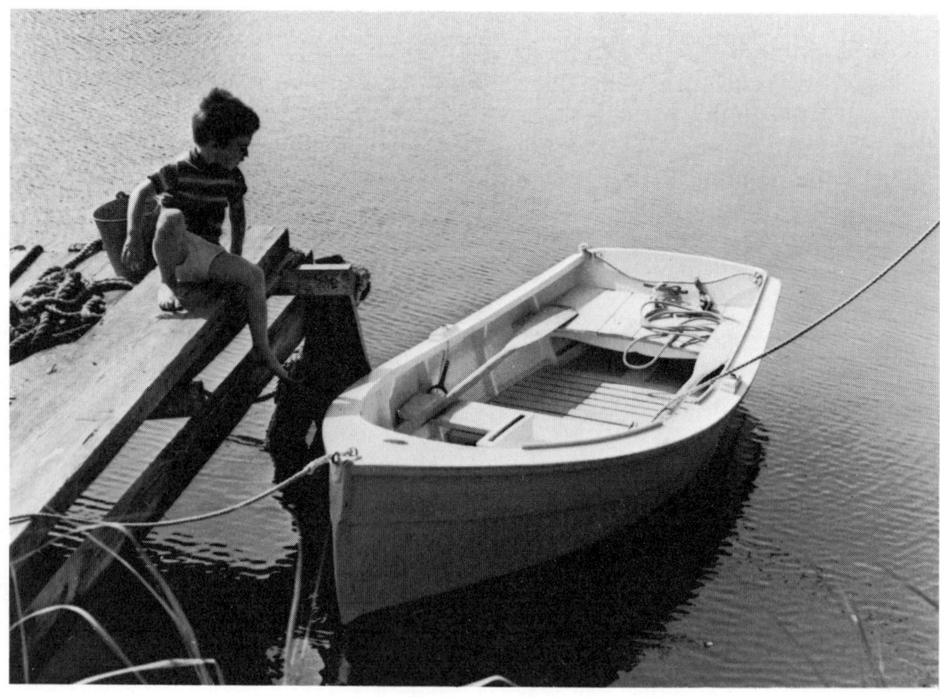

The skiff was a favorite with the children.

Some days I'd even get up early and go sailing before breakfast. I'd generally head across the river so as to get a better view of the sunrise.

Maybe the best times were when I got home after working late in the evening and there was a breeze and a moon. Going to windward in just the right breeze, I'd sit in the bottom of the boat leaning back against the weather side (her flare made that just right) and she'd roar along with her rail just down. Sail like that into the path of the moon and you've got something going for you. For one thing, you'd swear she's going about 20 knots. Out there on the river in the wee small hours, you had the whole world to yourself.

That's when the secret of the universe would be revealed. You couldn't remember what it was next morning, but you knew that the next time you caught the moon and the breeze that way again, there'd be another revelation.

You learned a few tricks doing all this sailing around. To keep your centerboard out of the weeds on various far-ranging shoals, you'd memorize a range to keep you clear. There's a big shoal on the south side of Ferry Point just west of our outside dock. Going out into the river you can see to skirt the edge of it, but coming back from across the river you want to end up just off the shoal's edge without having to change course. To accomplish this navigational feat, all you need do is keep the right-hand light pole on the end of Jim Glose's dock on the ridgepole of the yellow cottage with the red roof up the creek.

When making or stowing sail at the outside dock, I'd tie up by taking the end of the painter around a piling and bringing it back on board to belay. Then when I cast off, I didn't have to leave the boat: just let go the end and pull the painter back on board around the piling. It saved ten or fifteen seconds when I'd be in a hurry to get underway.

Happy was the day I discovered that the skiff could execute a North River jibe perfectly every time no matter how hard it was blowing. Yes, it was I who introduced the North River jibe to the South River. The natives were amazed and delighted. The North River jibe is where you slam the boat right into a jibe with the sheet full out as if you didn't know any better or were trying to destroy her, and then keep her spinning so fast that by the time the boom swings over, the wind is so far forward that instead of the boom's fetching up on its sheet with a jarring crash, it mushes into a cushion of new-found headwind like a prizefighter punching cotton candy. Then you immediately head right back off on the new tack, having made a fast S-turn that wouldn't harm a cargo of Ming vases. Of course you do this with studied nonchalance, letting the boom just miss your head so that any onlookers will be confused as to whether you are lucky or good.

I got so I could come roaring into the creek in a fresh

southerly, make a North River jibe around the corner of the outside dock so close aboard I scared myself, run through the narrow cut into the cove, round up off the end of the inside dock, and be all furled up and tidy by the time she drifted in to her berth. You don't have this kind of fun if you get underway only once a week.

The place the children liked to go best in the skiff was the cove behind Cedar Point across the river. Dean, in particular, would say, "Let's go to 'the quiet place.' " To get in there you have to pass close by the upended roots of a fallen submerged tree that show except on a very high tide. Once inside, you're landlocked. The wind soughs in the pines up on the bluff overhead, and right up at the head of the place, where it gets all swampy and jungly, the sounds of the birds defy sorting. We used to just let her drift in there for an hour at a time.

Once Dean and I took a camping trip in the skiff over to Cedar Point. We loaded a tent on board and set off after supper. It was drizzling, and we had to beat over. We beached the boat, set up the tent, and snuggled in for the night. Rain comes right down steady. Pretty soon we're all afloat. No ditch around tent and ground cloth extends out beyond the roof. Some campers! Given the square footage of material we had to work with, there was no way we could have trapped more water. Bailed out and settled down soggily. Woke at dawn, found rain had stopped, so walked down to the beach for a look around. Just starting to get light in the east. Watch says midnight. Must be the glow from the great city of Annapolis. We stuck it out till breakfast time and then sailed home.

A rather decrepit-looking skipjack sailed out of Glebe Creek one day and started slowly beating down the river. I made sail in the skiff and gave chase, catching up easily with what turned out to be the *Eddie Leonard*. I quote the log for January 7, 1967 (yes, I kept a log for this little skiff): "Tacked behind her and caught up easily to weather of her, as her board wasn't down far enough, and she was making considerable leeway. Off Melvin Point, they put the wheel up, but without letting the jib go, she wouldn't go about. I asked if they were having trouble getting her around, and the fellow at the wheel nodded. I suggested they slack the jib. They did and got her around. One fellow said to another, 'Hey, he must know what he's talking about.' The fellow at the helm asked me to 'come aboard and help us sail her.' I came up astern and dropped the sail, made fast to a speedboat they were towing, and went aboard. She was falling apart all over, holes in the deck, holes in the sails. We eased the sheets and filled her away to get her going, then worked her to windward down the river. I was going to suggest slacking the main lazyjacks, set up taut and fouling the sail, but then was afraid to put the weight of the boom on the sail. That she would go at all was a wonder. Dropped off, set sail, and ran back up the river and into the cove. Tied up at 1700. The *Eddie Leonard* came back into Glebe Creek, but without benefit of slacking the sheets off the wind. So ends an adventurous little sail."

The *Eddie Leonard* fell on hard times and was eventually abandoned, aground, on the south side of Glebe Creek. Somehow, the poor old vessel held a fascination for me, and I would find myself making her an objective when sailing. I'd sail over to her, go round the lonely vessel, and sail home. Once I did that in a light breeze and as I was sailing away from her the thought struck me what a wonderful study she'd make for Andrew Wyeth. As I looked back at her again, the breeze stirred a bit more, and suddenly a long lazyjack, hanging loose from high on the mast, swung out in a graceful arc just like the curtains in the third floor window of the Olson house in Wyeth's painting *Wind from the Sea.*

After a few years, I put the skiff on the schedule of the Chesapeake Bay workboats, keeping her in commission through the winter and hauling out to paint in the summer. This regimen increased the use of the vessel markedly. Of course some winter weather was a bit too much for her, or, more likely, for me.

On January 23, 1966, I went for a late afternoon sail. "Clear and cold, blowing a gale from northwest. Underway from the skipjack [by this time we had our own skipjack and kept her in the cove in the winter] at 1700, intending to sail in the creek. Ran out of the cove. Took a heavy puff in the entrance, let go the sheet, and two parts of it unrove. The sail streamed out ahead, fortunately not carrying away the gooseneck. Trimmed sail in and ran ashore on McGee's Point, raising board as she went in. Jumped ashore and made the painter fast to a tree. Took in the sail, rerove the sheet and tied in a reef, intending to continue the sail. A few more heavy blasts undid this intention. Shook reef, furled sail, and rowed back into the cove to tie up. A short, but instructive sail."

The skiff just fit the stern davits on our skipjack, so of course we assigned her the duty of tender to the big vessel. I put in hoisting eyes. The forward fall led down through the mast hole to a big lag screw eye in the keel and the after fall hooked to the eye in a big galvanized cleat bolted through the transom. When the skiff was hoisted out, her mast, with boom and sail lashed up along it, went across the strongback atop the davits. Everything about the skiff went with the skipjack; the two boats seemed to get on well together.

My wife and children used the skiff more than any other boat in the family. Most of the boats I take up with they think are too cramped and tippy, but they didn't feel that way about this nice little skiff (or about the skipjack either, for that matter). The weight of two adults and a child turned out to be just too much for the skiff, making her somewhat tender and sluggish. She was generally at her best as a two-people boat or singlehander.

She was a fine training vessel for our four children. They often went out with me rowing or sailing, and I think they got their feeling for boats in this one. When we first sailed up the river in the skipjack, my son Roger rowed the skiff a long way down to meet us. Dean's first frustrating attempts to row made him laugh so hard he used to fall off the seat. When Rebecca bailed the skiff, she said she was "giving the water back," since "we don't need it." Stephen first went out in the skiff three days after his second birthday.

The last sail I logged for this skiff was on February 9, 1968. "Underway at 1400 under oars. Strong breeze from northwest. Set reefed sail outside. Stood full and by to far shore of the river. Considerable spray on board. Tacked, hove-to, bailed out. Filled away and smoked home on a reach. Dropped sail outside and rowed in." Typical.

I had more fun with this little skiff than with any other boat. Yes, more fun with this little skiff even than with the *Aria,* a 32-foot thoroughbred created by Nathanael G. Herreshoff. I'm not saying the little skiff has more greatness as a boat than the big Herreshoff, just that I had more fun with the skiff. Or am I?

2/ The *Sir Nigel*

Length: 12 feet
Beam: 4 feet 6 inches
Draft: 1 foot 7 inches
Sail area: 100 square feet
Displacement: 900 pounds
Designer: Donald V. Hotchkiss

Donald V. Hotchkiss treated the readers of the great British magazine *Yachting and Boating Monthly* to a two-part article — published in the November and December 1908 issues — on how to build a 12-foot sailing dinghy he had designed. Mr. Hotchkiss was trying to combine good sailing and rowing qualities in a boat that would be small and handy enough to be a good beach boat. I think he succeeded.

"There can, perhaps, be no alarming departure from historic design in the case of a dinghy," Hotchkiss began his first article, "yet as Dan Leno* said, 'There are eggs and *eggs*.' " Well, yes, and this egg has a shell of gentle curves. She's a handsome little boat, isn't she?

I like her lively sheer, hollow entry, and slightly raked wineglass transom. She's stiff, for she's quite beamy, and she picks up bearing all round her waterline as she heels. She has considerable bearing aft without too much drag. When upright, this boat has very little to her underwater, so she'd have a good turn of speed. You'd want to shift your weight to keep her trimmed as nearly level as you could.

Mr. Hotchkiss named his dinghy the *Sir Nigel;* she could be no more British if she had a Union Jack painted on her side.

The little vessel is 12 feet long, with a beam of 4 feet 6 inches, and a hull depth of 1 foot 7 inches.

Her sail area is a generous 100 square feet, and she needs it, for at the load waterline shown on the lines plan she is displacing nearly 900 pounds. Surely her carvel-planked hull, stout though it is, couldn't weigh over 400 pounds, so she is shown carrying some quarter-ton of people and gear. So loaded, she is drawing less than a foot with her centerboard up.

When I first saw this design, I thought immediately of the dinghy *Swallow* in Arthur Ransome's wonderful story *Swallows and Amazons.* That was a fictional reminiscence involving great adventures of youngsters camp-cruising on Coniston Water in England's Lake District. *Sir Nigel* would have fit right in.

I open *Swallows and Amazons* at random, and this is the first paragraph I read: "John and Roger ran to the harbour, cast off *Swallow*'s [or *Sir Nigel*'s] moorings, and scrambled in. John stepped the mast, paddled her out through the narrows, and then began rowing as soon as there was room to use the oars. You can't do much sculling over the stern against a southwest wind. He rowed round to the landing-place. Susan and Titty

*Thanks to Bob Bush of Williamsburg, Virginia, I can tell you that Mr. Leno was "an eminent British music hall comedian at the turn of the century."

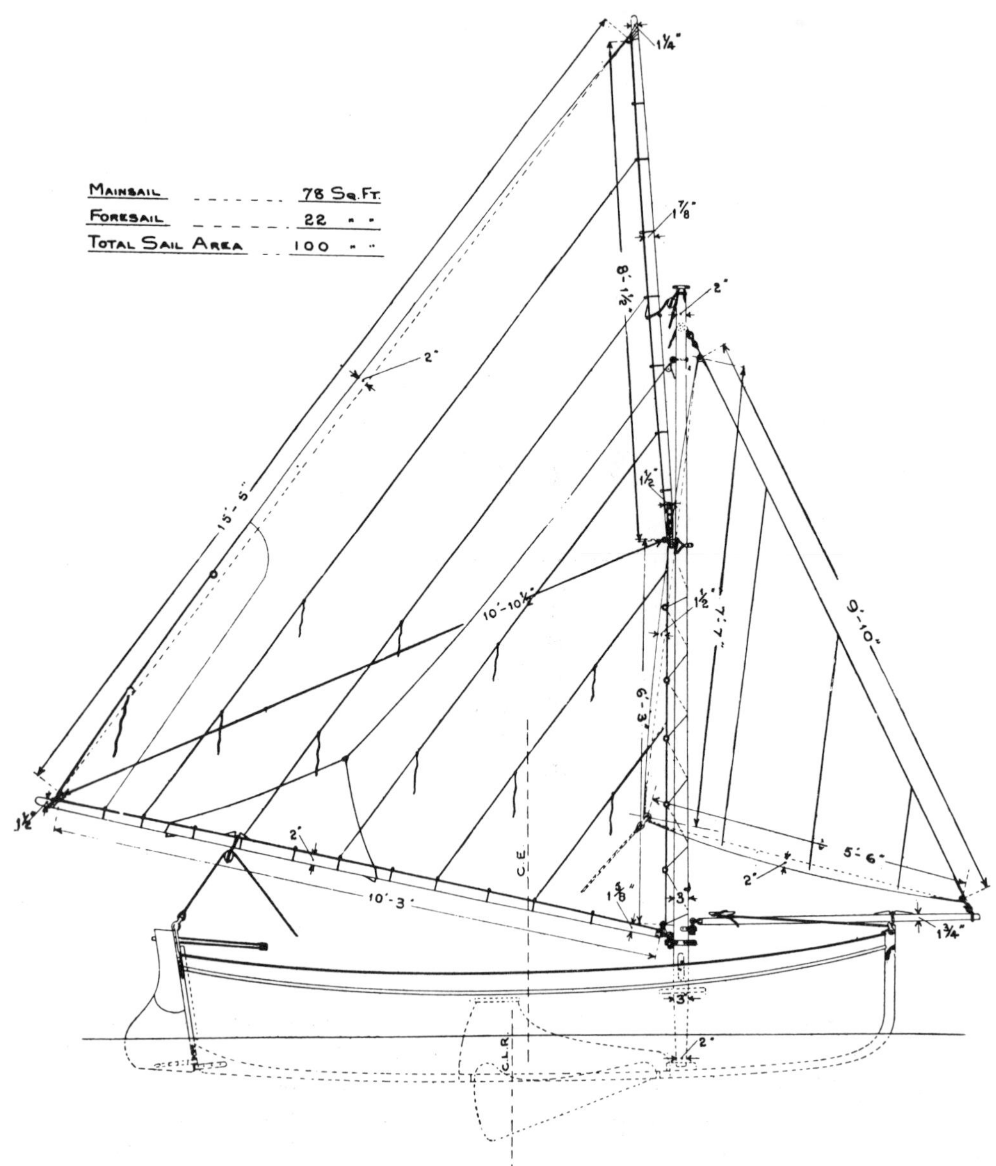

The sailplan of the Sir Nigel. (The Yachting and Boating Monthly)

were waiting there with a can of pemmican, a tin-opener, a knife, a loaf of bread, a hunk of butter wrapped up in a bit of paper, and four large apples. A moment later the brown sail was hoisted and set, and *Swallow,* with her whole crew aboard, was slipping out from behind the island."

Before he tells you how to build his dinghy, Mr. Hotchkiss gets right into the cost of the vessel. He lists 88 items you will need under these headings: "Timber for stocks, moulds, etc.; timber for boat; fastenings; ironwork; rigging tackle; paint and varnish; ropes; spars; sails; fittings; extra tools; and rent of shed for four months." The cost of all this came to something like the equivalent of 75 dollars, a lot of money for materials for a 12-footer 75 years ago. Good boats have never been cheap.

The dinghy's keel is of American oak, 4½ inches by 2½ inches; her frames, English ash, ⅝ inch by ½ inch. She has 11 natural-crook knees of English oak. The transom to be one piece of English elm, 3 feet by 1 foot 9 inches by 1 inch, "fairly 'mild.' "

Planking is ½-inch stuff, garboards and sheer strakes to be English wych-elm and the other strakes to be white pine.

The fastenings are copper boat nails with roves (clinching washers), mostly 14 gauge, 1¼ inches and 1½ inches in length.

She has an iron centerboard.

The "extra tools" are extra long bits, clamps, and a bead plane.

Under "fittings," Hotchkiss included one sponge at one shilling. I could have saved him that: an old towel works better.

The *Sir Nigel*'s smooth planking is varnished inside

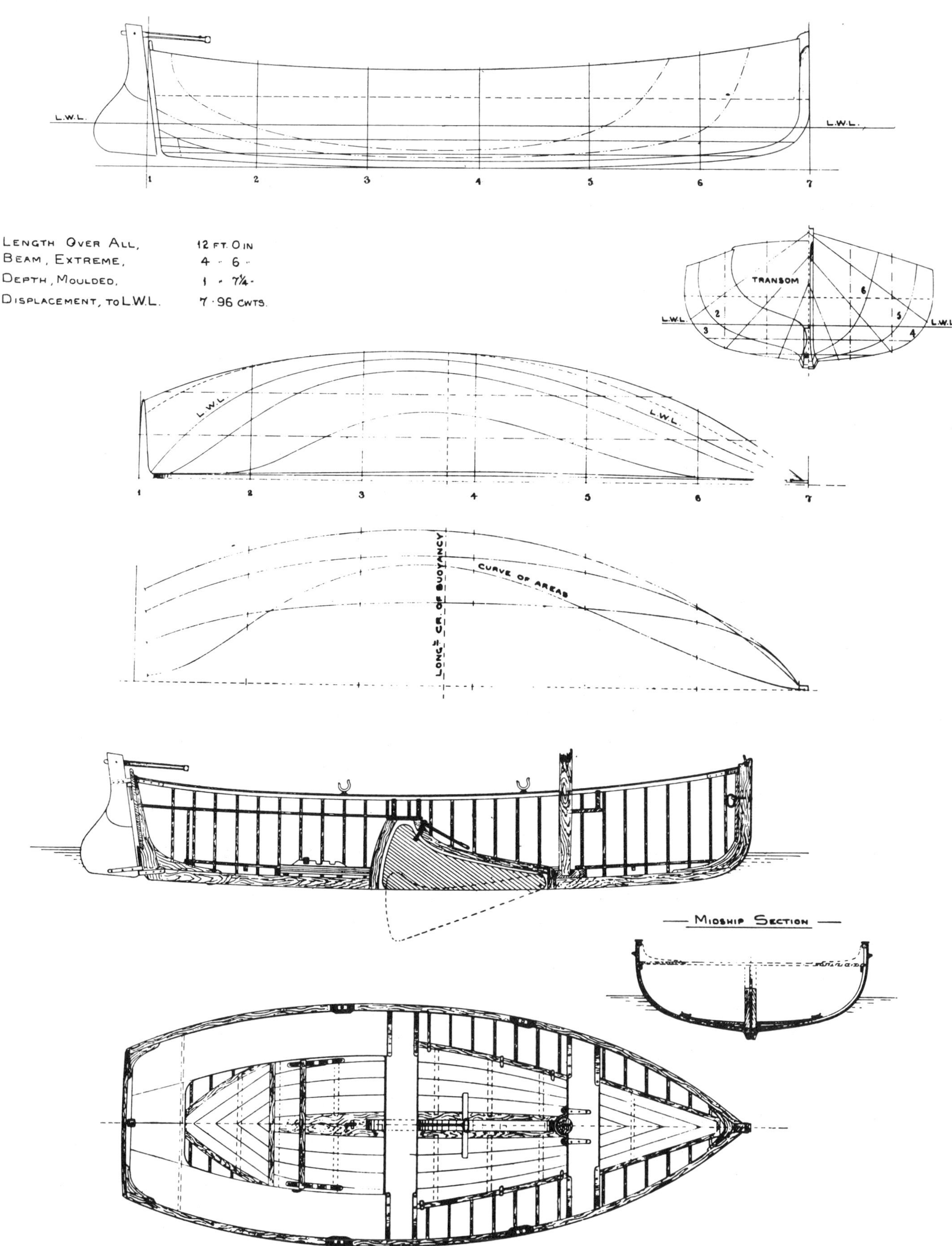

The lines and construction plan of the Sir Nigel. (The Yachting and Boating Monthly)

and out. She has a white enamel boottop and green antifouling paint on her bottom.

She could be easily transported overland. I can see her scudding down the River Alde, on England's east coast, running in half-a-gale from the northeast that's spitting rain now and then, bound from Aldeburgh to Orford, protected from the pounding North Sea outside by that long, high, gravelly beach that runs south all the way to Shingle Street. She has her tiny traveling sail set — a good deal smaller, even, than the two-reefed mainsail — and her crew of two are hunched down under their sou'westers staring ahead through the gloom, enjoying the fast progress signaled by the rollicking bow wave, and contemplating a timely arrival at an Orford pub's hot-meal time.

She'd be a nice steady boat to row; not fast, of course, being so heavy, but she'd carry her way well. She'd also be a fine motorsailer in light weather with a lee oar just ticking over to help her along.

The *Sir Nigel*'s gunter rig has been kept reasonably low to give her plenty of power without heeling her over too much. Her 22-square-foot jib sets flying on a portable bowsprit. I just love that sort of thing.

She has a fairly small lead (of the center of effort forward of the center of lateral resistance). I am told it's impossible to know just how much lead a small boat ought to have for good balance until you just put her in the water and try her. My guess would be that the *Sir Nigel* would have a fairly heavy weather helm.

The dinghy's vertical-cut, battenless sails are in keeping with her character and are strong and practical. Her two fairly deep reefs in the mainsail make great good sense. An advantage of the gunter rig is that the yard reefs down with the sail, so you don't have to leave the weight of a bare mast aloft, as you do with the Bermudian rig. She would, of course, need more parts than shown on her mainsheet.

That traveling sail that we saw on the River Alde was the jib turned round backward with its leech laced to the mast (we had to put grommets in the leech), its clew used as a tack, and its tack lashed to the boom for a clew. The topping lift was set up so the little sail wouldn't have to take the whole weight of the boom.

But I can see this boat, too, on this side of the Atlantic, roaring along with a fresh sou'wester abeam, making Eggemoggin Reach, on the coast of Maine, live up to its name. There's no sea, for the reach is well protected, and *Sir Nigel*'s crew of three are driving her to the limit with full sail, all leaning out for all they're worth on the weather gunwale in the puffs and then scrambling inboard in the lulls. Just foaming along, she is.

I'd want to add 4-inch-wide side decks to this dinghy. Just that little bit makes it so much easier to keep the water out when she heels to a sudden gust.

A deeper centerboard and rudder would help her to windward. Those shown would be better for exploring. Maybe she ought to have two centerboards and two rudders that could be interchanged, depending on her mission. That's the great thing about a little boat: you can have all kinds of elaborate spare gear without much investment. In any case, I think her shoal rudder should be bigger for better steering control, perhaps on the order of the barn door seen on the stern of a Cape Cod catboat.

And I'd prefer the high, rectangular centerboard and trunk that is the American style, because they give the lowered board so much more bearing in the trunk. The board ought to have a cross pin in its upper forward corner so that it can simply be hung from the top of the trunk in different positions to change the balance of the boat and so that it can be removed in a twinkling just by lifting it out. This arrangement not only makes for a highly versatile centerboard (or centerboards), but also makes maintenance of board and trunk relatively easy. And it eliminates one vulnerability: the underwater centerboard pin.

She ought to have a longer tiller, with a hiking stick on it. There's just nothing like being able to get up on the rail in a breeze to keep her on her feet when you're sailing alone. And such a steering arrangement would let you sit well forward in the boat to balance her when singlehanded; you could slide back and forth on her middle thwart when sailing in a light, puffy breeze so as to keep her trimmed right all the time. And yes, you *could* take a movable board sailing with you so you could sit exactly where you pleased.

I can even see the *Sir Nigel* well round the world from her native England, sailing the length and breadth of San Diego harbor so as to show her people close views of its fascinating collection of vessels. Here, on the wings of the afternoon westerly, comes a fine little brown-sailed brigantine with a bone in her teeth, a big gang of sightseers on board, and a young crew who have learned all about the timing of swinging yards when tacking. Over yonder goes a big tuna boat, putting to sea at 15 knots. Here comes, for heaven's sake, a handsome little pinky schooner beating laboriously up full and by. What's she doing out West? Far up to windward in the haze, having just swung in from sea past Point Loma, comes a guided-missile frigate, navigators fussing furiously so her big anchor will be let go exactly in the center of her designated mooring circle on the chart. Through it all foams the little *Sir Nigel,* sails bulging, sheets straining. Let's run her off for the museum docks and lie-to for a good long look at the complicated web of the *Star of India*'s rigging and the proportions of hull, deckhouse, and funnel of the *Medea,* a lovely little Scottish steam yacht. She's a vessel the *Sir Nigel* ought to get acquainted with.

3/ The Tin Canoe

My earliest memory of any kind of boat is being told to climb carefully into a long, dark-green one and to stay very still, sitting in an aroma emanating from sun-baked, crackled, black varnish, acres of which surrounded me on all sides and came right up to eye level. This must have been a family trip in the old canvas-covered canoe up Mud Cove, a tiny body of water at the west end of Quonochontaug Pond, back of the Rhode Island beach.

When we rented out our house on the nearby Pawcatuck River during World War II, that canoe went with the place. The renter was a large man of considerable exuberance. When peace allowed us to return home, we stared up in disbelief at the canoe resting on her garage rafters. In her bow was a huge hole. Pop said when our tenant hit the rock, he must have been paddling her at about 20 knots.

Eventually, the poor boat came down to be converted into an ultra-light cruising dinghy for the Buzzards Bay 25-footer *Aria.* This was accomplished by chopping her ends off, thus neatly removing the hole, boarding them up, and renewing her canvas.

The shortened canoe was, of course, christened the *Ano.*

Thanks to her small size and light weight, the *Ano* was easy to stow on deck and easy to flip in and out of the water. When asked to ferry passengers to and from the Herreshoff sloop, however, she balked.

One person of average weight could travel short distances in her in flat water. It was foolhardy for two lightweights to set forth in her if there were ripples. One night, in Great Salt Pond, Block Island, a man disobeyed an order not to embark in her, and she nearly drowned him.

The ends of a canoe seem to be rather important.

When Burt Coffey left Maine for a couple of years on the West Coast, he decided to leave his 15-foot Grumman aluminum canoe behind. He offered the vessel for sale, and I made him an offer he couldn't refuse. She had some dents in her where Burt had bounced her over some rocks on the St. George River on one or another of his early spring, wild, whitewater rides. But she had a bow, as well as a stern.

The first thing I did when I got my hands on Burt's boat was to give her oarlocks. The first paddler who — perhaps accidentally — fetched his paddle up against a fulcrum and used the thing as a lever really accomplished something. A great thing, the oarlock. I was in a big hurry to take advantage of the invention, so I went right out and bought a Grumman rowing rig: seat, 7-inch outriggers, and oarlock sockets all in one metal structure, fastened to the gunwales with four U-bolts set up with eight wing nuts. I cinched down on those babies, and they have never moved since.

The Grumman people made the relationship of the various heights in their rowing rig just right for rowing: that is, the seat is the right height above the bottom of the canoe, and is the right height with respect to the height of the oarlocks. The result, though, is that when you first get in and start rowing, you feel as if you're sitting up too high in the boat. Your perch seems a little dangerous until you get used to it, though I must say I have never felt that she was going to throw me out, even in rough water.

Of course she flies under oars, just flies. And I haven't been greedy: I use a pair of mere 6-footers with big blades. She rows easily and fast, and you don't even have to cross your hands.

In a following sea, as a big one comes in under you, you sense the opportunity to shoot it with real speed and can't resist pulling like anything. By going like a windmill with short, rapid, powerful strokes for a few seconds, you can really keep her shooting down a wave. It's some exciting.

Whether rowing fast or slowly, in rough water or smooth, the great thing is to watch her high, pointed stern slipping along silently. In contrast, the other end of the boat, with its flat sections, pounds vigorously when going into a head sea, and the aluminum hull sets up a terrific racket.

A canoe is very maneuverable under oars. With no draft to speak of, she spins round like a top. She makes plenty of leeway in a breeze, of course, but she's very easy to steer under oars, and you just head up more into the wind to make allowances.

You say you want to see where you're going? If there are obstacles to be dodged, spin her round and back her down. You can push her backward with the oars for some distance at speed before you tire.

Two people can sit in the normal paddling positions, the stern person pushing with the oars, without changing the position of the rowing rig. Or, since the rowing rig is positioned to put her down by the stern a bit with one on board, the second person can sit in the bottom of the boat amidships while the other rows normally, without putting the boat out of trim.

Few places where a canoe goes are too narrow for a pair of 6-foot oars, but in really tight places there is nothing that says you can't ship the oars and break out the paddle. We always carry a couple, and one of the great pleasures of using this boat has been that it gives me an occasional excuse to dip a skinny, hardwood paddle that Pop brought back from the Philippines.

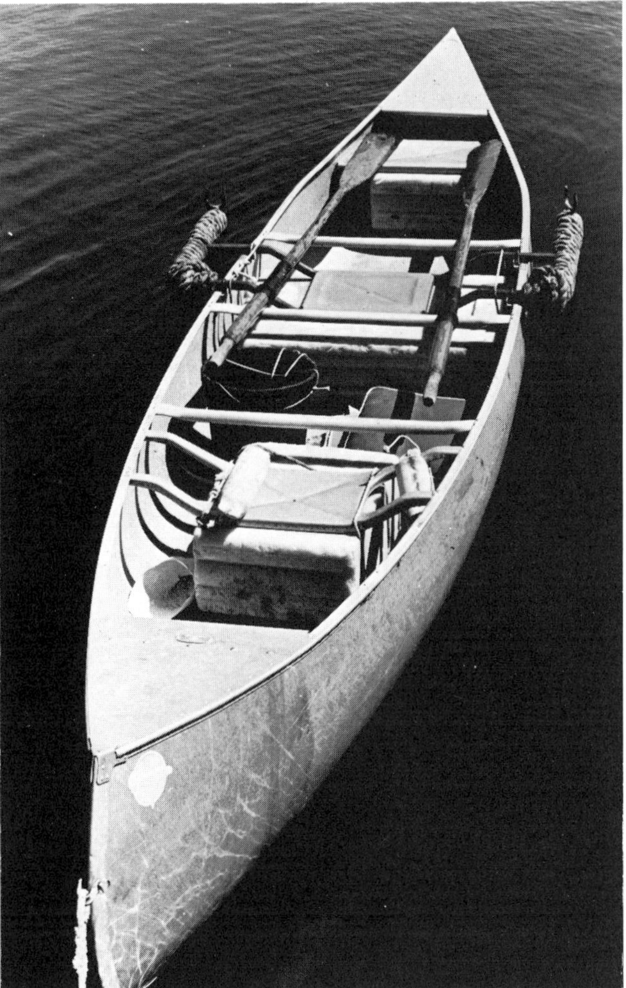

The tin canoe ready to travel. (Neal Parent)

Of course you can row *and* paddle with two people if you're in a hurry or it's cold. Sometimes I go canoeing in company with Sam and Susan Manning. You never know what mode of propulsion they are going to unveil next; simultaneous use of oars, paddle, and sail is merely where they start.

Listening to Burt's St. George River yarns and looking at the dents that proved there was at least some truth to them, we figured the poor tin boat deserved a little peace. So far — except for the occasional lazy breaking wave on Penobscot Bay — we have kept her right away from white water. We've been on the St. George River, all right, but only down far enough where he's close enough to salt water to know he's going to make it and can afford to calm his headlong rush. One of our favorite haunts is a tiny tributary of his, a tickle grandly called the Oyster River. Happiness is going up the Oyster River with the flood, picnicking way up in the

Sliding across Camden Harbor. (Neal Parent)

woody saltings at high water, and then coming down with the ebb.

We've also done plenty of quiet cruising on Lake Megunticook. And one of our most memorable trips was a gentle moonlight row in the shadow of mountains way up north on South Branch Pond.

The great thing about this metal boat is that she's automatically always in commission. She used to lean against the garage, ready to go, 365 days a year. Recently, I've taken to tying her up at the Public Landing in Camden Harbor all winter. Neither ice nor snow bother her in the slightest, and it's fine to know you can get afloat quickly from December through March. Maintenance? Just clean her when you use her.

The tougher the boating conditions, the more advantages accrue to the tin canoe. She came into her own when we lived a quarter of a mile up through the woods from the steep, rough, rocky shore of Penobscot Bay. One day I woke up to the fact that I had a boat that could live and work down there. There was plenty of snow on the ground, so it was no job at all to move her from the house down through the woods to a ravine in the 20-foot ledges. This was a great little spot, very steep, but indented just enough to be a rare hiding place in a fairly straight shoreline. Pirate's Cove, I named it.

The canoe's resting place down there was halfway up the steep ledge at the very head of the ravine. I rigged a block and tackle to a tree so I could haul her up easily, well above the reach of waves sent breaking against that shore by a northeaster.

She was only 50 feet from the water at high tide, but considerably more than that at low. To launch and recover, you had to haul her bodily over whatever distance the state of the tide decreed; and it was all sharp, broken rock until you got down to the more rounded, rockweed-covered boulders well below high-tide line. Well, if Burt could bounce her over the rocks of the St. George River, I could bounce her over the rocks of Penobscot Bay. She announced her emergence from her hiding place in the ledges with great clashing of cymbals and bonging of metallic drums.

The waves had to be less than three feet before I would dare put to sea in the canoe off the rocks. Even two-footers required a quick decision, an unhesitating strong shove out, and careful balance while getting seated. Landing again, I would hang off in the surge outside the little break studying the situation a long time before I found a quiet enough spell to pull on in fast, slow her to a reasonably gentle bump alongside a handy rock, jump out, and scramble her quickly over the rocks a ways. I don't know what other boat could have been so used at Pirate's Cove.

Using the canoe year-round, I have to think about tipping over in cold water. I discovered in the summer lake that the small amount of built-in flotation in the very ends of the boat was sufficient to float her hull, but could not float me too. Throwing the minor aesthetic considerations of the tin canoe to the winds, I purchased a quantity of extremely lightweight plastic stuff whose surface reflected a color that seemed about halfway between orange and pink. Under each of the three seats of the boat I lashed tightly the biggest cube of the material that would possibly fit. This flotation has become a permanent fixture. It transforms what was a sinkable metal shell into an unsinkable cork, sheathed with metal for propulsion efficiency, and incorporating enough holes for people's feet and dunnage.

By way of adding a belt to my suspenders, I always carry as part of my gear, one of those fancy life preservers that is disguised as an ordinary jacket. It lets you wear a life jacket without looking foolish. Of course fooling around the Maine coast in winter in a tin canoe without obviously wearing a life jacket probably looks very foolish indeed. One problem with this type of fancy life jacket, though, is that when you wear it you turn your life over to a zipper. I'd rather depend on buttons. What if the thing should jam at the bottom?

Another piece of gear that stays right with this boat all the time, tethered to her with a lanyard, is a bucket.

In the lake in summer, I've experimented with climbing back into her swamped. I can't get in over her gunwale, but I can get in by hoisting myself across one of her end decks and then swinging into the boat.

It was fun working the canoe along the rough and rocky shore of the bay, operating from Pirate's Cove. Depending on wind direction, I'd go out to Davenport Ledge and work cautiously round it, watching the seas break, sometimes with a loud harrumph. There's something about watching waves surge in and over a low-lying ledge out in the middle of deep water. Kind of scary. Or, I might row up into Rockport Harbor, or over around Indian Island with its handsome lighthouse, or go down the shore the other way to Glen Cove to explore round its guardian island. Lots of times I'd make it a real voyage, take along some food, and heave-to by just letting her drift, carefully shifting from the rowing seat to the bottom of the boat amidships. She'd blow along sideways, and I'd occasionally pull on one oar or the other to swing her round to change from a view of the hills to a view of the islands.

Occasionally, when I was out rummaging around on the bay in the tin canoe, I'd meet up with a lobster fisherman pulling his traps. These guys don't wear their emotions on the sleeves of their slickers, so I never saw one of them tap his head knowingly or actually point and laugh, but they must have thought I was nuts. They were probably right.

4/ Sliding-Seat Rowing Boats

It was high water at Steamer's Restaurant, way up the Damariscotta River in Maine, so the wide veranda, with its picnic tables for outdoor-minded customers, overlooked blue river wavelets pushed along by a moderate southerly, instead of mud flats. An ideal time to try the restaurant owner's boat.

Loyal Sewall has a lovely, fine-lined, 18-foot Whitehall pulling boat built by Dick Shew, of Shew and Burnham, down the river at South Bristol. Loyal has her fitted with a sliding seat.

I pulled her down the river a mile or so with Dick as passenger. He outweighs me by quite a bit, and I worked reasonaby hard, though not very efficiently, at the oars. She made excellent progress against the wind, and we thought the Damariscotta River at high tide a very pretty place indeed.

Dick Shew also outweighs me considerably in knowledge of sliding-seat rowing. A thorough boatman in every respect, he has gotten all excited about the sliding seat in recent years. Really gone into it.

We let her gradually coast to a stop and then just drift, beam-on. Dick spouted information and ideas about sliding-seat rowing techniques: the proper paraphernalia, from the rolling seat itself to outriggers, oarlocks, and oars; the right sorts of boats for such powerful propulsion; and the kinds of people making and selling all this stuff and doing the rowing.

"A recreational boat ought to make her owner happy," Dick said. "It doesn't make any difference if she's faster or slower than the next boat, and it doesn't make any difference if she's wood or fiberglass."

Not that the speed of a sliding-seat rowing boat isn't important; it's a huge part of the fun of the things. But anyone choosing one of these boats will row her first, and she'll either seem fast enough, or she won't. (Clue: The lighter, longer, and narrower the boat, the faster the boat. Standard: A typical *racing* shell weighs 28 pounds, is 25 feet long, and is an uncompromising 11 inches wide.)

I started pulling back up the river so we'd get back to the float at Steamer's before the ebb got a hold of us. Took it easy, mostly letting her blow along with the wind.

"You can put a sliding seat into any good pulling boat," said Dick. This Whitehall, with her handsome, gentle sheer and nicely flaring sides, her smart paint, varnish, and red brass, wasn't designed for a sliding seat but certainly rowed beautifully with one.

Loyal Sewall met us as we carried the oars up the float ramp, put some beers on one of the picnic tables, and we sat down to talk it over. I made sure I sat facing the river, for the Whitehall had been paddled out and left on a mooring, where she sat on the water like a bird, turning slowly in the first eddies of the ebb.

Above: *Dick Shew.* **Below:** *It's easy to stop rowing in one of Dick Shew's nice boats and just feast your eyes on the shape of her transom. This is an 18-footer, which Dick feels is a big improvement on the mere 16-footer. (Dick Shew)*

Thomas C. Mendenhall, in *A Short History of American Rowing,* says that not until "sometime after 1,000 B.C." did man first see the advantage of rowing over paddling. I doubt it. I don't dispute Mr. Mendenhall's scholarship, but I'll bet it didn't take nearly that long for watermen to discover the great advantage of the pry. It will probably be like the evidence of man's very existence: earlier and earlier fossils will be found. Why, a fossilized oarlock carbon-dated to 25,000 B.C. or so wouldn't surprise me a bit.

Bringing the history of rowing quickly up to the last century, John Gardner has reported rowing led all American outdoor sports in the decades between 1850 and 1880, in an article called "Early Days of Rowing Sport." Rowing was taken seriously; nor did interest wane in the early years of this century. News item: "Jake Gardaur, the famous oarsman, slipped on the ice while curling at Rat Portage, Ontario, the evening of February 21 [1903] and broke a shoulder bone. His surgeons declare that he can never pull an oar again." It was if Ruth's bat or Ali's jab had been silenced.

Out of such popularity and fervor was born the sliding seat. If you pull as hard as you can on an oar (as you would if you were a famous oarsman rowing a famous boat in a famous race), you find that as you strain every fiber toward making the boat leap ahead, your seat also leaps ahead, a bit, over the seat of the boat. Then, as you recover for the next stroke, you have to scrunch aft again to regain your position. It was reasoned that if

this process could be aided and abetted, the boat would go faster.

Thus originated the "Buckskin and Butter" school of rowing. Students of this school screwed down to the seats of their boats ¼-inch-thick pads of close-grained cherry, smoothly polished, and with the grain running fore and aft. They reinforced the seats of their pants with leather. They applied grease to the cherry and grease to the leather. If their boat was too wide to contain their slippings and slidings with its gunwales, they put flared wooden sides on the cherry pads to confine their wanderings to the proper axis.

The notion of making the seat itself slide back and forth in the boat came, in 1857, to one John C. Babcock. He put such a contrivance into his single shell, the *Experiment,* at Chicago. He didn't think much of it.

Babcock kept fiddling around with his sliding seat and was still using it, though without much enthusiasm, in 1870. The trouble was, he never took the stops off the thing. His seat allowed only 12 inches of travel, and he wouldn't even use all of that, stating that "in rowing, the proper length of slide is from four to six inches."

By 1885, long slides had been tried and were in use, and rowers were traveling to and fro in their boats a proper 18 inches on every stroke. The sliding seat had added an interesting — and complicating — dimension to rowing.

The new contraption was viewed with skepticism by purists. This about the sliding seat from an English rowing text published in 1897: "We are inclined to the belief that its practical value and merits have been much overrated, and that, when our countrymen, who are fond of the oar, have become physically so well developed and trained by judicious, solid, and wholesome practice that they can by the aid of muscle alone bring into action every pound of avoirdupois they possess, we shall hear less of mechanical contrivances to effect this, and the secret of good oarsmanship will be better understood." And again: "It was imagined that swing was no longer necessary, and accordingly the rivers were filled with contorted oarsmen shuffling and tumbling and screwing on their slides. Veteran oars and coaches, to whom 'form' was as the apple of their eye, were horror-struck, and gave vent to loud lamentations, utterly condemning this horrible innovation, which, as they thought, had reduced oarsmanship to the level of a rough and tumble fight."

The purists lost, of course, and the sliding seat is ever with us in racing. And now, in the last ten years or so, the thing has made its way steadily into recreational rowing. As someone who has been rowing for 45 years on seats that stay where boatbuilders put them, I view this unsteady base of operations with a little anxiety and a lot of curiosity.

* * *

The Stonington Pulling Boat is a fiberglass beauty built by Justin Camarata's Golden Era Boats at Noank, Connecticut, to the lines of a very fine, 16-foot Whitehall type designed by Rob Pittaway in 1973.

I tried her at Noank, rowing alone for a couple of hours in the middle of a crisp, clear day in late fall. Got familiar with the boat while prowling slowly along the shore that leads from the cove where Golden Era is to Groton Long Point, sheltering from a moderate westerly breeze. I fell in love with her high-tucked, wineglass transom. It's an elegant thing to watch as you row.

The boat seemed just the right weight. She carries her way beautifully, yet accelerates easily.

Even though wind was with tide off Groton Long Point, there was a bit of a rip. There must be big boulders on the bottom just off the point. I skirted round outside the little breakers, preferring the more stately chop of Fishers Island Sound. Pulled quite hard to get round the point against the wind, tide, and sea, and then headed, crabwise across the current, along its western shore.

This course brought the sea nearly abeam; I hoped no weekend cottagers had their binoculars trained on me as I struggled to keep the oars somewhere near covered right and maintain some semblance of a regular stroke. You really need short oars for such work.

The Stonington Pulling Boat is tippy, of course, but she has just enough flatness of floor and flare above the waterline so she doesn't scare you, even your first time in her.

I found the blind entrance in the jetties to the lagoon back of Groton Long Point and rowed into its smooth water for a peaceful change. Of course, I had to go up to the very head of the lagoon, by now hoping somebody might notice my comparatively smooth and effortless strokes. At least I hoped they looked effortless; every one of them took considerable mental concentration, thanks to the sliding seat. Nobody was around except a guy so busy scrubbing off the bottom of his fat dinghy that he didn't even notice me flash by in my lean greyhound.

Back out in the sound, now with fair wind and tide, I took it easier, but still made plenty of knots over the bottom. It really *was* pretty rough for a low-sided boat, and I was glad to remember about this boat's built-in flotation.

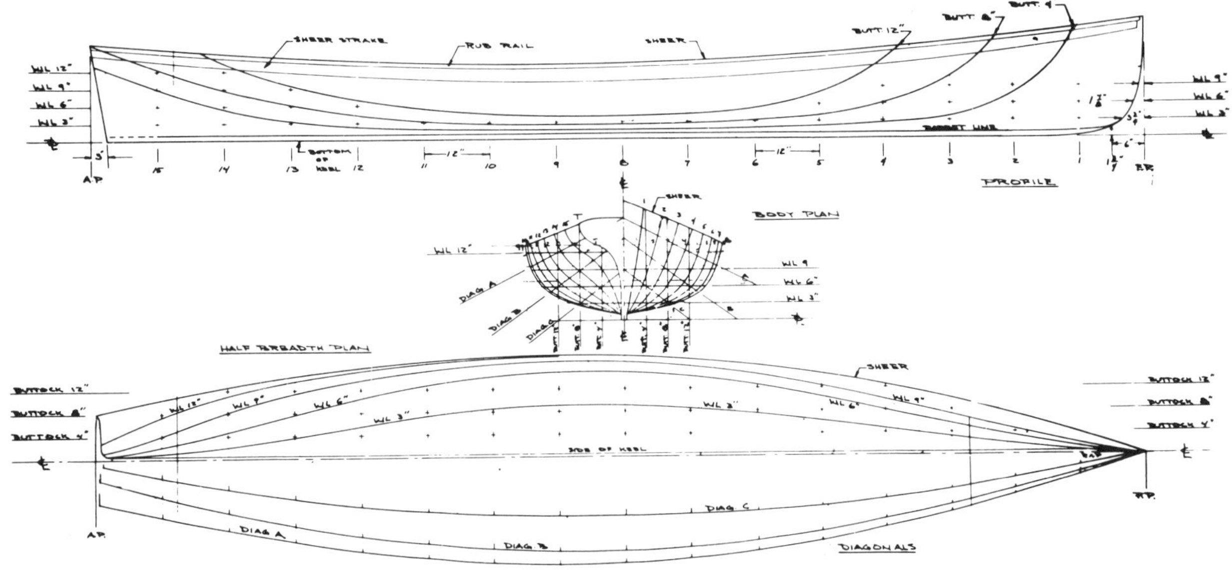

The lines of the Stonington Pulling Boat. (Golden Era Boats)

The Stonington Pulling Boat under a fair head of steam. (Golden Era Boats)

A funny thing happened on the way back to the cove. These used to be my home sailing waters, but the notion of Fishers Island Sound as a place in which to *row* had never crossed my mind. But in this boat, whipping off the face of a sea and flying along in a welter of foam, I looked over to the Dumplings and even way out to Race Rock and thought to myself, "Why, I could row over there." Those places, miles away, really did seem just "right over there," even in a rowing boat. Somehow, I had never before felt quite such a oneness with Fishers Island Sound. I felt as if the whole place was in my grasp, as if I could patrol it at will, just by pulling on oars. Heady stuff.

But the best was yet to come. With a fair wind there was no point in staying close under the east side of Groton Long Point, so I let her go offshore a bit — and found what the surfers call the perfect wave. A whole succession of smooth, round, 3-foot swells coming in dead under the stern. Now you get in a fast rowing boat in such a perfect following sea and just see how long *you* can keep *your* cool. Mine lasted one sea, and then I was off, seeing how fast I could make her go. Those beauties

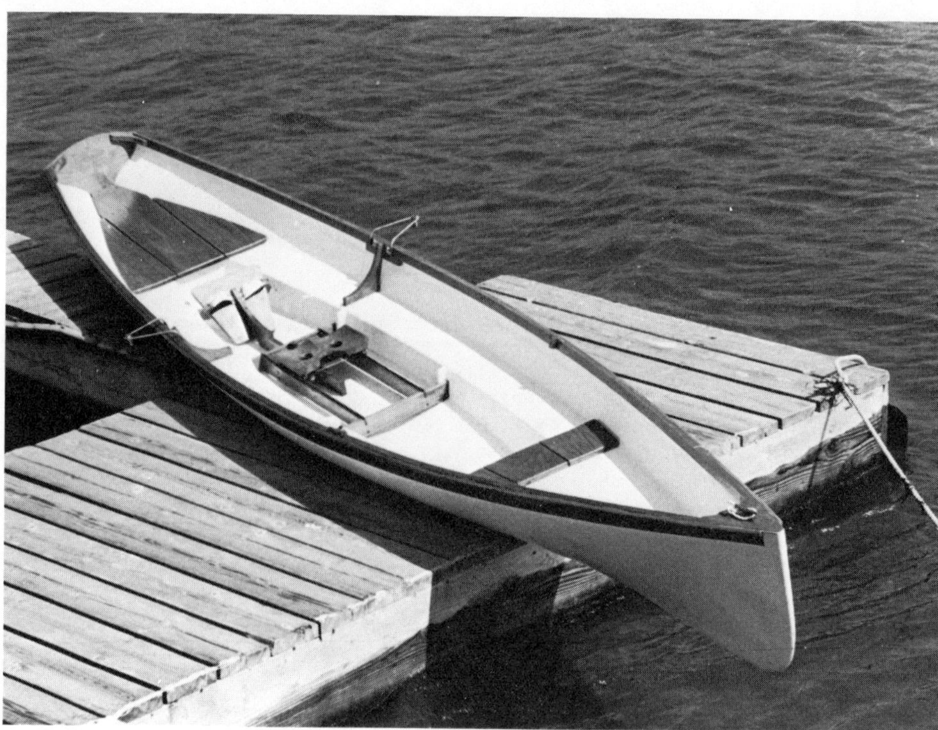

The Stonington Pulling Boat has a pretty shape from any angle. (Golden Era Boats)

would roll in under the stern, I'd feel her lift and start to take off, and then I'd give everything I had to about four quick strokes. Damn near got her planing, I did.

By the time I tied up, I was all tuckered out.

* * *

If, like me, you are one of those old-fashioned, fixed-seat sort of rowers who wants to learn sliding-seat techniques, read the accompanying instructions, numbers 1 through 12. They were written by one R.C. Lehmann in a day (1897) when many a serious racing oarsman was making the same transition.

And now to the business of instruction. Remember and endeavor to apply all the lessons you have learnt on fixed seats. Slides add another element to the stroke. They do not alter the elements you have previously been taught.

(1) Beginning — Get hold of this just as you would on a fixed seat, with a sharp spring of the whole body, which thus begins its swing-back without the loss of a fraction of time.

(a) The natural tendency of a tiro will be to drive his slide away before his shoulders have begun to move. This must at all costs be avoided. In order to secure the effectual combination of body-swing and leg-work, it is essential that the swing should start first.

(b) It is equally reprehensible to swing the body full back before starting the slide; you thus cut the stroke into two distinct parts, one composed of mere body-swing, the other of mere leg-work. Therefore:

(2) When the body-swing backwards has started, but only the smallest fractional part of a second afterwards — so quickly, indeed, as to appear to the eye of a spectator almost a simultaneous movement — let the slide begin to travel back, the swing meanwhile continuing.

(a) Remember what was said in fixed-seat instructions as to the use of the toes and the ball of the foot at the beginning of the stroke. On slides this is even more important.

(3) Body and slide are now moving back in unison, the feet pressing with firm and steady pressure against the stretcher, *and the arms perfectly straight.* As the slide moves, the leg-power applied must on no account diminish. If anything it ought to increase, for the body is beginning to lose its impetus, and the main part of the resistance is transferred to the legs, the blade all the time moving at an even pace through the water.

(4) The body must swing a little further back than on a fixed seat.

(5) Body-swing and slide-back should end at the same moment.

(6) As they end, the knees should be pressed firmly down so as to enable you to secure the last ounce of leg-power from the stretcher. Simultaneously with this depression of the legs, the hands [and particularly the outside hand, which has been doing the main share of the work of the stroke all through] must bring the oar-handle[s] firmly home to the chest, sweeping them in and thus obtaining what is called a firm hard finish. As the knees come finally down, the elbows pass the sides, and the shoulders move back and downwards . . . .

The blade, as on fixed seats, must be kept fully covered to the finish, and there must be power on it to the last fraction of an inch. If a man takes his oar out of the water before he has fairly ended his stroke, and rows his finish in the air, or if he partially uncovers his blade and rows "light," he commits in either case a serious fault. In the former case his whole body-weight, which ought to be propelling the boat, not only ceases to have any good effect, but becomes so much dead lumber, and actually impedes her progress. In the latter he can only exert half, or, it may be, one quarter of his proper power during an appreciable part of the stroke.

(7) The drop of the hands, the turn of the wrists, the shoot-out of the hands, and the straightening of the arms must be performed precisely as on a fixed seat, but the legs, meanwhile, are to remain braced, so that knees may not hamper hands. As soon as ever the hands have been shot out, and *immediately* after the start of the forward swing, the slide comes into play, and the knees consequently begin to bend outwards and upwards. It is very important not to pause or "hang" on the recovery.

(8) The recovery movements ought to release the body smartly, but care must be taken not to hustle the body forward with a rush before the arms are straightened. The body *begins* to swing *from the hips* as soon as the hands release it, but the swing is to be a slow one.

(a) Do not begin to slide forward before you swing. Let your swing just have the precedence, and let it then carry your slide with it.

(9) The pace of the swing forward must be slow and unvarying, and the slide, therefore, must also move slowly. The time occupied by the swing should be the body's rest.

(10) Remember the fixed-seat instructions as to balance against the stretcher with the feet during the swing forward, and especially during the latter part of it. The fault of tumbling forward over the stretcher is far too common, and can only be avoided or corrected by maintaining the pressure on the stretcher. In fact, never let your body get out of control. You ought to feel and to look as if at any moment during the swing forward you could stop dead at the word of command. Swing and slide should practically end together, the body "snaking out," as I have heard it expressed, in the final part of the swing, but without "pecking" over the front-stop. There must be no over-reach with the shoulders.

(11) When the body is full forward the knees should be opened to about the breadth of the arm-pits, the flanks closed in against the thighs. The knees should bend steadily and gradually into this position, and at the moment of beginning they must maintain themselves there and not fall loosely apart. Such a movement entails a great loss of power at the beginning of the next stroke. Nor, on the other hand, ought the knees to be clipped together as the stroke begins.

(12) Remember, finally, that grace, erectness, straightness of back and arms, and a clean precision, balance and elasticity of all movements are as important now as they were on fixed seats. A man who on slides rounds his back, humps up his shoulders, and hollows his chest *may* do good work, but it will be in spite of and not because of these serious disfigurements. Only by carefully observing fixed rules and by prolonged practice will you be able to attain to the harmonious ease and elegance by which a comparatively weak man can so economize his strength as to outrow and outlast some brawny giant who wastes his power in useless contortions.

Actually, we shouldn't even be talking about "rowing." Technically, "rowing" is pulling on one long oar. Pulling on two short oars at the same time is called "sculling," and oars so pulled are not oars at all, but "sculls." Oh dear, I just can't handle this. I want to learn to pull from a sliding seat, really I do, but I just can't bring myself to call it sculling. That's what you do with an oar (scull?) in a figure-eight motion over the stern. So I'm afraid I am going to keep right on talking about rowing.

Rowing from a sliding seat ain't easy. Mr. Lehmann wrote: "The muscles and joints at first absolutely refuse to accommodate themselves to this new strain, and you will see a man as he slides forward, taking his heels well off the stretcher in order to ease the strain upon his ankles and moving his shoulders back long before his oar has gripped the water in order to relieve his hip joints. This results in his missing the whole of his beginning, striking the water at right-angles to his rigger instead of well behind it, and having absolutely no firmness of drive when it becomes necessary for him to use his legs." Well, I know that feeling. The most surprising strains and pains crop up all over the place.

The hardest thing for me is twisting round to see where I'm going, because now, all of a sudden, my feet are high, close together, and strapped in. You don't get to bend your knee and move your foot when you twist round to look over your shoulder to avoid collision, the way you naturally do when you twist your body to look ahead when rowing from a thwart. (Do your feet really have to be laced in to enable you to pull the sliding seat aft again during recovery? Has anyone given any thought to a padded toe-bar above the stretcher for pulling yourself back aft again? That way you could take a foot off the stretcher and put it back again quickly and easily when twisting round to look ahead. Pete Culler, a rower of many kinds of boats, wrote that he hated to lace his feet into a small boat. It seemed a bit dangerous to him. Gives me a funny feeling too. You see how we fixed-seat rowers try to hang on to every little vestige of comfort we can.)

I have only a couple of pointers to add to Mr. Lehmann's instructions. Don't be too greedy. That's been my problem. I thought that being an old hand at the oars, I could jump into one of these sliding-seat boats and have it all down pat in about six strokes. It's just like any other rowing, I reasoned, only you just give a shove with your legs as you pull the oar. So that's what I did, expecting everything to work out just perfect. It didn't. Too greedy.

Now I can tell you the obvious: Take it easy at first, letting the very fact that your legs are now totally involved in the rowing gradually give you the extra speed you crave. Just using the sliding seat, even gently, gives you a longer stroke and keeps your oars covered longer. This means speed without strain. Don't strain. Don't feel at first (as I did) that every stroke has to be a long, perfect one with the seat sliding a full 18 inches. Use the half-slide stroke for a while. Then, when you get your balance and feel more comfortable with the whole business, gradually lengthen out. And gradually pull harder. And good luck.

* * *

Ken Bassett builds boats in north central Vermont. Calls his one-man shop the Onion River Boat Works. One of the boats he builds is the Firefly, a wonderful, plywood, V-bottomed, near-double-ender that he designed for sliding-seat rowing. The single is 18 feet long; the double, 22. I journeyed inland to row one of the doubles with Ken at the height of the foliage season.

Ken is fascinated by the sliding-seat recreational rowing movement. He says he sells half his boats to rowers, half to non-rowers. In the latter group, he says, are a lot of converts from cycling and jogging.

The owner of the Firefly double we were to try is John Perry, a furniture maker. He is new to rowing (and to boats, for that matter). He's soaking it all up fast and obviously loving every minute of it.

John had the boat loaded atop his VW van when we got to his house in Montpelier. During the sometimes-bumpy ride out to Curtis Pond near Maple Corners, Ken explained some of the dos and don'ts of roadsmanship. He said a car top gives a boat a much better ride than a trailer, because a car is much better sprung than a trailer. Obvious, when you think about it, but I hadn't. He said plenty of soft padding is a must and that you want to lash the boat down really hard on it.

The first thing John did when we got to the shore of Curtis Pond was clamp to the Firefly's narrow transom a pair of wheels he had designed and built. We untied her, shoved her straight aft off the top of the van, and lowered her stern to the ground. John wheelbarrowed her to the water's edge. We turned her over. Off came the wheels. John said it's easy to do this singlehanded. A neat rig.

We launched her and John went off by himself, saying that because the boat has a co-owner, he doesn't get a chance to row much alone.

Ken Bassett. (Onion River Boat Works)

Ken and I stood and admired the Firefly underway. She's a pretty boat, every bit as pretty and sophisticated as, say, a Whitehall. Ken gives all the credit for her design to his mentor Donald C. Rosencrantz, a man Ken says knew one heck of a lot about boats and rowing.

Ken, like Dick Shew, believes that recreational rowing has room for all kinds of people and all kinds of boats. The point, he says, is to promote the idea of people getting afloat. He likes to share what he's learned with others.

If you buy a boat from the Onion River Boat Works, it comes with a canvas cover, because Ken has learned the importance of keeping the inside of a boat really clean. And he won't leave you alone. He calls up his owners every year: "How's the boat doing? Anything need fixing?"

I tried the Firefly alone. It was lucky for Ken and John that Curtis Pond is a fairly small body of water, because boat, day, and scenery were all exquisite, and I would have been tempted to go for a week if we'd been on Lake Champlain. But I returned shortly to pick up Ken, and we rowed double. We took it easy; Ken said the beat he set was only about twenty strokes a minute. Yet the bottom of the pond seemed to fly out from under us. Maybe she was going 5 knots, but being close to water and bottom, it seemed much faster. She knifed through an unwanted outboard wake as if it weren't there. She passed youngsters rowing a great, clumsy skiff with mere fixed thwarts as if they were anchored.

Reluctantly we returned to John, who had his fishing

The Firefly *double about to leap ahead. (Onion River Boat Works)*

rod out by this time, and transferred the boat easily from water to van top.

I liked these guys. Their talk of boats was right down to earth. Somebody mentioned lapstrake construction, and John wanted to know what that was. Ken told him, "It's like clapboard." I just love to see that kind of learning about boats going on.

* * *

There are other ways of using your legs when rowing than sitting on a sliding seat. William M. Lightbowne, down in Florida, makes a device involving a fixed seat and sliding oarlocks. The stretcher is hooked up to the outriggers, and as you pull the oars, you drive the oarlocks aft with your legs. This is a bit tricky to visualize until you realize that you could row the boat with your legs alone, just holding the oars out perpendicular to the boat. I suspect Mr. Lightbowne has named the invention after himself; he calls it the Silver Fox. I don't dare try the thing for fear I'll foul up my rowing for fair.

The Chinese — always way ahead in maritime matters — have for centuries been using their strong leg muscles for rowing. The champions of Chinese foot rowing were the mailmen. Their 25-foot sampans went twice as fast as boats of comparable size propelled by mere arm and back muscles, nor did they tire as quickly as did their compatriots. One wonders why everybody in China didn't take up oars with their feet, or, indeed, why we backward westerners don't take up the practice today.

You sit facing forward, comfortably ensconced against a back brace, and shove a single oar to starboard with both feet. A flat wooden pad on the inboard end of the oar helps with the feathering. The right foot grasps the loom and draws it back on the recovery. Here's where I might settle for somehow having my feet tied to the oar. The oars were 8-footers with big blades. You get to use a paddle to port, to keep her from always turning to the left. (Left-footed people would, I suppose, switch sides.) Foot rowing allows you to see where you're going without getting a kink in your neck. The authority on such matters, the late G.R.G. Worcester, wrote in his monumental book *The Junks and Sampans of the Yangtze,* "So expert did these men become that, while rowing, they could cook, eat, smoke, or play the flute without relaxing speed."

I don't know how you're going to beat that for recreational rowing.

* * *

"If it weren't for Arthur Martin," Dick Shew told me, "we'd still be back in the Dark Ages of sliding-seat recreational rowing." Arthur designed and built the first Alden Ocean Shell a dozen years ago. I remember seeing his first advertisements for the boat and thinking, "There. That really makes sense."

Martin Marine Company, at Kittery Point, Maine, has probably sold as many sliding-seat recreational rowing boats as has all the rest of the movement. Besides the single Alden Ocean Shell, there's also a double; a faster boat called the Martin Trainer; two lovely double-enders that also have sailing rigs, a 16-foot and a 19-foot Appledore Pod; and a plywood kit boat called the Kittery Skiff.

On a sprinkly day in early spring, I went to Kittery to row the Alden Ocean Shell. She's a fiberglass 16-footer that somehow reminds me of a skinny tadpole. Sort of a cod's-head-and-mackerel-tail shape, at least at the deckline, though there isn't an ounce of fat on her.

She really pulled very easily, I thought, but I had to work at the oars in order to keep up with Arthur, pulling moderately along in one of his Appledore 19s, as we started out of his narrow, quiet tickle toward the Piscataqua River. It's fun to row in company with another boat, for you get to see what you look like skimming along in one of these low, fast machines. Not that my rowing looked anything like Arthur's: he's been pulling oars from a sliding seat every day for years, and it shows.

Out in the river there was a light breeze and just a little occasional slop. Enough to make me really spoil a stroke now and then. It didn't seem to bother Arthur any.

We had to dodge plenty of lobster buoys and moored boats on our way up the eastern shore of the river. I had my usual crick-in-the-neck problems and had to think really hard about staying balanced upright every time I looked over my shoulder. The Alden Ocean Shell is not a boat in which you can jump up and down on the gunwale.

Our destination was Arthur's Energy 48, a long, narrow, low-powered motorboat that Arthur has developed for sensible cruising. Climbing up onto her from the outriggered shell without doing something very embarrassing was just possible. We lifted the shell easily onto the top of her deckhouse. Put a towline on the Appledore Pod and ran the Energy 48 down the river, outside a ways into a bit of swell, and back again. The Pod towed just fine.

Then we rowed home, and going up the flat water of the tickle, I finally began to get the feel a little more of

Above: *Arthur Martin and some of his boats. (Ann Grinnell Welles)*
Below: *The Appledore Pod double. (Arthur Martin)*

the tiddly shell. There were times when I could even enjoy watching the nearby shoreline flash past, as I tried to make the boat live up to something not too far from her potential. I envied Arthur the opportunity to do this sort of thing every day, year-round.

My friend Dave Jackson bought his son Matt one of the 16-foot Appledore Pods. Matt was still in college, as it happened, so Dave had to keep his boat for him for a while. It seemed only right that he should make sure the new purchase worked.

One summer morning Dave and I tried her, rowing double, on Lake Megunticook. We took it easy in terms of both speed and distance, and marveled at how easily she went even under our far-from-expert efforts. This boat has a really lovely shape, being a beautifully stretched-out whaleboat.

By now I was thoroughly confused as to which sliding-seat recreational rowing boat was my favorite.

* * *

I was intrigued with the 18-foot Tad Single, because she is all decked over, with just a tiny watertight cockpit for the sliding seat and your feet. When I revealed this interest to Tad Spranger, the man who created the boat out in Costa Mesa, California, nothing would do but that he ship me one to try right away.

"What color do you want?" I was asked.

"What colors have you got?" I responded. (What the heck.) I finally settled for a dark blue hull with a cream-colored deck. When I slid her out of the biggest carton I've ever seen in my life onto my lawn, she looked absolutely gorgeous.

She's another skinny tadpole sort of boat, really sleek and graceful. I liked the idea of such a tippy boat being fully watertight. Screw-in ports in the cockpit give access to a small amount of dry storage space. There's a drain in the deck at the very stern, so if any water should get inside the fiberglass hull, you can tip her over on land and drain it out.

Her sliding seat and foot pads are built right in, the latter being adjustable, of course. Her tubular metal outriggers are very easy to put on and off. There's a little brass plate that slips into a notch in her bottom, back aft, so you have a skeg to help keep her going straight.

I tried her on Lake Megunticook in the cold weather of early winter. Thought mighty hard about not tipping over, for when I waded in barefoot to install the oars in the locking-type racing oarlocks, the water was painfully cold. The watertight deck and cockpit did give me a sense of security, but in such frigidity I sure didn't want to test my ability to right her, get back aboard somehow, and resume rowing. I made short miles of it around the lake and was grateful to get back dry. But then I had to go wading again to retrieve my oars. (Haul

The Tad Single at speed.

her out, silly, you say, but there's that little bendable skeg sticking down.)

How these fliers do shrink a body of water! I often row and sail on the lake, for I live nearby, and it's always seemed a fairly big place to me. Rowing on it in a sliding-seat boat is akin to skating on it: you get where you're going and back again before you know it.

* * *

I approached the Saroca with considerable skepticism. Her very name put me off. You can sail it, row it, use it like a canoe, claimed the advertising, and the promoters named the boat accordingly. I found myself wondering if the thing could also walk, talk, and crawl on its belly like a reptile. After sailing, rowing, and paddling the boat, my skepticism changed to a healthy measure of respect.

Jan W. Dorfman, the innovator who designed this new and different kind of boat, kindly had a Saroca trucked right to the Public Landing at Camden Harbor, where she was at my disposal for a couple of weeks in midsummer.

The Saroca turned out to be the most stable of all the sliding-seat rowing boats I tried, with the exception of one that cheated by having more than one hull. She's 16½ feet long with a beam of 56 inches and a weight of 140 pounds.

And the Saroca turns out to be well named after all, for she is first and foremost a sailing boat, second a rowing boat, and last a canoe. In hull shape she's sort of a skinny IOR racer, and I found her light 'n' lively under sail, very fast — and quite wet in anything of a head sea. She was not unduly tender under sail.

Under oars, her great stability did away with my nemesis, feeling as if I were going to tip over every time I twisted round to see where I was going. One day I rowed her across the harbor in thick fog and discovered a new problem. You go so fast in a sliding-seat rowing boat that when it's thick, you spend the whole time with your body contorted, trying to keep a proper lookout. There's hardly time to row. Even at that you have a hard time holding her back so you could stop her in half the distance of visibility.

This boat carries a passenger very well. Rowing with a passenger is really living: the passenger becomes the lookout, points out a safe heading with a vertical palm (fingers together, extended), and all you have to do is pull harder on one or the other of your oars to bring the passenger's palm to the centerline.

The Saroca has a deep daggerboard for sailing, of course, and a short daggerboard for rowing. This gives her something to spin round on; she turns very easily under oars, not a common attribute of the sliding-seat rowing boat.

The three-cockpit arrangement is great. You sail and row in the midships cockpit. With the boat under oars, a passenger can sit at ease in the after cockpit on an elegant cane seat. You can close off these cockpits with waterproof covers when any of them are not in use. The "bridge deck" between the midships and after cockpit is useful. You can sit on it and push with the oars when maneuvering, such as making a landing. By far the easiest way to handle her.

As a two-handed canoe, with a paddler in each of the end cockpits, the Saroca suffers a bit from the typical IOR malady: not enough buoyancy forward.

I had a lot of fun rowing and sailing this boat. She was different enough to be really interesting.

* * *

It was a great experience breaking into the edge of the sliding-seat recreational rowing movement. I have a few lasting impressions to carry me forward into my next semester of sliding-seat rowing.

You are rowing along in one of these long, skinny boats, struggling with every stroke. First your right oar digs too deep. You start to lose your balance on the next stroke and almost have to abort. On the next one, your left oar pops right up out of the water with a great splash. Oh dear, oh dear. So you take it a little easier just trying to get the rhythm. And suddenly you put about five strokes together that seem effortless, and looking aft, you notice that your skinny boat is pulling up something of a swell behind her. You have her going nearly at hull speed. Beautiful.

Yet the great thrill of sliding-seat rowing is not the speed so much as the distance you feel you can cover. As children, we used to talk about rowing from the Rhode Island beach the dozen miles out to Block Island. We weren't serious, of course. But with a sliding seat under me, I could get serious about something like that.

You're so low to the water in a sliding-seat boat that you feel an unusual oneness with sound, bay, river, or lake. You're right down with the water, right among the waves. You feel like an incredibly fast swimmer, almost as if you had truly returned to the sea.

* * *

The Rowcat hardly noticing powerboat waves.

Stephen Richardson is a Renaissance man. His profession is medicine. His modern house, facing Long Island Sound at Riverside, Connecticut, holds a lot of books on all kinds of things. He plays a lot of music and goes to a lot of concerts. Drama fascinates him. He keeps dogs. He runs miles every day to stay in shape.

He's also a lifelong seaman. He has earned his living in merchant ships, sailed a wide variety of different kinds of boats, and raced under oars. He's a good oarsman, but he's also a real sculler.

Stephen is also the owner of a Rowcat. It's a sliding-seat rowing catamaran designed and built by Art Javes in Gulfport, Florida. Now I just *had* to try that one.

Stephen kindly fit me into his busy schedule, with the result that we got underway at six o'clock of a wintry morning. We trundled the boat down from Stephen's house to the shore on a practical, two-wheel dolly that he made to just fit her. With the drill he has worked out, this all went very smoothly, despite the fact that the Rowcat is quite a big contraption. They come single or double; Stephen's is a double, which means that the hulls are 24 feet long. She weighs 90 pounds. One thing I noticed right away: the Rowcat's 62-inch beam neatly solves the outrigger business.

A fresh westerly breeze was pushing up some decent-sized waves out on the sound, but it was nice and quiet where we launched, for Stephen's beach was protected by a point of land. We rowed on up the cove, skirting round another little point where a bit of sea was making in from the sound.

Here was a whole new thing. You sit in a narrow, low-slung half-fuselage, just wide enough to take your sliding seats and supported by hulls at such a wide stance that the question of stability never crosses your mind.

The question of wetness does, though. Your bottom clears flat water, but most any wave worth the name can reach it for a little slap. At first you wince (at least I did), but then you remember that it's not your bottom that's getting slapped but that of the catamaran's fuselage. Meanwhile, seas sweep right over the low, thin hulls. No matter. They're watertight, of course, and filled with flotational stuff anyway.

Farther up the cove we found smooth water, and then

the houses and docks swept past. We turned her round, somewhat laboriously, to be sure, and headed back out. There was a bit of a slop going back round that little point, but, restraining ourselves, we slowed her down and stayed dry.

A fast boat with all this stability raises some interesting possibilities. Stephen envisions using his Rowcat as a cruising vessel, for instance. Build a light platform across her, take a tent and sleeping bags, and use a golf umbrella for a sail. Without the platform, he has used her as a perfectly safe training boat for neophytes pulling their very first oars of any kind; and with the platform, he has used her as a means of getting a relatively immobile invalid afloat.

As we eased the Rowcat back to the beach in front of Stephen's house, our early rising was rewarded by a spectacularly bright, half-cloudy sunrise. Yes, the light was certainly beginning to dawn.

5/ The Noank Smuggler

Length: 17 feet
Beam: 4 feet 10 inches
Draft: 1 foot 6 inches
Sail area: 105 square feet
Displacement: 550 pounds

Jaxon Vibber looked none the worse for wear, even though he had spent the night in the somewhat cramped quarters of my Tancook whaler (see Chapter 41). Jaxon used to be a boatbuilder at Justin Camarata's Golden Era Boats in Noank, Connecticut, and he was on a sort of busman's holiday, trailing one of Golden Era's fiberglass reproductions of the 17-foot Newfoundland skiff Down East for some sailing and demonstrating. He'd launched her into Camden Harbor late the day before, and had tied up for the night alongside the Tancook whaler.

So it was from this berth that we got underway on a nice summer morning, without much breeze as yet, to row down the harbor and out into Penobscot Bay.

The Newfoundland skiff, Howard Chapelle tells us in *American Small Sailing Craft,* is a type that originated in Nova Scotia, where it was known as the Toulinguet boat; it was introduced into Newfoundland sometime before 1870. The boats were round-bottomed, with well-raked ends and a wineglass transom, and a deep enough full-length keel to enable them to work to windward without a centerboard. They were used for sealing, fishing, and — doubtless — for fetching and carrying.

The Newfoundland skiffs were jib-and-mainsail boats with sprit rig. Justin kept the sprit rig in his first replicas but was a little disappointed with the sailing qualities of the boat, particularly in light weather, and so tried a gunter rig. He was so pleased with the way the change smartened her up that he decided to call his gunter-rigged version the Noank Smuggler.

It was a Smuggler, rather than a mere skiff, that Jaxon and I were rowing out of Camden Harbor. I found her quite a heavy boat to row; that is, it took a few hard strokes to really get her going. Once you had expended that effort, however, it was easy to keep her moving right along. She carries her way beautifully between strokes. (Because of this characteristic and her low freeboard, she'd be a fine boat to row against a breeze, if for some reason you didn't want to make sail.)

She doesn't turn when you don't want her to; when you do, she turns majestically. The oars we had were fine except that they were blade-heavy; needed more weight in the inner looms.

The Noank Smuggler is 17 feet long, with a beam of 4 feet 10 inches, and a draft of 1 foot 6 inches. Her hull weighs 550 pounds, of which 150 pounds is outside lead in the keel. Her sail area is 105 square feet.

Her hull has lots of flare, which looks good and gives her bearing as she heels. The flare is carried out into the handsome wineglass transom. She has a pronounced hollow in her waterlines both forward and aft. "The boats have an exceptionally long fine run for an open boat," wrote Mr. Chapelle.

As we rowed out past Curtis Island, a breeze was

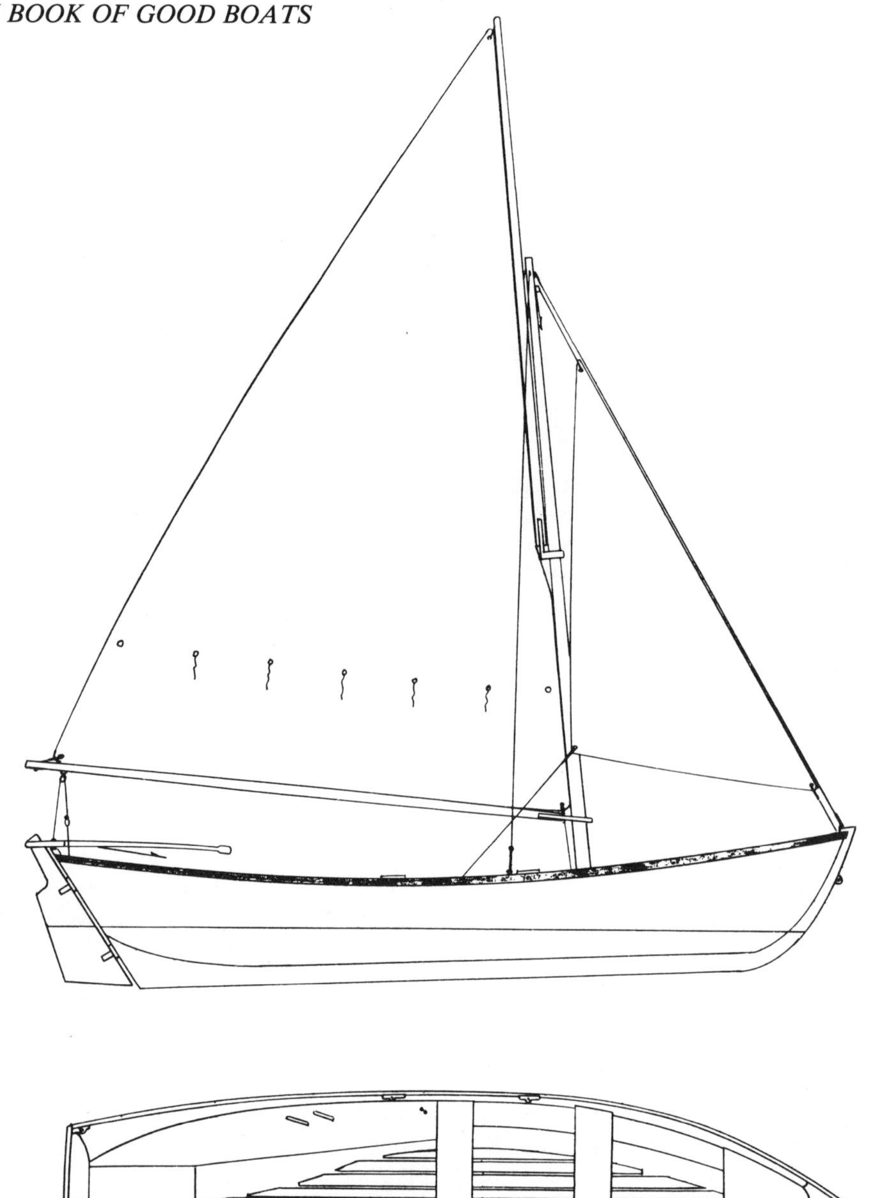

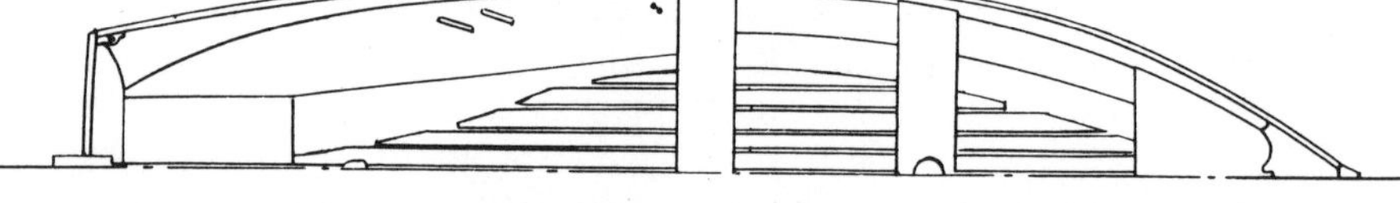

Profile and interior half-breadth plans of the Noank Smuggler. (Golden Era Boats)

darkening the water to the southeast, so Jaxon set up the rig and hoisted mainsail and jib. No great chore, I noticed. There is a topping lift on the boom, so you can get the spar up out of your way when rowing toward your breeze.

The gunter rig is taller than the sprit but has been kept fairly low, which is only proper, for this boat doesn't have huge amounts of stability. She would profit from my narrow side decks. The Noank Smuggler has plenty of flotation built into her unobtrusively under her bow and stern seats and all along her sides.

As Jaxon was making sail, I noticed that the spars and their fittings were very nicely made: the work I believe, of Rick Conant when he was at Golden Era. And the boat herself shows much evidence of the competence and care of her builders. Her heavy mahogany gunwales, mahogany seats, and oiled fir sole are all nicely made; and her fiberglass hull is strong and without blemish.

Breeze and boat reached each other; we shipped the oars and we trimmed her in close-hauled to weather the ledges at the mouth of the harbor. Jaxon went up into the bow and curled up looking aft to watch her go, so I slid aft so she wouldn't be down by the head. There was

Left: *The Noank Smuggler on her trailer. Note the Seagull outboard clamped to the transom.* **Right:** *The Smuggler chuckling along with Jaxon Vibber grinning in the stern. (Golden Era Boats)*

quite a little lop of left-over sea for her to pitch into. And pitch she did; she went up and down more than she went ahead. What a disappointment! Of course our weight in the ends of the boat wasn't helping her, but still. I had just begun to compose the paragraphs of a diplomatic letter to Justin commiserating with him about the sailing performance of his boat when Jaxon moved aft again and I slid forward automatically to keep her balanced. With an "It's about time," the Smuggler picked up her skirts and started off, footing just fine, thank you. Getting the weight out of her ends made a much more enormous difference than I anticipated. I tore up my letter to Justin.

We headed out across the bay toward Mark Island, full and by. The Smuggler has a handy cleat on either side so you can take a turn with the mainsheet to leeward on either tack. Jaxon showed me a new kind of slippery hitch to use, a turn round the horn with a bight jammed under such that a yank pulls it completely free of the cleat instantly. A useful trick in a small, open boat.

Windward ability is not a top priority for the Noank Smuggler; nor was it, of course, in the working Newfoundland skiff. She foots very well close-hauled, but she does make a bit of leeway. It's just a trifle discouraging to sail her to windward trying to make every foot to weather that you can on each tack, until you remember the sort of vessel you are in and get yourself into the frame of mind of a master of a coasting schooner who expects to have to be patient to make big gains to weather. Meanwhile, you can revel in the fact that there is no big centerboard trunk cluttering up the best part of the boat. One thought, though, would be to put a very short daggerboard trunk just abaft the mast: it wouldn't take up much room, and a narrow, deep board would give you the option of hanging on a bit better and tacking faster when working to windward in deep water.

We stood two-thirds of the way to Mark Island with a fine little sailing breeze, but it was getting thick in the outer bay, so presently we tacked back in for the land. She weathered Beauchamp Point after a couple of short hitches. We snuck through inside Indian Island, grateful for our shoal draft but still watching closely ahead for stray rocks, and ran up into Rockport Harbor.

Jaxon unerringly picked out all the interesting boats at anchor — there are lots of them in Rockport — and as we sailed past them we nitpicked sheerlines, sterns, and rigs. We made a landing alongside the float at the marine park at the head of the harbor and ate our picnic up on the bulkhead so we could look down on the little vessel and admire her.

With that accomplished, we beat out of Rockport into a rising southerly. I had sailed her to Rockport, so Jaxon sailed her back to Camden. It breezed up to moderate, maybe even fresh at times, and Jaxon sailed the Smuggler out nicely, planning his tacks among the anchored boats, keeping her footing fast, and allowing only a few dollops of spray from the making chop to climb over the gunwale. Yes, she does throw spray, like any boat of her type, when beating into a steep, nasty chop. Again we cheated Indian Island and Lowell Rocks by going inside them instead of beating out around.

When we freed her sheets, to run up the shore to Camden, she took off like a wild hunted thing. Not that she was hard to steer, even though she was flying. I was afraid Jaxon might fall asleep back there, he looked so relaxed at the tiller.

Fly she did. Of course she has a nice long waterline, which you tend to forget somehow, in an open boat. If you're sitting fairly well forward in the bottom of the boat, the nearby crests whip past right at eye level.

This was real *Bounty*-launch stuff. I was off watch trying to sleep, but unable to avoid peeking, fascinated, at the big seas that would roll up high astern. The boat tore along down them, Jaxon guiding her around their broken tops automatically and, looking ahead from their heights, trying for the thousandth time to decide if the palm trees ahead were real or imaginary. A hand drooped overboard into the water of Penobscot Bay startled me out of this tropical reverie.

We ran into Camden Harbor inside Curtis Island, and Jaxon elected to bring her up and tack in the moderate breeze rather than jibe her, a seamanlike choice. This we did, and then smoked up the harbor on the other tack. We rounded up to land at an empty moored float in the middle of the inner harbor, stowed the rig, and then rowed on up to the head of the harbor to tie up again alongside the Tancook whaler.

Two little vessels from away Down East. Finest kind.

6/ The Lightfoot

Length on deck: 21 feet
Length on waterline: 18 feet 3 inches
Beam: 6 feet
Draft: 1 foot
Sail area: 156 square feet
Displacement: 750 pounds light
Designer: Robert K. Johnson

Just as Rick Smith handed over to me the tiller of his Lightfoot sharpie, running down a foamy Kennebec River with one of her two spritsails set to a fresh northwester occasionally gusting to strong, she jibed.

None of us could have cared less. Her high, sprit-rigged boom slammed over harmlessly well above our heads, she heeled slightly, and we went flying along on the other tack faster than before. The accidental jibe was so benign that nobody had to apologize for it. Certainly Rick's wife, Sue, and their tiny son, Micah, sitting forward, were unconcerned. They just kept right on enjoying the sail.

As did we all. It was one of those glorious, bright, sunny days. We were the only sailing craft on the river.

Robert K. Johnson designed and built the Lightfoot sharpie for his own use as a family day boat in 1975. He was inspired, of course, by the New Haven sharpie. For his purposes, he increased the beam and freeboard of the type, thus sacrificing beauty and speed for stability, carrying capacity, and dryness. The funny thing is that those changes appear to be more appropriate to converting a pleasure craft to a workboat rather than the other way around, but I suppose the true, narrow, low-sided New Haven sharpie looks extreme to many eyes today. The point is that the Lightfoot is merely a handsome sharpie instead of being exquisitely beautiful. In particular, she's not as low and fine aft as the best-looking New Haven sharpies.

The Lightfoot is 21 feet long on deck, with a waterline length of 18 feet 3 inches, a beam of 6 feet, and a draft of about 1 foot. She displaces about 750 pounds light. Her sail area is 156 square feet.

Bob Johnson's original wooden Lightfoot sharpie sparked enough interest to convince him to set up a company to build fiberglass copies: Traditional Watercraft, in Indian Rocks Beach, Florida. Reuben Trane of the Florida Bay Boat Company in Miami has since purchased the molds and now produces the Lightfoot sharpie.

Rick, Sue, and Micah Smith keep their Lightfoot on her trailer in their backyard. We had put her overboard at the fine launching facility on the Bath side of the Kennebec. She launched easily once her trailer was backed far enough in so the boat was nearly afloat. She seemed reasonably light to handle around the trailer, and this was with her rig, motor, and all her gear stowed on board.

Usually when sailing a small boat, you start off to windward so as to keep some weather gauge in your pocket for going home. Not so on the Kennebec River. The tide floods at 3 to 4 knots and ebbs at a couple of knots more than that. You keep uptide, rather than worrying about weather gauge. Thus, we started off running down the river over the young flood.

And a beautiful river it is, big and majestic. When Mark Twain was debunking the glories of Europe, he belittled Mount Vesuvius by conjuring up the image of pouring "old Kennebec down her crater." "That'll still her fiery nater," he claimed. I wouldn't doubt it for a minute. The Kennebec moves a lot of water. She has well-wooded, bold shores whose ledges and rocks are well scoured by her strong tides. Our Lightfoot must have looked pretty on the river that day, with her dark green hull and tanbark sails. She stood up well to half her sail area and fairly flew in the gusts.

The vessel has enough plywood built into her bottom and decks not only to stiffen these flat surfaces, but also to give her positive flotation if swamped. She has the traditional sharpie's balanced rudder, given a modern, airfoil shape. I'd want a protective skeg for the rudder and also for the propeller of the outboard motor.

The boat's centerboard is offset by 9⅝ inches, to get it out of the middle of the cockpit and put it just inside the port seat locker. It's a heavy board, raised and lowered with a winch consisting simply of two drums of different diameters. I noticed that the board was off-center before we got underway, but must confess I forgot all about it once we were sailing. She seemed to sail just as well on one tack as she did on the other.

The Lightfoot's tiller is well inboard of her rudderpost, so it turns a quadrant linked to another quadrant on the rudderpost by a ⅛-inch, 7 x 19 wire steering cable.

We ran on down the river under the bridge, past the busy Bath Iron Works and to Doubling Point, where we jibed again, this time intentionally. Upon doubling Doubling Point, we found some nice quiet water up under the weather shore. After a breather in this lovely millpond, we turned round and commenced to beat back up the river. It was time to face the music — plenty of closely spaced whitecaps with a few tide rips thrown in — but we would be encouraged in our ordeal by that greatest helpmate to a sailor beating to windward, a strong fair tide.

When we poked our long, straight bow out from behind the protection of Doubling Point, she heeled a bit, speeded up, and began to slap and pound. When she hit one wrong, the pounding was accompanied by a bit of spray. Micah, who had fallen asleep off the Iron Works despite the interesting naval vessels tied up there, awoke only when a trickle of river water ran down off the oilskin pants thrown over him and dripped on his nose. How many 21-foot boats go sailing around in a fresh and gusty breeze with children asleep on board?

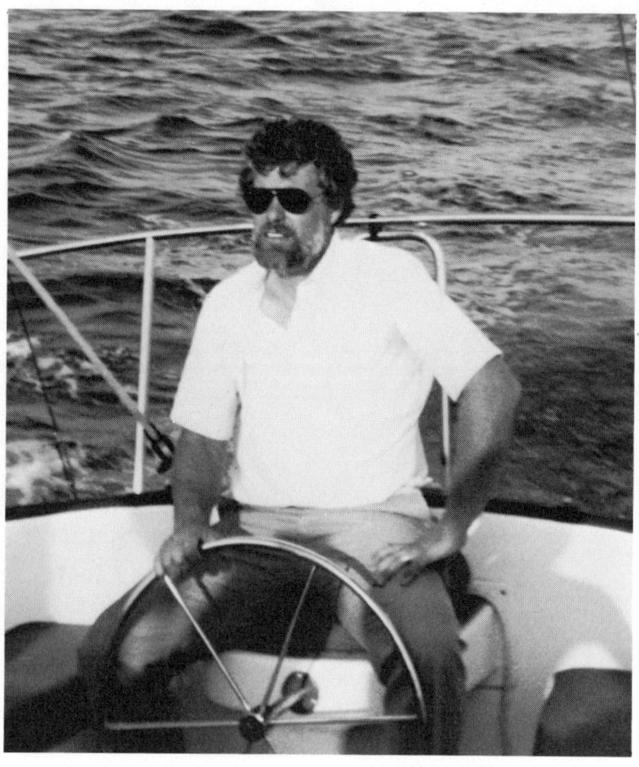

Robert K. Johnson.

The Lightfoot felt very lively going to windward in the gusts. She accelerated like mad and was in no danger whatsoever of being overpowered. She didn't heel much, hence the pounding. In a flat-bottomed boat, pounding is just something up with which you have to put. She lost quite a bit of way when tacking, but I think this was due more to the fluky conditions (you know what a northwester is like in New England) than to the boat's design.

The Lightfoot's rig goes up easily and can be struck easily. The masts are interchangeable; they are unstayed. Masts and sprits are all 14 feet long and stow handily in the huge spaces opened by the hinged cockpit seats. All the spars are aluminum, the masts being coated with epoxy. They are light to handle. The sails lace to their masts, and you set them and furl them by rotating the masts by hand in their steps. The sprits and booms set up easily, the former to hold the peaks up and the latter to hold the clews aft and down. There's only a two-part purchase on the sheets. Not enough. It ought to be three. I found it hard work holding the sheet when the northwester came breezing on.

The rig is the traditional cat ketch of the New Haven sharpie (though that craft was rigged with leg-o'-mutton sails) and of many other small American working craft. For sailing with one mast — as we were — there's a

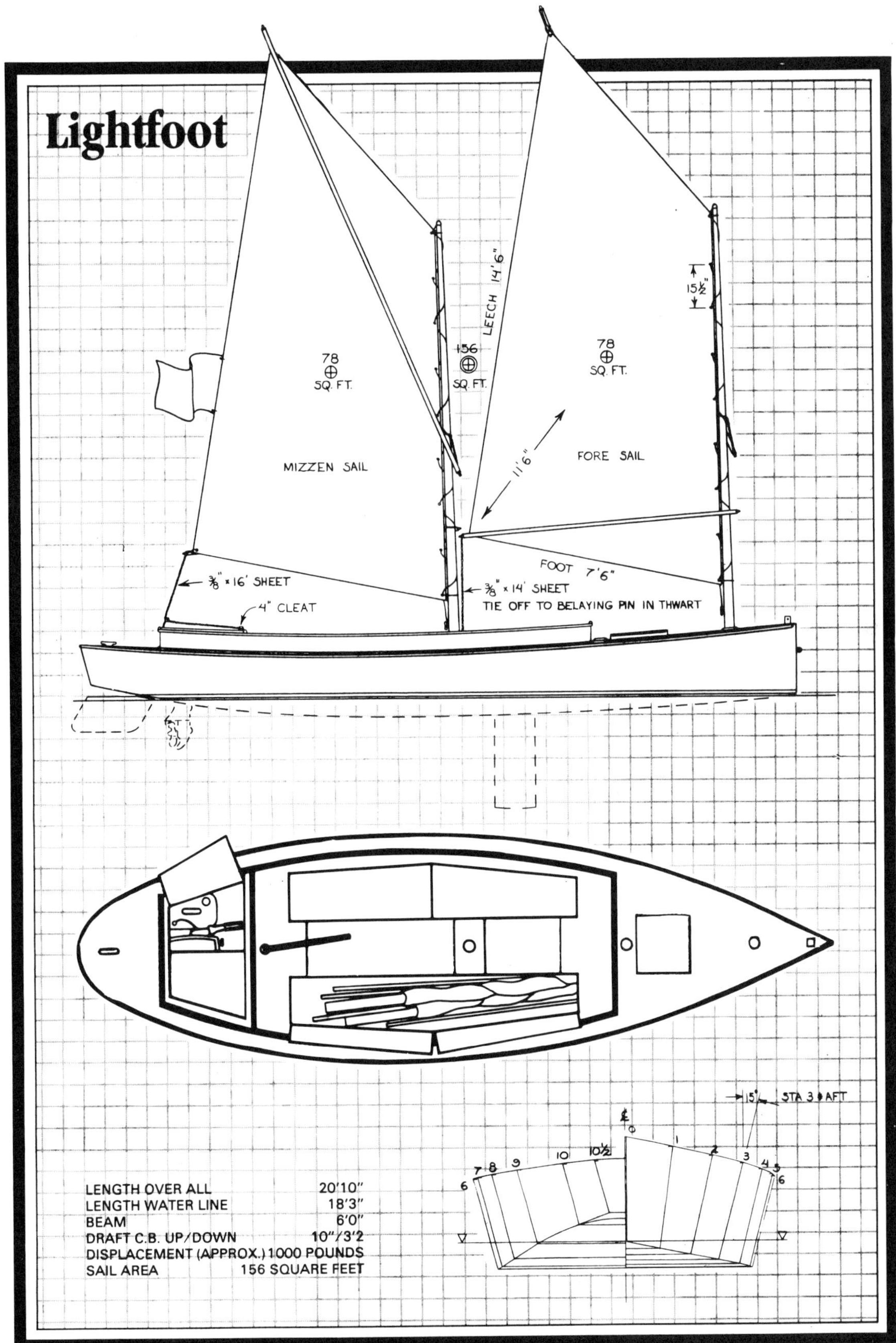

Plans of the Lightfoot sharpie. (The Small Boat Journal)

Ah, shoal draft. (All photos courtesy Robert K. Johnson)

Wing-and-wing.

Under power.

The whole rig can be stowed "below."

The engine room.

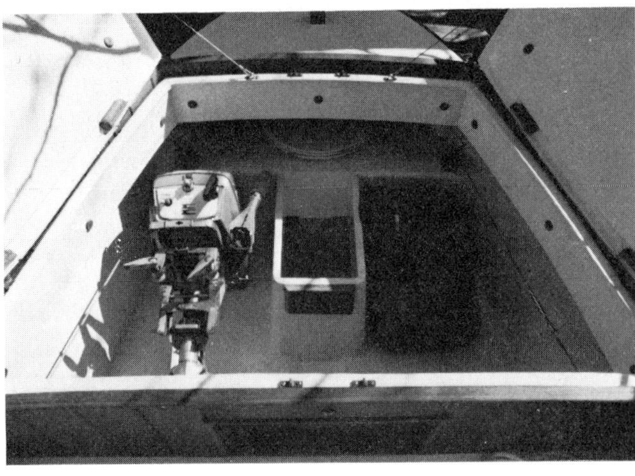

third mast position to put the single sail amidships and keep the boat balanced. This is a great rig that lets you shorten the rig right down by half very easily. I'd want at least one fairly deep reef in each sail, too, so you could shorten down less than 50 percent and so in a hard chance you could scud along with just one sail, reefed.

With our strong fair tide, we made short miles of it back up the river. We did all right through the water, and we did just marvelously over the bottom. Is there anything more fun than working to windward with a strong fair tide under you? We let the tide wash us back under the big bridge and waved back to some youngsters doing a bit of daredevil climbing on the railroad tracks.

The Lightfoot is steady on her helm, has a very light, easy helm, and responds to her rudder with certainty. There isn't quite the normal direct sensitivity of tiller to rudder because of the quadrant-and-cable arrangement, but all in all she's a great pleasure to steer.

She has a majestic, purposeful appearance to her as you glance fore and aft from the tiller. Part of this look comes from her long, straight bow, part from her nicely rounded sharpie stern, and part from her substantial bitts on bow and stern. There's also something that grows on you about the squareness of her fairly high cockpit coaming and her engine room "house," the very squareness that may put you off a bit at first sight. It did me. The square coaming is not as comfortable to lean against as one slanted outboard, and it's so high that you can't see the lee gunwale. But somehow the structure goes with the simple and homely (in the best sense of the word) character of the sharpie.

The cockpit is huge for a 21-foot boat. The seats are wide; the footwell is not too wide. The footwell floorboards can be raised to make one huge, flat surface for sleeping on board under a tarp. The whole boat is open under the cockpit seats, and besides plenty of room for the rig and any spare gear you might want to carry, there's room down there for about four people to stow away. (Good idea to check before getting underway.) She also has a big forepeak under the hatch in the foredeck.

The Lightfoot has the least obtrusive outboard motor installation I have ever seen. She has a separate engine room, insulated to keep the machine quiet. The motor can be left mounted in its well, ready for instant use, or it can be hauled inboard and laid down flat in the engine room. In either case, a fairing plug is lashed into place in the well opening. An exhaust line leads out through the side of the boat. There's a sliding door in the forward bulkhead of the engine room so you can get at the engine controls without opening the engine room hatches. You can rig a remote shifting control through the bulkhead. It's a well-thought-out engine installation. A 6-horsepower motor drives the boat at 6 knots. She'd make a fine motor launch. You can also row her with a pair of 10-foot oars. The Connecticut oystermen did plenty of that.

Above the bridge, we tacked over to see the Key West smackee that had been recently launched by the Apprenticeshop of the Maine Maritime Museum. A very handsome boat indeed, we thought, and she ought to be a flier with her big rig. So a New England type of boat built in Florida paid her respects to a Florida type built in New England. Oh, the wonders of the modern world.

We landed at the Smiths' float on the Woolwich side of the river so Sue and Micah could go ashore and walk home through the woods. Then we sailed back across the river to the launching ramp. There was no room to round up at its float to kill her way and make a landing, so I began mumbling to Rick about rounding up off the float and letting her drift in. Rick shrugged unconcernedly and said that if I'd sail her in to the float, he'd take a stern line ashore. Then I remembered that our sail was really a flag that we had simply not let fly all afternoon, instead using it to catch wind. So we simply eased her in alongside the float with our flag flying like a flag over the bow. Duck soup. The possibilities of sailing a boat with flags instead of sails are limitless. A shiphandler's delight. Slow down all you want to off the wind. Lie-to instantly on any point of sailing. What boat could be safer?

Rick and Sue and Micah Smith are exceedingly happy with their Lightfoot sharpie. "Occasionally," Rick says, "you get a material possession that exactly suits your intended use for it. This boat is one of those rare finds." He says she's a great picnic boat for the Kennebec River, sailing well in a light breeze or a fresh one, and, with her shoal draft, able to put ashore nearly anywhere. She's also a true 50—50 boat, as good under sail as she is under power, and as good under power as she is under sail.

I think the Lightfoot is a great family day boat for sheltered water. The simplicity and speed of the sharpie type is wonderful.

7/ The Doughdish

Length on deck: 15 feet 10 inches
Length on waterline: 12 feet 6 inches
Beam: 5 feet 10 inches
Draft: 2 feet 6 inches
Sail area: 140 square feet
Displacement: 1,500 pounds
Designer: Nathanael G. Herreshoff

Bill Harding hoisted the jib on his Doughdish with the mainsail still in stops, and I was just about to shoot him a questioning glance when he sheeted the little sail flat, spinning the boat round and running her off the wind. I hadn't even seen him cast off the mooring.

We loosed the mainsail and set it. Bill motioned me to the tiller, and off she went on a broad reach out of Hospital Cove, Cataumet, Cape Cod, with full sail set to a fluky southerly that was gentle to fresh at times and mostly moderate.

The first thing I noticed is that you can see all around in this boat, for the boom rises at a jaunty angle.

The second thing I noticed was that she feels like every other Herreshoff I have ever sailed: fast, responsive, and a thoroughbred in every way. The Doughdish has the usual Herreshoff weather helm, and in this case the boat is so tiny it's light as a feather.

She is pretty to watch go through the water when you're not on board her, as I learned when Bill dropped me off on the stern of a moored sloop out by Scraggy Neck so I could take some pictures.

Then we set out into Buzzards Bay, and I realized a lifelong dream: sailing in a Herreshoff 12½-footer — in the very waters for which the boat was created.

This dream had endured some hard times. To be sure, Pop was a great enthusiast of the 12½-footers, but another of my mentors, Ed Cabot, used to heap great scorn upon them. The poor little boats were always the butt of his Buzzards Bay racing stories, and he could say Doughdish so quick it had only one syllable and you had a hard time believing in a boat with such a no-count name. But of course Ed used to race in the E class, the big Herreshoff 15s, and those great racing yachts would sail rings round a measly little 12½-footer. My dream was sustained one rough day, when we came upon a 12½-footer in the middle of Buzzards Bay reaching happily along under full sail with six grown-ups on board.

Some of the E boat racers thought their boats too much of a handful for their children learning to sail. Robert W. Emmons and others went to Nathanael G. Herreshoff in 1914 and asked him to design a smaller boat, more suitable for their children but still able to cope with the strong winds and big, steep chop of Buzzards Bay.

For Nat Herreshoff and the Herreshoff Manufacturing Company at Bristol, Rhode Island, 1914 was quite a year. A New York Yacht Club syndicate wanted him to make sure once again that the America's Cup stayed on the west side of the Atlantic; he kept the big mug here with a 75-foot-waterline cutter, the great *Resolute*. A wealthy yachtsman wanted a huge cruising schooner;

Herreshoff designed one and the yard turned out the 115-foot-waterline beauty, the *Katoura.*

And that same year the Wizard of Bristol was conjuring different versions of his two-year-old *Alerion,* a 22-foot-waterline sloop with whose creation he was well pleased. In 1914 the Herreshoff yard produced a near sistership, the *Sadie,* and two classes of larger modifications: four Buzzards Bay 25-footers and three Newport 29s.

Nat Herreshoff thought the *Alerion* type would do well too for this "Buzzards Bay Boy's Boat," as he called the little 12½-foot-waterline vessel on her sail plan (1914 was pre-E.R.A.). She is the sort of boat a boy might draw while looking out the schoolroom window on a spring day, with her nicely curved bow, raked transom, strong, simple sheerline, and high-peaked rig. The 12½-footer has as handsome a hull as you can find.

Bill Harding thinks Captain Nat may also have been inspired by the keel catboats in which he had learned to sail. And the 12½'s stern is quite reminiscent of the pretty transoms of the Bahama sharpshooters. I doubt that there is any Bahama connection, though. Probably Captain Nat gave the Buzzards Bay Boy's Boat her lovely, raked, wineglass transom, rather than the short counter sterns of the other *Alerion* types, just to get maximum room, carrying capacity, and stability in such a short, beamy boat.

We went out into the Bay full and by on the port tack. It wasn't one of those real rough-and-tumble Buzzards Bay days when the sou'wester whistles and the seas heap right up, but the southerly had worked up its own lesser breed of chop, and there were some decent waves for a small boat. She would thrash into a series of them, taking all your attention for a minute. Then when it calmed down you would look back over the lee quarter to see if all that commotion had stopped her, and lo, she's still charging along, just seeming greatly to enjoy the whole business. We knocked her off a point and, of course, she really loved that. A little container ship came out of the canal and rumbled past to leeward. Efficient looking. Plain, to put it kindly. I wouldn't want to have to steer her. The pilothouse is so far forward that the jackstaff on the bow would be right in front of your face. The only way to gauge her swing would be to look aft. Her steep bow wave was a lee sea for us, so we bore off a few seconds to take it on the bow.

After we headed up again, we decided we had time to go to Marion before turning back. Being in a small boat, we could cut inside Bird Island, so rather than having to jam her right up on the wind, we held our close reach. She went along just fine. Bill and I were enjoying ourselves hugely.

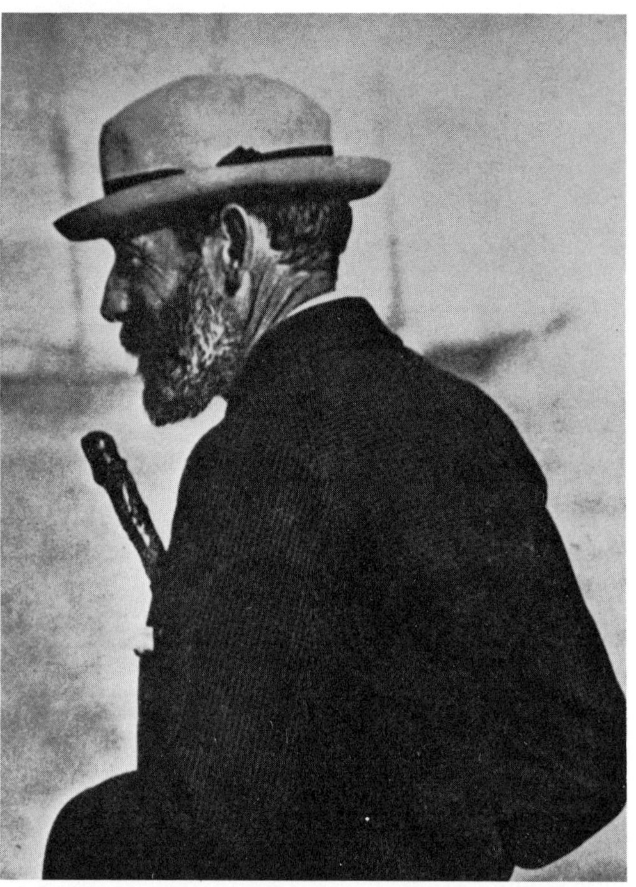

Nathanael Greene Herreshoff. (Captain Nat Herreshoff *by L. Francis Herreshoff, Sheridan House, New York)*

When the 12½-footers came out of the Herreshoff yard, they were called simply the "Buzzards Bay Class." The first one, contracted for on October 30, 1914, at $420, was Herreshoff Hull Number 744, the *Robin.* The dimensions given on the company's record of contracts are: length on deck, 15 feet 6 inches; waterline length, 12 feet 6 inches; beam, 5 feet 10 inches; and draft, 2 feet 5 inches. This record is handwritten; as near as I can make out, the name of the *Robin*'s owner is Stewart Duncan.

Eighteen more boats in the class were put under contract on November 14, 1914. These 19 boats were delivered for the 1915 season.

They caught on. A few more were built every year, another 38 boats having been added to the class by 1924. By this time the price had more than doubled, to $900. In the next seven years, the class really took off; by 1931, another 154 boats had been built. There was another big building spurt between 1935 and 1943 that produced 146 boats. This made 357 Buzzards Bay Class 12½-footers turned out by the Herreshoff Manufactur-

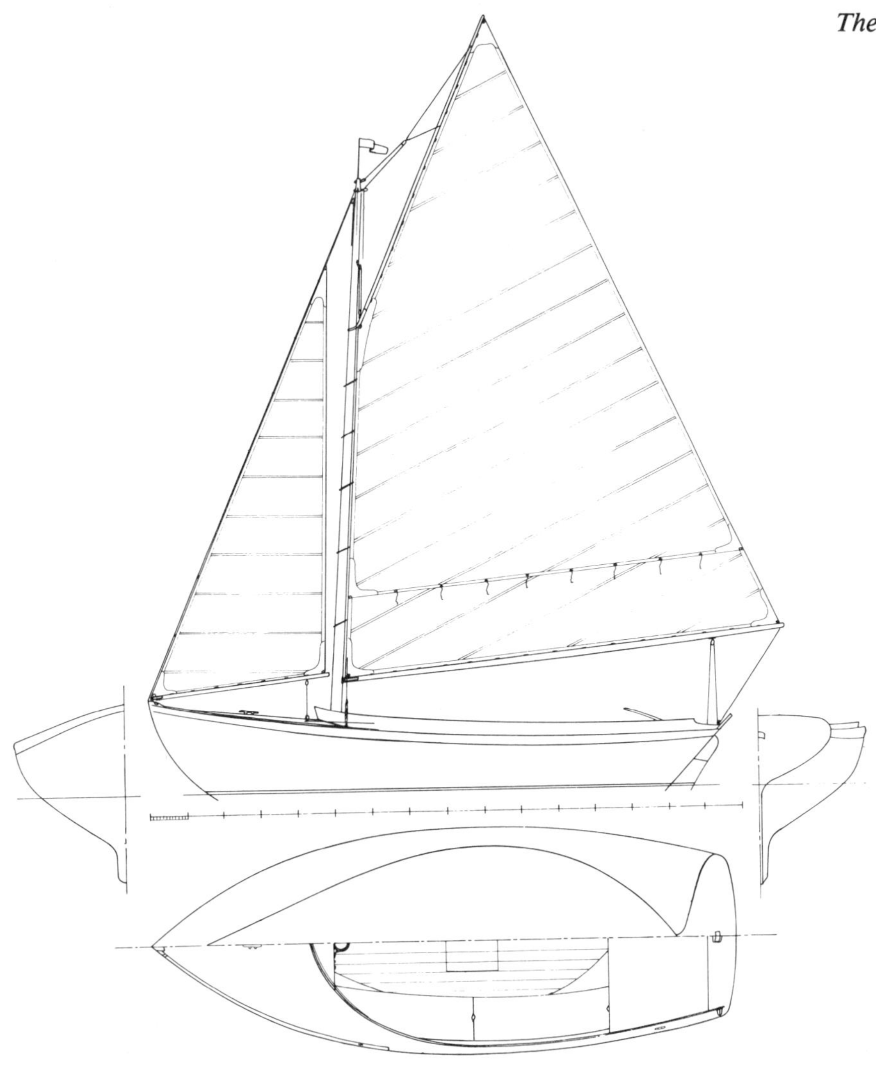

Plans of the Herreshoff 12½-footer Doughdish. (Doughdish Inc.)

ing Company. The price per copy had climbed to a high of $1,100 in the late Twenties and then dropped back to a Depression low of $790.

The first 12½-footer built with a marconi rig was Hull Number 901, D.W. Flint's *Wanderer Jr.;* she came out in 1924. The company began calling the marconi-rigged 12½-footers Bullseyes. By then scornful E-class racers were calling the gaff-rigged 12½s Doughdishes. To this day, Bullseye implies a marconi-rigged 12½-footer and Doughdish implies a gaff-rigged boat. Buzzards Bay sailors have kept to the gaff rig, while more fashionable racing classes in places like Marblehead and Fishers Island have fancied the marconi.

The boats may have been designed for boys to learn to sail, but girls, men, women, and old-timers of both sexes couldn't keep their hands off them. The 12½-footers were raced from the beginning, racing being thought to be good training for the young and good experience for the not-so-young. To say nothing of fun for all. Along the way, a single-luff spinnaker was added to the boat's basic equipment. In 1937, the Beverly Yacht Club had a fleet of 75 of these boats racing.

The last 12½-footer turned out by the Herreshoff Manufacturing Company was Hull Number 1518 in 1943. In 1947 and 1948, the Cape Cod Shipbuilding Company built 30 of these 12½-footers. The Quincy Adams Yard built 10. Occasionally you still hear of another 12½-footer being built. Just a few years ago McKie Roth built one for Andy Nixon at North Edgecomb, Maine.

Cape Cod Shipbuilding later came out with a fiberglass version of the Bullseye. They used the basic design of the 12½-footer, but the idea was not to duplicate the

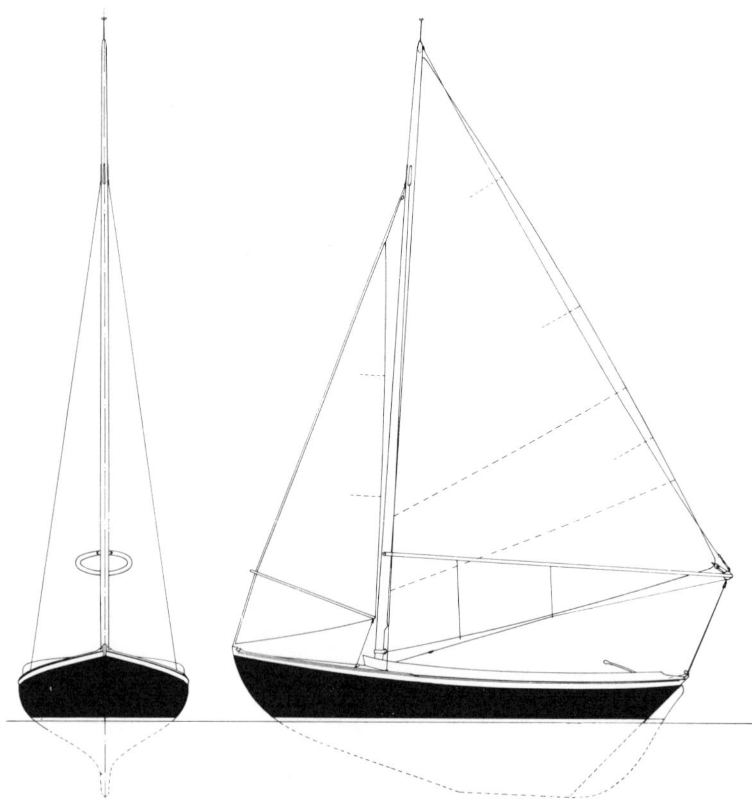

About 1935, the Herreshoff Company came out with a "modernized" sailplan for the Bullseye with wishbone booms on both sails.

wooden boats. The Cape Cod Bullseye has less displacement than the original, has a cuddy molded into the deck piece, and has aluminum spars. Some 700 of these boats have been built. Willard Wight has several for day charter in Camden, Maine, and every fall the locals race them in the harbor before he hauls them out. I crewed in one of these autumnal extravaganzas on a very blustery northwest day and was well impressed with the ability of the Cape Cod Bullseye to stand some heavy gusts. You just can't beat a good design.

Bill Harding estimates that some 250 original wooden 12½-footers are still in commission. Many of these boats are a half-century old; all are over 25. The biggest concentration is still in Buzzards Bay.

The H Class Association was formed in 1972 for the purpose of ensuring that the 12½-footers would keep on racing. The association held its first regatta in July of that year, and the next day Bill Harding got the idea of making a fiberglass reproduction of the 12½-footer that would duplicate the wooden original just as closely as possible. It seemed the only way to keep the class going indefinitely. To many Buzzards Bay sailors, a bay without Herreshoff 12½-footers would be no bay at all.

Bill Harding teamed with Peter Duff, of Edey and Duff, builders of the Stone Horse and other fine vessels, to develop the construction details of a foam-core fiberglass 12½-footer and to produce the boat. Naturally, they called their reproduction the Doughdish and their company Doughdish, Inc. Bill runs the business; Peter builds the boats. The company's headquarters is at Bill's sail loft (Harding Sails) in Marion, Massachusetts.

For a model, Bill took the lines off his own Herreshoff 12½-footer, one built in 1936. He also measured quite a few other boats to satisfy himself that his boat was typical.

The given dimensions of the Doughdish are: length on deck, 15 feet 10 inches; length on the waterline, 12 feet 6 inches; beam, 5 feet 10 inches; and draft, 2 feet 6 inches. Her displacement is 1,500 pounds, with 735 pounds of outside lead ballast. Her sail area is 140 square feet.

After a season of reproduction Doughdishes racing with originals, the class organization accepted the reproductions into the class. Doughdishes seem to sail about even whether they are built of wood or foam-core fiberglass. (The Doughdish beats a fiberglass Cape Cod

The Doughdish on her trailer. (Doughdish Inc.)

Bullseye in a breeze, but the Bullseye is a little faster in gentle going because of her lighter displacement.)

A reproduction Doughdish looks just like the original except that she has no frames visible inside and no seams visible inside or out. Bill Harding still has his 1936 12½-footer. She has been well cared for and is in excellent shape, but her hull is nowhere near as fair as that of her replica on the next mooring.

Bill Harding and Peter Duff have done a very satisfying thing in keeping alive one of the greatest small boat designs ever.

As we sailed along, Bill kept looking admiringly at the little boat he knows so well. He has sailed in a 12½-footer, just as we were doing, hundreds of times, but I could tell he still was fascinated to watch her go. "I couldn't live without one of these boats," he said. When he's not sailing a 12½-footer or making sails for one (or for some other boat), he likes to carve half models of 12½-footers. (His shop is right off his kitchen, so the models are handy to work on.) Bill says he never gets tired of carving that hull shape and of going over their form with a piece of sandpaper.

Bill Harding is a good sailor. In between watching that his little vessel was being sailed all right, he would stare hard around the horizon so as not to miss anything going on in his home waters. He would tend his peak halyard as the wind breezed up or eased off, or as we changed our point of sailing.

Once past Butler Point, we let her go off on a broad reach up into Marion. A big, handsome catboat came out making stately progress to windward. Bill the sailmaker noted how flat her big gaff mainsail looked in profile but how drafty you could tell it was after she went by and you could see the sail edgewise.

The boat population in Marion is 10 times what it was last time I was in there, some few years ago, to be sure. I was impressed by the general ugliness of the fleet, emphasized by the loveliness of the little boat we were sailing. We did find a Newport 29 hauled out at the head of the harbor and the Herreshoff Fishers Island 31 class sloop *Torch* on a mooring without her mast stepped yet (she was the *Scorpion* when she came out in 1930).

On a mooring up near the head of the harbor we found a green Herreshoff Fish class sloop that I used to

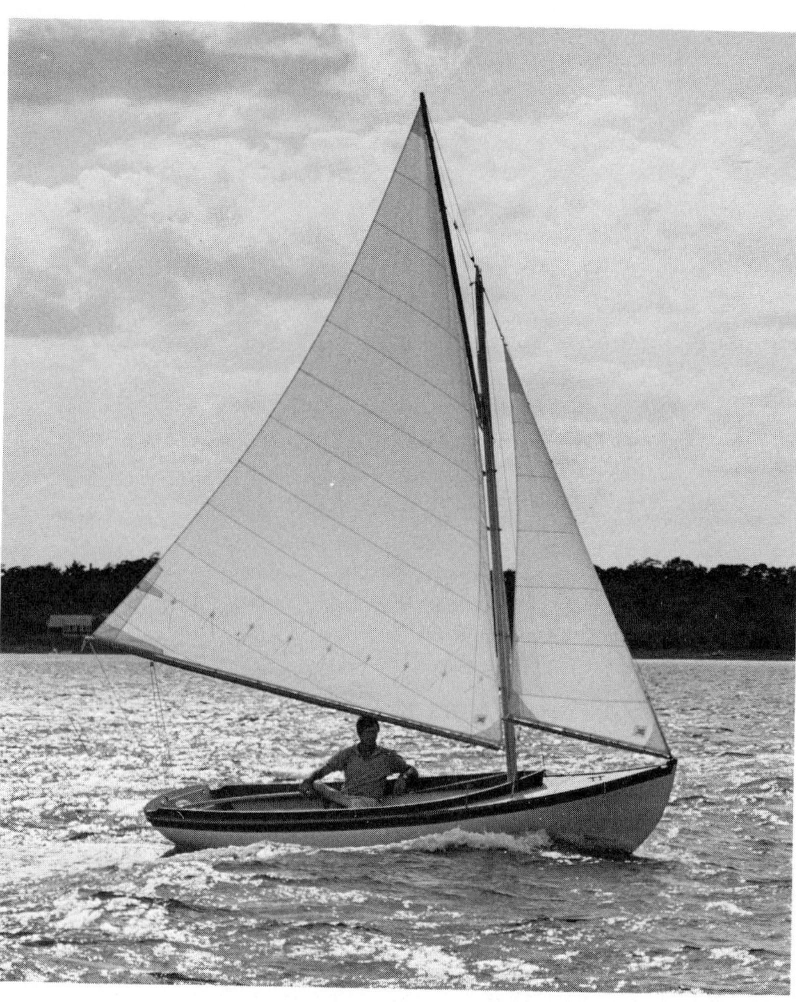

The Doughdish lifting along on a fast reach. (Doughdish Inc.)

see out cruising years ago. The Fish is a 12½-footer blown up to a waterline length of 16 feet. Bill luffed the 12½-footer right alongside the cruising Fish boat. She was as I remembered her except for the open cockpit, which I had thought was watertight. Her cabinhouse comes fairly well aft, so her cockpit is much smaller than that of a standard Fish boat. It's surprising to come upon a boat like that all of a sudden after not seeing her for 35 years.

We beat back out through the moored boats and worked up under the weather shore well out toward Blake Point before putting her about on a final starboard tack for home.

The Doughdish's Airex hull is ¾ inch thick; the material gives her a very strong, tough hull. She's generally less vulnerable in case of accident than is a wooden 12½-footer; and should she be damaged, is more easily repaired. One of the reproductions got ashore on Wing's Neck and pounded on the rocks for quite a while. Most of the damage she sustained was superficial, and she was repaired for $150.

The Doughdish has fiberglass decks and bulkheads. The decks are finished nonskid. The wood in the boat is teak. The beautiful stuff is used on the inner facing of the transom, the cockpit sole, the long cockpit seats, the nicely shaped coaming, the rail, and the wide sheer strake, molded to the traditional Herreshoff shape.

About 600 pounds of net positive flotation is built into the ends of the boat in the form of expanded foam behind the bulkheads. (The original 12½-footers had air chambers fore and aft for flotation.) So if she should swamp in a hard chance, she will keep you afloat until you can get her bailed out with a bucket or two. Two buckets take up the space of one bucket, but unless you are singlehanded, they bail twice as much water. Buckets are a great investment under any economic conditions.

The 12½-footer has a seaworthy hull. Her motion in rough water is corky but not uncomfortable, because all the lurches are damped out by her heavy keel. She won't pound or slap.

She can be wet because she's really very small, yet is

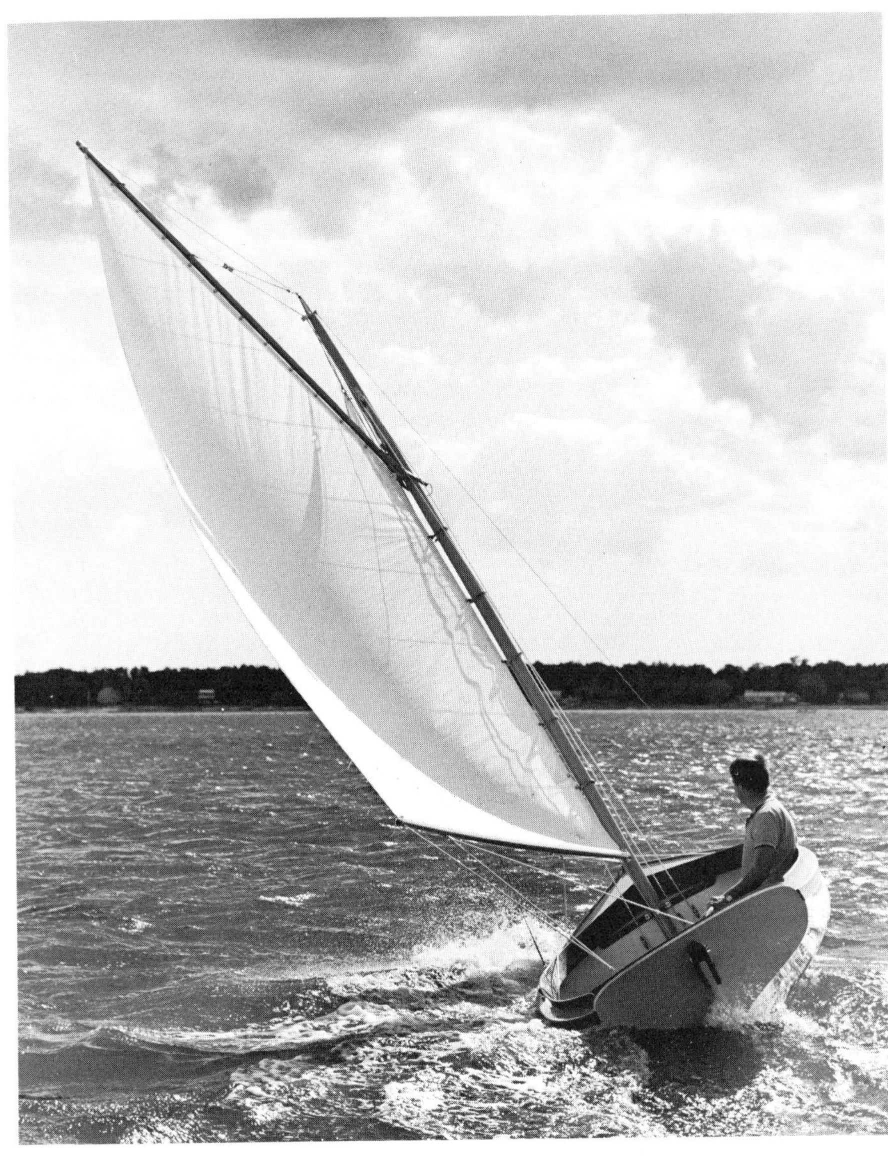

Hard at it. (Doughdish Inc.)

so seaworthy that you don't think twice about taking her into rough water — until the spray begins to fly. She is certainly drier than most boats her size.

The Doughdish's gaff rig is low and seamanlike. She has dainty Sitka spruce spars. Single shrouds lead from a cone-shaped masthead fitting that also takes the peak halyard blocks. She needs no backstays. A mast collar holds the mast up against the forward bulkhead while you set up the rigging, after which there is no strain on the collar.

The stemhead fitting is a neat bronze casting that makes the stem looked raised in profile like that of the original boat; it forms a sort of little breakwater for the eye for the headstay and jib club gooseneck.

The sails have no battens. They are nicely made of Dacron, many of them tan, by, of course, Harding Sails.

The mainsail has one shallow reef. Usually I don't have time for shallow reefs, but I have to remember that this is a racing boat. I would have another deep one for the hard chance I hope always to avoid. I would judge that when sailing to windward the Doughdish would be helped by a reef when it breezes up to 18 or 20 knots.

She has one of those "self-tending" jibs that you have to push another inch to leeward every tack before you're really satisfied with its trim. The 12½-footers originally came with a storm jib, but the working jib is small enough so that such a sail is probably not necessary.

The Doughdish's running rigging is all sensible and

seamanlike as to size, purchase, and hardware — except that the boats have no topping lift on the main boom. And after all my preaching about what good and faithful servants topping lifts are! Ask a topping lift to hold the boom up out of the way for a minute or an hour and he jumps right to it. Tell him you no longer need him and he slacks right away without complaint, being careful not to spoil the set of the sail he serves. Why would anyone fail to ship such a crew? The Doughdish does have a nice little boom crutch, which is useful when the mainsail is furled.

Our starboard tack took us full and by back between Butler Point and Bird Island. Then we could crack off just a bit and head back for Cataumet, bearing off a little extra to let the tide set us up under Scraggy Neck. The breeze increased a little, particularly after we passed Scraggy Neck and began beating up into Hospital Cove. In fact, the day began to feel decidedly raw. True, we were a bit damp around the edges, for although the boat is so maneuverable you can run her bow right off with a cross sea, rendering it harmless, the occasional little wave would shoot up the side with glee to let its top blow in over the coaming. The veed coaming makes a good breakwater, but it's not always high enough.

Oar and spinnaker pole lash up under the cockpit seats out of the way. Bill says the way to row a Doughdish is to push with one oar and steer. Under the cockpit sole, Bill carries the little bronze Herreshoff anchor that came with his 12½-footer of 1936 vintage. There is a small stowage compartment worked into each bulkhead.

Some of the early 12½-footers had a thwart across the cockpit about a third of the way aft, and the side seats ended at the thwart. I think that would be a fine rig. You could shift your weight anywhere across the boat to trim her just right when running or in a light breeze. You could sit facing forward or aft as well as to the side; and the forward end of the cockpit would be unobstructed for sailhandling or scrunching down out of the wet. It might be intriguing to try a little spray hood over the forward end of the cockpit.

Steering, you can sit on the after end of either cockpit seat or also sit up on the stern deck facing forward if she's not heeling over too much. I always wondered if on a lazy run in a 12½-footer you would lollygag about all the way aft using the transom as a backrest. You wouldn't; it's not high enough. (Besides, your crew would have to go way up forward to keep the boat in trim.)

The great thing about the cockpit of the 12½-footer is that it has no centerboard trunk. All the boats this size I have ever sailed in have had them. I used to get yelled at when racing because I couldn't hurdle the thing and trim the jib at the same time. I am here to tell you that sailing in a little boat with no centerboard trunk is some kind of luxury.

It was nice to beat up into Hospital Cove in smooth water. Ahead of us, on high ground, was the nice old family cottage that Bill winterized for living in year-round. Below it, at the edge of a sandy beach, was the little boathouse where the Doughdish spends the winter.

We got in and tied up in time for a late lunch. The forecast had promised us rain all day, but since we hadn't paid any attention, it didn't get started till ten minutes after we got ashore.

I think it's just grand that the small Herreshoff classes — the 12½-footers, the Fish class, the Herreshoff 15s, and even the *Alerion* herself — are again available in well-built reproductions. Of all of them, the Doughdish is the most faithful to the look and feel of the original boats turned out by the Herreshoff Manufacturing Company.

If I had any sense at all, I'd trade my soul for a Doughdish and put her by for my old age. Put her by?

8/ The *Dog Watch*

Length on deck: 16 feet
Length on waterline: 15 feet 6 inches
Beam: 7 feet 6 inches
Draft: 1 foot 9 inches
Sail area: 211 square feet
Designer: S.S. Crocker, Jr.

Join me, if you will, for an imaginary sail in a tiny cruising catboat — a mere 16-footer — designed by S.S. Crocker, Jr., nearly 40 years ago.

We join ship in the middle of a summer morning, running dead before a light southwest breeze that has just sprung up at the elbow of Cape Cod. We are heading up Chatham Harbor, that long, narrow estuary that is Chatham's quiet, main street, protected from the sea by Nauset Beach.

Now we have to mind our p's and q's going up through here, for there are plenty of sand flats to stop strangers who aren't watching the chart. Anyway, we've got a fair wind and a fair tide; what more could anyone want?

I think it's time to jibe that mainsail over to the starboard side and cross back in from the Nauset Beach side of this place to the Chatham side. The chart shows a big looping bar ahead, and the way around it is to the left. In this little breeze, you can just grab all three parts of the mainsheet together and haul the sail right on over.

Isn't this as pretty a little catboat as you've ever seen? If we duck down out of sight, she'd look like a 26-footer from a distance.

Her profile is certainly pleasing. I like the way the stem curves back a bit beyond the vertical, the way her springy sheer is carried out by the steeve of her bowsprit and the lines of her house sides and coaming. Her transom is raked just enough.

She has a nice, hollow entry that quickly widens out, giving her enough beam forward to keep the bow from plunging when running. Her waterlines are well balanced for a catboat, so her stern shouldn't lift too much when she heels.

She has plenty of stability, thanks to her great beam and also to the flare in the sections above the waterline, especially aft. Her transom wouldn't drag much, yet it gives her added bearing as she heels.

She has a well-formed run for such a short boat, a great advantage of shoal draft. In fact, there is just not much to her underwater. This is a very easily driven hull.

It's interesting to compare the rather sharp curves of her waterlines with the sweet ones of her diagonals.

This little vessel is 16 feet long on deck and 15 feet 6 inches long on the waterline. She has a beam of 7 feet 6 inches and a draft of 1 foot 9 inches.

But let's not get mesmerized by her hull shape. Time to jibe again and swing along past Tern Island. Don't you love to sail along like this in a deep channel with bare sand banks close aboard, just covered by the tide? Real *Riddle of the Sands* stuff.

Now let's look sharp, because there's one little bank

ahead, probably just covered up, that we've got to skirt around by eye. I think I see it right ahead, so keep off a mite and we should just clear it. There she comes, just on the weather bow.

I suppose it would be no great catastrophe to run up on that thing and have to wait an hour for the tide to lift us off, but as they say, "I'd rather be sailing." Now let's jibe her over one more time and put her on a reach past Allen Point.

This boat has some interesting construction details. She has so much in the way of partners and knees up around the mast that nearly the whole deck forward of the house is laid on heavy timbers. You'd want to be mighty fussy about keeping that deck tight so rot couldn't get at the heavy stuff.

Her big, heavy mast step forms an integral part of her backbone, well bolted to both stem and keel. A catboat's mast is always trying to twist the bow right off her, so it's well to build her Achilles heel mighty strong.

Her centerboard has a 14½-pound chunk of lead let into it so it will sink when lowered.

What do you say we try beating up through Bassing Harbor into Ryder Cove just to see what it's like up in there? We'll probably hit the board plenty and may even get hung up for a bit, but what the heck? The tide's coming.

Up into the narrow waters she goes, making tiny, short tacks with one person on the tiller paying the closest attention to the exact color of the water just ahead and the other holding the centerboard by its pendant as if it were a precise measuring instrument.

Her board slithers over the sand more than once, but that doesn't slow her enough to keep her from answering her helm and coming around to try the other tack. She's gaining across the pretty little harbor yard by yard and soon will be entering the relatively unobstructed, though narrower, water of the cove.

Here we are at its head. Let's anchor for lunch. Up comes the board, down goes the helm, and she rounds up and skids to a stop almost within her own length. The anchor is let go off the bowsprit, the sail is dropped before it can get her underway again, and a stop is passed casually around the boom and gaff end in case the breeze picks up.

A catboat, even a small one, has quite a heavy rig. This boat's boom is 16 feet long; her mast is 5½ inches in diameter at the deck. I'd put lazyjacks on her if she were mine — might as well get some automatic help in handling the mainsail.

A nice thing about a gaff-rigged catboat is that there are no shrouds on which to break the gaff jaws when you ease the boom broad off running in a breeze.

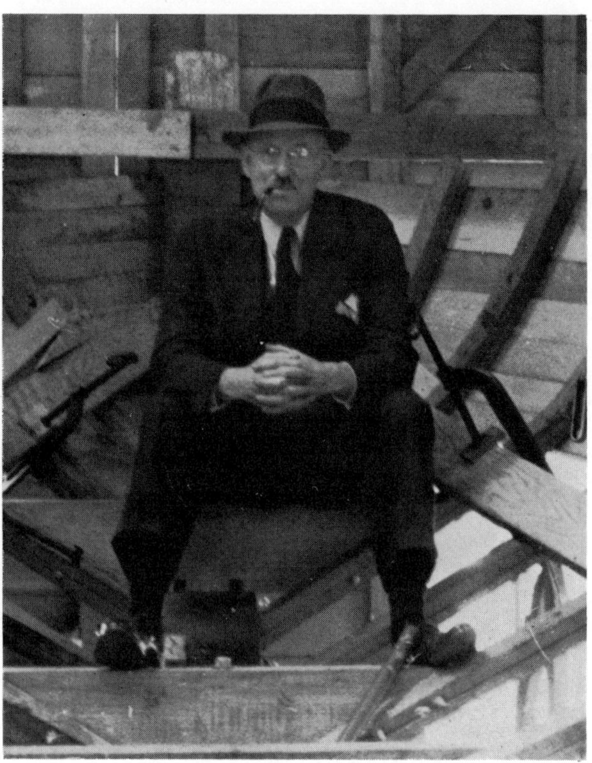

Sam Crocker. (Sturgis Crocker)

Her mainsail has 169 square feet, and that lovely roller jib adds another 42 square feet, making 211. The mainsail is nicely peaked up and has three good reefs. The jib can help lift her along in a light breeze (we've been too lazy to fool with it this morning) and really comes into its own on a broad reach when it's blowing hard, for then it helps hold her head off and eases the helm a lot. Shortening down off the wind, you'd want to leave the jib set and start reefing the mainsail, but shortening down on the wind, you would take the jib in first.

She was originally built with a short bowsprit and no jib, as shown in the construction plan, and was later given the longer bowsprit to take the headsail. Well worth it. And the longer bowsprit gives you a place to keep an anchor, which otherwise you'd have to handle from the cockpit. The foredeck of a catboat has about as much working space as the top of a flagpole.

The catboat rig has little windage, even taking the big, round mast into account, so her motor can drive her to windward easily. And even with the motor box right in the middle of the cockpit, she's still very roomy for daysailing. There are two 6-gallon gas tanks back in the quarters.

Well, I suppose if we're going to try to get all the way up to Meetinghouse Pond for the night, we'd better get

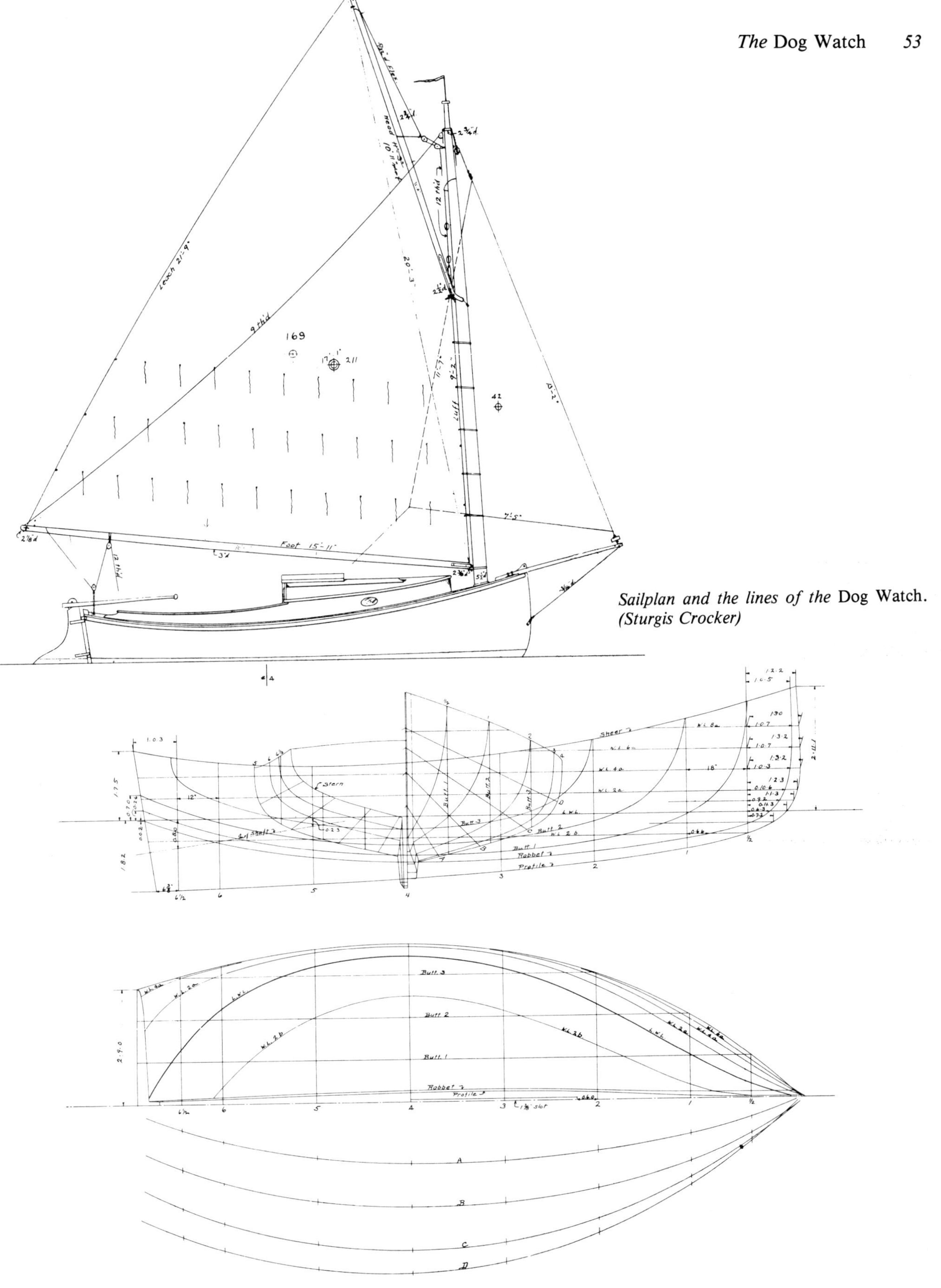

Sailplan and the lines of the Dog Watch.
(Sturgis Crocker)

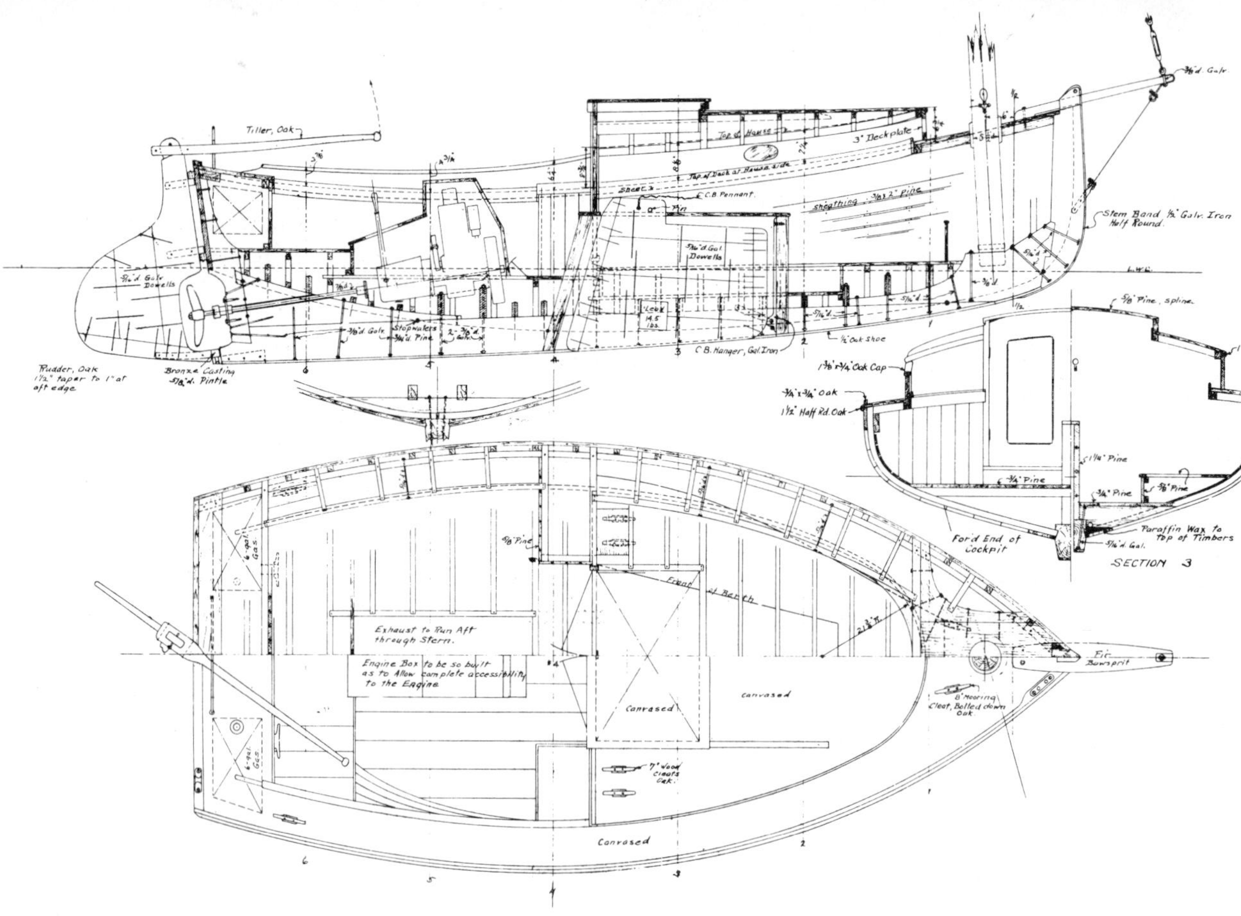

The construction plan of the Dog Watch. *(Sturgis Crocker)*

A sister to the Dog Watch *built by the Landing Boatshop, Kennebunk, Maine. (The Landing Boatshop)*

going. This breeze has some pretty good puffs to it now, even way up in here. Shall we tuck in a reef before we start, or would you rather brave it? Single-reef her, you say? Why not? We've been pretty lazy up to now. No sense in spoiling our record.

Up comes the anchor, to be triced up under the bowsprit as we coax her to fill away to reach and run out of Ryder Cove, across Bassing Harbor, and jibe her way down past Strong Island. With the breeze now moderate to fresh, these are no casual, grab-everything-and-throw-her-over jibes, but rather carefully coordinated efforts by helmsman and sheet man to get the sail well trimmed in before letting the boom lift across and go right out fast on the other side. The last jibe allows her to come up on a fast reach heading for the middle of Pleasant Bay.

It's a distinct relief to reach the deep water of the bay, but it really didn't take us long to sail across it. Now we're faced with deciding whether to jibe again or tack to head for the narrows at Sipson Island. We'll stay conservative and tack, letting her up and trimming her in so she can slash along close-hauled.

This is fun! She's doing so well that we can let her romp along this way for a while before she's tacked and run off for the narrows.

Sam Crocker designed this little cat in 1945 as an old-age boat for a Mr. Dimmick of Hartford, Connecticut. Mr. Dimmick named her the *Dog Watch.* She was later owned by Lois and Louis Darling, an artist-and-writer team. The Darlings named her the *Sibling,* feeling she was "related to the entire world's small sailboats, work and play."

The Darlings cruised in their *Sibling* a lot and didn't seem to mind the cramped cuddy despite Louis' height of 6 feet 1½ inches and the fact that they liked to take along their 70-pound golden retriever, Tasha. But the bunks are 6 feet 3 inches long, and in good weather, you can slide her wide hatch forward to open the whole place up to the sky. She does, in fact, have tremendous space for a 16-foot boat.

Eleven jibes later the little catboat has whipped through the narrows, skirted round the western shore of Little Pleasant Bay, passed Namequoit and Oldfield points and run up the river through Frostfish Cove, round Lucy Point and, finally, into Meetinghouse Pond.

By the last jibe, it's late in the afternoon, and with the wind really whistling, even way up in these narrow waters the reef is appreciated. The anchor goes down again, and this time, after the sail has been lowered and the reef shaken out, it is given a real harbor furl.

9/ The *Cockle*

Length on deck: 18 feet 9 inches
Length on waterline: 15 feet 11 inches
Beam: 6 feet 3 inches
Draft: 5 feet 1 inch
Sail area: 330 square feet
Displacement: 5,470 pounds
Designer: James R. Purdon

I was reminded of one of my favorite boats, the *Cockle,* cutter, when a copy of her plans as published in *The Rudder* for March 1915 arrived in the mail from Bill Garden. Mr. Garden is a versatile naval architect with years behind him of designing all kinds of wonderful vessels in Seattle, and now more years behind and (I trust) ahead of him of doing more of the same on his great little island up near Victoria. He has the delightful habit of chucking a boat plan in the envelope when he sends me a letter.

When the plans of the *Cockle* arrived, they reminded me that I hadn't paid homage to the little vessel in some time. These days she stays tied up, but at least is still in the water, at the Mystic Seaport at Mystic, Connecticut. High time I went down to the sea wall to spend some time staring at her. Care to join me?

Ah, there she is right over there on a mooring between the *Charles W. Morgan* and the *Joseph Conrad.* Isn't she a handsome little boat, though? Deserves the name cutter, too, tiny though she is, for she has nearly all the spars, sails, and gear of a cutter of twenty times her displacement.

The *Cockle* was designed by James R. Purdon and was built in 1913 at Marblehead, Massachusetts, by James E. Graves. She's had some name changes, unfortunately, being called the *Galena,* then the *Fox,* and now the *Galena* again.

Mr. Purdon wrote, "*Cockle* was designed to give two lads [when this was written, women hadn't even gotten a vote, much less a boat] experience with as much of the sails and rigging of the cutter type as it seemed reasonable to put in a very small boat . . . ." Lucky the lads on whom such attention was lavished. One was Frederic Tudor, son of W. Starling Burgess, who, between the ages of nine and nineteen, got to sail her out of Provincetown, at the end of Cape Cod.

The *Cockle* was designed as a daysailer, but was meant to do some traveling and had a small cuddy in case the lads were caught out overnight. Say, what about taking her out for a little spin today? I see her mainsail is bent on, and I'll bet there's a fair array of headsails bagged up below. The museum folks wouldn't mind, do you think? Heck, this is supposed to be a living museum.

By the way, I have it on good authority that taking these visionary voyages is perfectly all right, that imagining getting underway when you're actually only sitting in a chair doesn't necessarily mean you're losing your grip. Mike and Nancy Samuels, who have done a lot of research and thinking about this sort of thing, wrote in a book called *Seeing with the Mind's Eye:* "Although a person is convinced of the reality of his visualization, he need not confuse it with external reality. He can treat it with all the respect he would accord

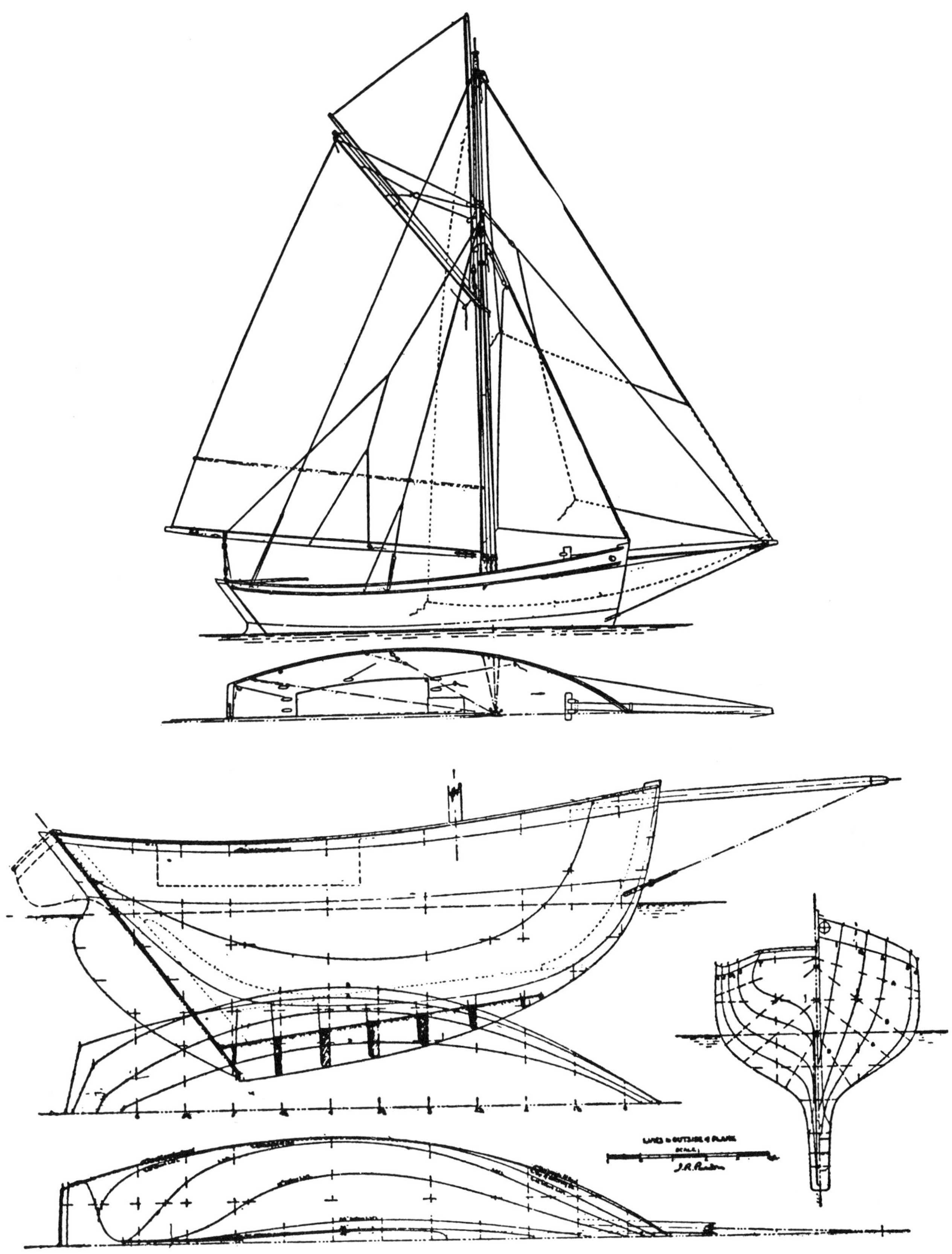

The sail and deck plans and lines of the Cockle. (The Rudder Treasury)

an external event, while knowing that it isn't one. He can have an attitude of full participation without attachment." So, as you can see, everything's going to be all right.

Let's put a little bit of this fresh, summer northwester, blowing nearly straight down the Mystic River, to work. Not only will we have a fair wind down the river; I think we'll be just in time to catch the first of the ebb.

I'll set up the mainsail, if you'll let all those various backstays go. Then see if you can find a bag in the cuddy marked forestaysail. Throat halyard set up pretty hard for the fresh breeze. Don't think she'll need a reef off the wind in smooth water. Set up the peak to give her some wrinkles. Good. Run up that forestaysail and let's clear out of this before someone in authority stops us. If you'll back the staysail to starboard for a jiffy or two, then let it draw and haul the mooring down the starboard side, we'll be off on the starboard tack. That's the stuff. We're away.

No use strapping that mainsail down hard, let her luff a little mite in this breeze because we'll be paying off directly we go round the *Conrad* and head on down the river.

A couple of guys — or are they gals? — on the *Conrad*'s fore topsail yard wave to us. That's a good sign. And off tears the little *Cockle,* foaming down the channel toward the bridges. Sure hope they open for us.

The tiny cutter is 18 feet 9 inches long on deck, with a waterline length of 15 feet 11 inches, a beam of 6 feet 3 inches, and a draft of 5 feet 1 inch. Her sail area is 330 square feet. She displaces 5,470 pounds, of which 2,850 pounds is outside ballast.

She *does* look kind of pitchy, with her fine waterlines forward and deeply curved bow and buttock line. Her sections are certainly powerful enough; she needs them to take her considerable sail area on short forays into deep water. Her high freeboard is to keep us lucky lads dry. She ought to be weatherly enough. I surmise she gets this nice speed she's showing us from the combination of her fine waterlines and her power to carry plenty of sail. Not that she's really fast, but she sure ain't no dog, is she?

You're way ahead of me finding that foghorn. Give him that new signal, a prolonged and a short, and let's see if we can stop a little downtown Mystic traffic. My goodness, there he goes already. Some luck! So the *Cockle* whips through the opened bascule road bridge, flies through town, finds the railroad swing bridge open (!) and just manages to run through it without jibing. There. Now we can settle down to a nice reach down past Willow Point and Mason's Island to Noank.

Want to give her the jib? We might as well drive her a little while we have a good chance, and it will help hold her head off. This tiller is about to break my back.

Let's look up what the *Cockle*'s designer had to say about her performance in that old *Rudder* and see what kind of vessel we have under us. Mr. Purdon wrote:

> In all sorts of weather, winter and summer, she has shown the most satisfactory capabilities. Her odd appearance and rather extreme proportions might lead one to suppose that her gait would be a disappointment, but the little boat has shown quite unexpected speed for one of her size and type. She has gone out into heavy easterly weather off Marblehead, when none but the saltiest salts cared to try the "dust" and has sailed into it like the little ship she is, as dry as the proverbial bottle afloat with the cork in. Of course, to windward, in a sharp sea of her own length, she does a rather abandoned rocking horse act, but off a little and with a longer sea, she climbs up and down the watery hills like a roller coaster. In smooth water, she slides along as well as anyone could ask.

Well, we can already vouch for his last sentence. Mr. Purdon goes on:

> The little boat is stiff and carries all sail easily in anything but the heaviest weather. Lying to in a "breeze o' wind" is her special forte; she will stay put as long as you choose to leave her, riding as light and dry as a gull. Her balance is nicely adjusted under various combinations of sails and even works out well with only foresail and reefed mainsail. This makes her very comfortable to handle and as a matter of fact she has been sailed practically singlehanded under all conditions through the year, with much pleasure, ease and benefit to her "crew."

It sounds as if we have little to fear. Why don't we go out around Race Rock and back, just for the fun of it? Do you think this breeze is going to hold up? Probably for much of the day, anyway.

So the *Cockle* swept close by the docks of Noank, ran off to round the spindle, hauled her wind to weather Whale Rock, and soon enough shot out past Groton Long Point to meet a strong ebb, setting to leeward in Fishers Island Sound.

Keep her up to about west southwest, will you, so we'll weather the North Dumpling? My, but doesn't she love this nice fresh breeze abaft the beam? Pretty nice going, I calls it.

The cutter has a pole mast, one minor concession to simplicity. A separate topmast might be taking things a little too far. Her off-center bowsprit is canted to bring its outboard end back to the centerline.

How do you like all her backstays? We won't have to

The two lads, sailing their fine little cutter. (Edwin Levick, courtesy Mystic Seaport)

shift the lower ones when short tacking, and unless her topsails are set we won't need to bother too much about the upper ones. Of course we've got both weather backstays set up now, because we're on a nice long reach. I suppose jibing her with the topsail set in a moderate breeze, you'd pay attention to the upper backstays and leave the lowers slack till after the smoke cleared.

The North Dumpling comes and goes, and then she makes easy work of the whole west end of Fishers Island. There's a big shallow harbor down there to leeward beyond that low spit of land. Hay Harbor. I could tell you a story about one night in there when we heard some girls over on a pier — hang on. The tide going out through The Race is already starting to catch hold of us. We'd better keep her right up high so we don't get set down on Race Rock. We're going to have quite a tussle after we get round and have to fight our way back in. I'll tell you about Hay Harbor later.

Round Race Rock she flies, going sideways nearly as fast as she's going ahead. We run her off and jibe her. Easy as pie with the strong fair tide cutting down the wind strength.

Round she continues, coming up hard on the wind, port tack. Strap everything in and put her to it. It's not blowing quite as hard, is it? Sure hope this breeze doesn't take right off. We'd have to anchor to keep from being swept out to sea!

In she comes toward the nun off Race Point, trying to make it but fighting a losing battle against the tide, pitching into a bit of a rip and spitting off the little seas to leeward. We let her go nearly halfway from the buoy in to the point, cheating the tide a little under the protection of the offlying rocks.

The Cockle *on the ways. (Mystic Seaport)*

Let go the upper backstay, set up the lee lower one and we're ready to go about. I'll cast off both lee sheets as I put her about and will at least hold the staysail on the new tack till you get the jib in tight. Round she goes, and stands off to fight the tide again, starboard tack. Sure catches her the minute we get out from under the rocks, but we just barely weather the nun, and then it's tack, tack, tack, right into the teeth of wind and tide, gaining a few yards every time, until we dare let her go in and work along Race Point as a lee shore so the tide won't set us bodily to leeward.

I suppose if we had the jib topsail set we'd still trim the jibsheet first when tacking, then get in the jib topsail, and still leave the staysail for last. When you have more headsails than people, you just have to set your priorities.

The breeze is holding up nicely, thank goodness. We probably won't get to use her light sails. The club topsail has been kept small, so it's not hard to handle by its halyard; tackline; and sheet to the gaff end, thence to the throat, and down to the deck. The topsail is a great sail, even in a little boat. Makes her seem like quite a vessel. I'd love to see that big ballooner on her.

Glad the clew reef pendant is all rove off. It would be tricky to reach it with the boat jumping around a little. I think she ought to have two more deep reefs in that mainsail. You've got to be able to shorten right down in a little boat like this. I'd want a reef in the staysail, too.

I should think she'd go well to windward in a breeze with single reefed main and jib, with the staysail down. If it blew harder, you'd take in the jib, set the staysail, and pull down a second reef in the mainsail. More wind yet, and she'd want a reefed staysail and close-reefed mainsail. And I'd want a tiny spitfire jib to hold her head off reaching in hard weather. She's an able little vessel, and would stand up to some real weather as long as you could keep shortening her down without throwing her out of balance.

This day she stands up to all plain sail — her three lowers — and just romps along, retracing her steps toward the Mystic River. Gradually the starboard tacks can be shorter and the port boards longer as she weathers the northwest corner of Fishers Island, splits North and South Dumplings, and then makes a long port board back across Fishers Island Sound.

The breeze is moderate, even down to gentle at times as she goes back to short tacking to weather the rocks west of Ram Island. I suppose we could put up some topsails or something, but I'm too relaxed to think of it, how about you? I thought so. Let's just work her back up the river like this and enjoy the scenery. To say nothing of the boats.

The floor of the *Cockle*'s watertight cockpit is fitted with special cushions made just for the space. Pretty fancy. They double as safety gear, for they are stuffed with cork shavings and designed to keep the lucky lads afloat in the unlikely event their education included driving her under. Such a thing is always possible, of course, but it would take some doing.

You can sleep on the cushions at night, for the cockpit is 6 feet long, and you can rig a tent over the boom. Or, in case you're not subject to claustrophobia, a pair of pipe berths has been squeezed into the cuddy.

She has no house to spoil her looks, but I suppose for longer cruising, or maybe for some of us older lads, there could be a booby hatch abaft the mast to give her a little sense of space and light below.

My goodness, here we are up the river making our last tacks back to the museum. I don't even remember beating through the bridges, do you? You say we had to shoot the railroad bridge and just barely made it? And had to make a tight circle at the last second when the guy on the road bridge refused to make a big hole in Main Street just when we wanted him to? How could I have forgotten? Must have gotten too wrapped up in that story about the Hay Harbor girls.

Anyway, better slip the tack of that jib aft to blanket it behind the staysail and get it off her. Kind of nice to have the jib set flying so you don't have to go out on the bowsprit after it. A little cutter like this would be down by the head a bit with somebody climbing around on her nosepole. Of course you'd have to do it to bend or unbend the jib topsail.

Staysail off, mooring picked up, mainsail lowered into the lazyjacks. Coil down all the slack of the topsail sheet. Just like a big vessel.

You know, I just thought of something. This is the first northwest wind I can ever remember that was really quite steady. But I mustn't get too attached to *that* visualization, must I? Anyway, thanks for going sailing. And thanks to Mystic Seaport for keeping the *Cockle,* cutter, in such fine shape, so we could try her out.

10/ The *West Wind*

Length on deck: 24 feet
Length on waterline: 20 feet 5 inches
Beam: 7 feet 9 inches
Draft: 4 feet 4 inches
Sail area: 368 square feet (gaff sloop)
Designer: Philip L. Rhodes

It would be interesting to know if Julian Cendoya of Santiago, Cuba, ever got to put to sea in any of the fine vessels he had Phil Rhodes design for him — to say nothing of how it was that the designer's first client came from so far away from his office in New York.

At any rate, Rhodes designed the 24-foot cruising boat *West Wind* for Mr. Cendoya in 1921. She's one of those diminutive vessels that looks so able that she makes you want to take her right offshore and go voyaging.

She has a strong sheer, an element of hull shape that was to become a Rhodes trademark throughout his long career.

Her bow seems a bit long for the stern; I think she looks better with a boomkin and no bowsprit (with ketch rig) than she does with the bowsprit and no boomkin (with sloop rig).

Being short and needing freeboard to stay reasonably dry in rough water, she has to have fairly steep bow and buttock lines, but her run, if not flat, is at least fairly straight.

While we're looking at her profile, consider those three portholes. Cover up the middle one with your forefinger. Is it my imagination, or did the vessel just gain stature and lose cuteness? Phil Rhodes never worked for John Alden, in whose office that middle porthole would never have survived.

But now let's take our departure from mere minutiae and move on to notice that the *West Wind* has just the tiniest trace of hollow in her entry at the load waterline. I believe she is just full enough forward to avoid serious rooting when her buoyant stern is lifted by a following sea. Her transom stern is just right; the addition of a counter would have made her *too* buoyant aft.

She ought to have an easy motion, for she is not so deep that her keel ballast would snap her back after a roll. Her sections are deep to gain room in a little hull, with no hollow in the garboards until you get well aft.

The 24-foot *West Wind* has a waterline length of 20 feet 5 inches, a beam of 7 feet 9 inches, and a draft of 4 feet 4 inches. She has an iron keel of 2,270 pounds.

I like her deep outboard rudder. I also like a couple of her construction features: a pair of full-length bilge stringers on each side of the hull and a solid bulkhead right across the bow of the boat, just abaft the lower end of the stem.

Mr. Rhodes drew two very different sailplans for Mr. Cendoya to choose from: a gaff sloop rig with 368 square feet of sail, and a Bermudian ketch rig with 341 square feet. The mainsail on the ketch is a meas-

Philip L. Rhodes. (Philip H. Rhodes)

ly 169 square feet, as opposed to the sloop's mainsail of 287 square feet. I'd choose the sloop for longshore cruising and the ketch for offshore passagemaking.

The sloop rig has deep reefs in both jib and mainsail and is a generous enough sailplan so that she'd need to be reefed in a strong breeze, even though she's undoubtedly a stiff boat for her size. I'd want a permanent, strong gallows frame set up on the stern and reefing gear all rove off so you could haul out the leech cringles without taking to the air over the stern. And despite the deep reefs, I'd want a main trysail and a spitfire jib for that hard chance you hope never to have to face. And a balloon jib to set in time of peace. The ballooner would make a great sail to pole out when running off. Easy to control and easy to jibe, yet it pulls like a team of horses.

Why not have a pair of preventer backstays to replace anxiety with confidence when the mast gets to straining. (On the ketch, I'd want a permanent backstay on the mainmast leading to a pair of legs straddling the mizzen and a pair of mizzen preventers.)

The young Mr. Rhodes has tried to solve the age-old problem with Bermudian ketches — too much spar and not enough sail — by giving his sails lots of roach held

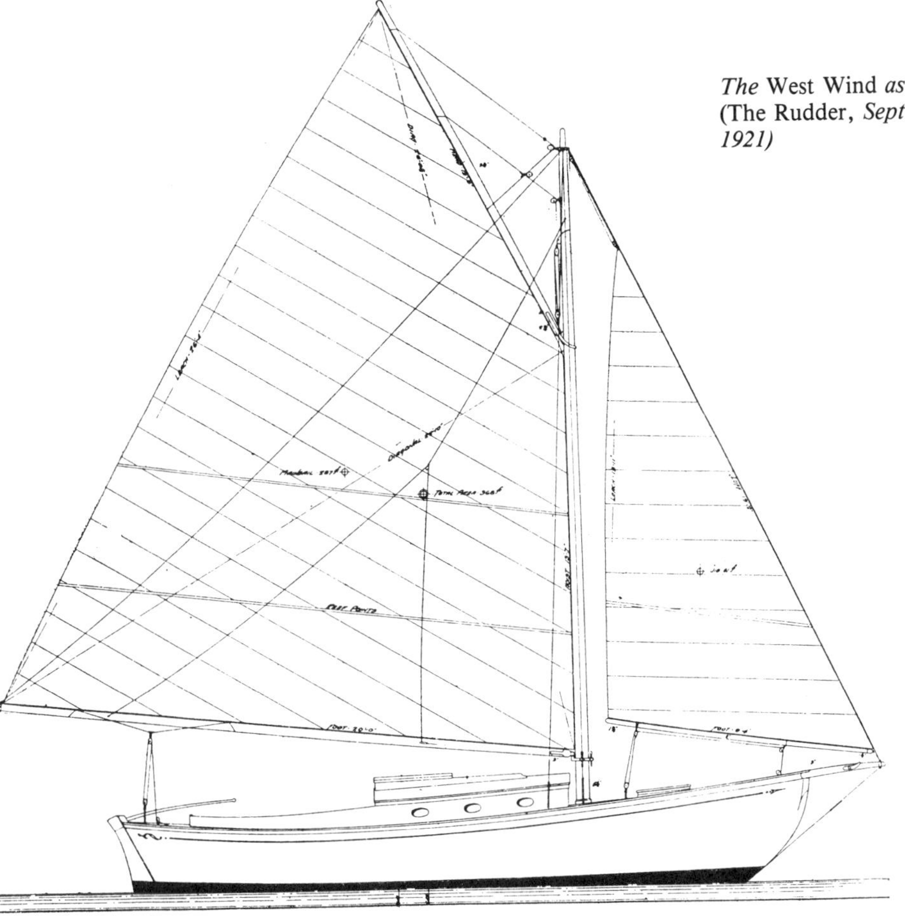

The West Wind *as a sloop.* (The Rudder, *September 1921)*

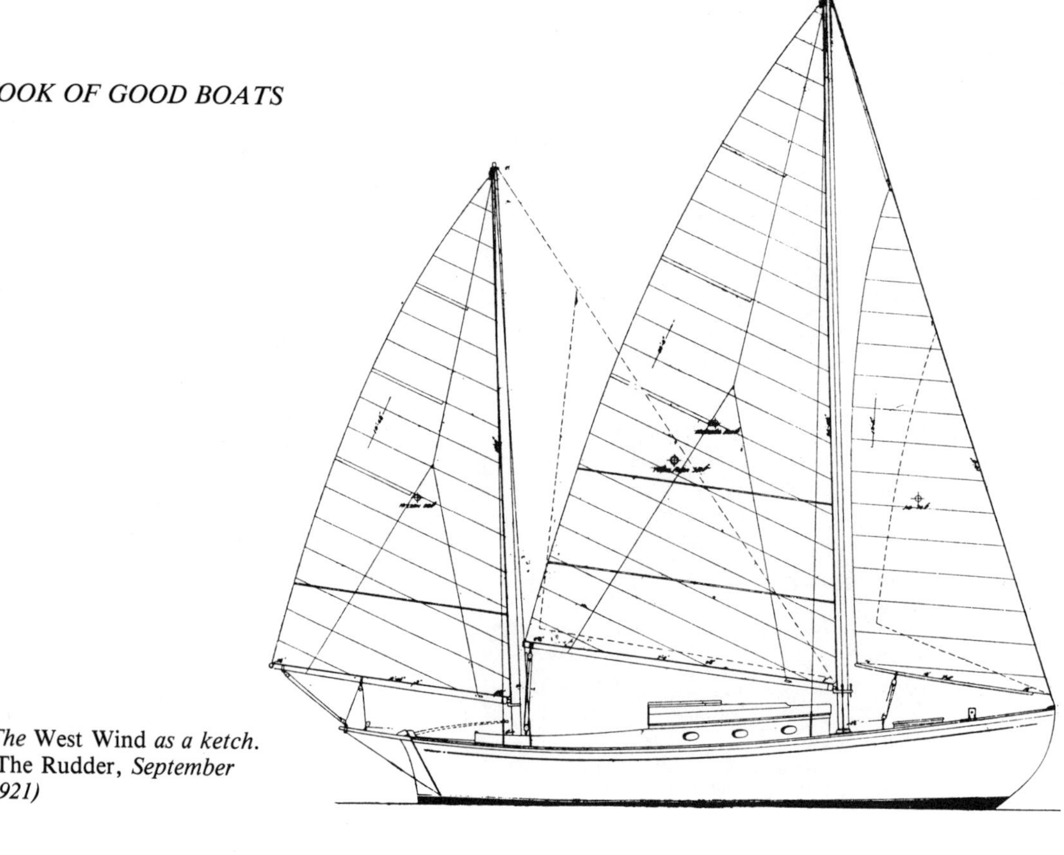

The West Wind *as a ketch.* (The Rudder, *September 1921)*

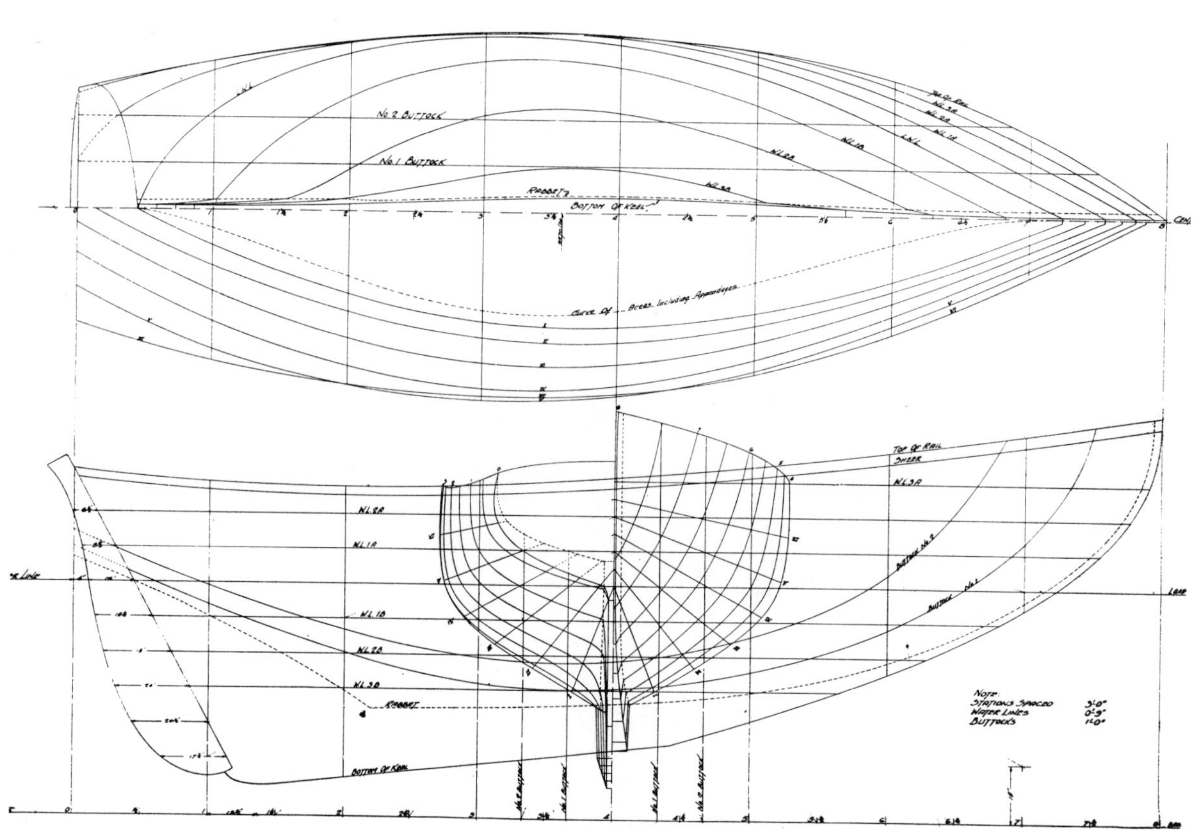

The lines of the West Wind. (The Rudder, *September 1921)*

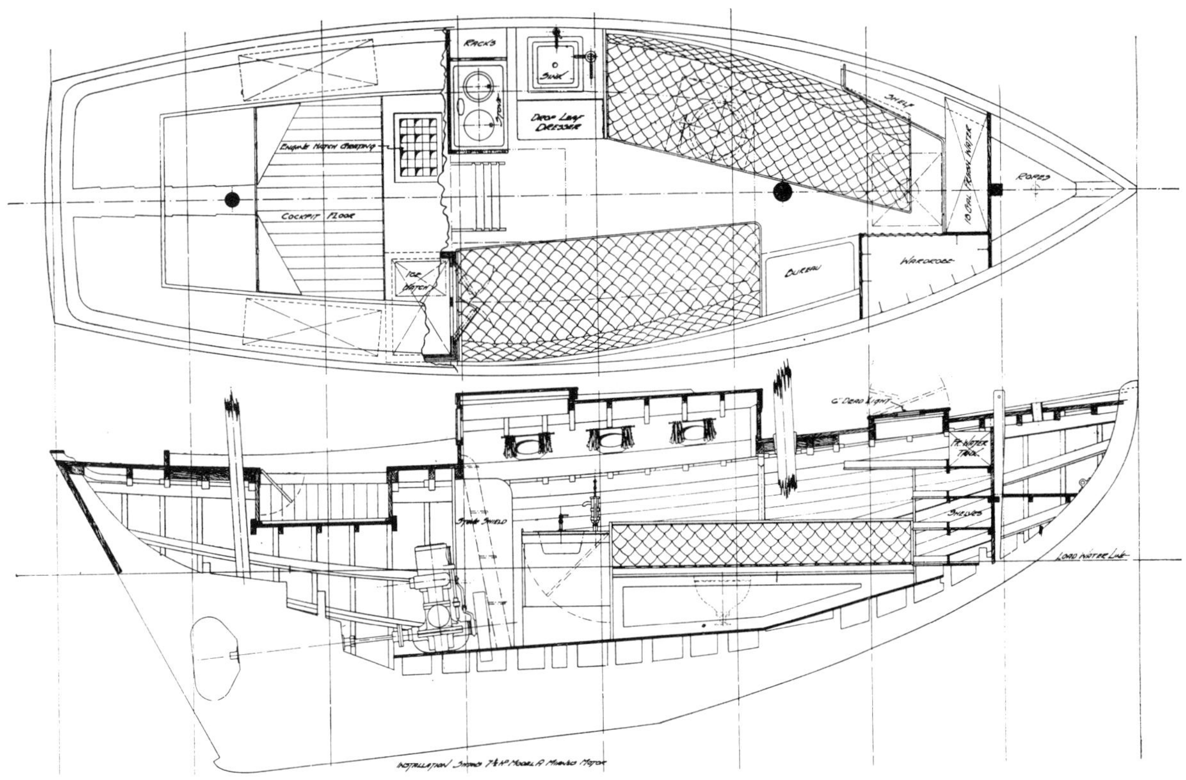

The accommodations plan of the West Wind. (The Rudder, *September 1921)*

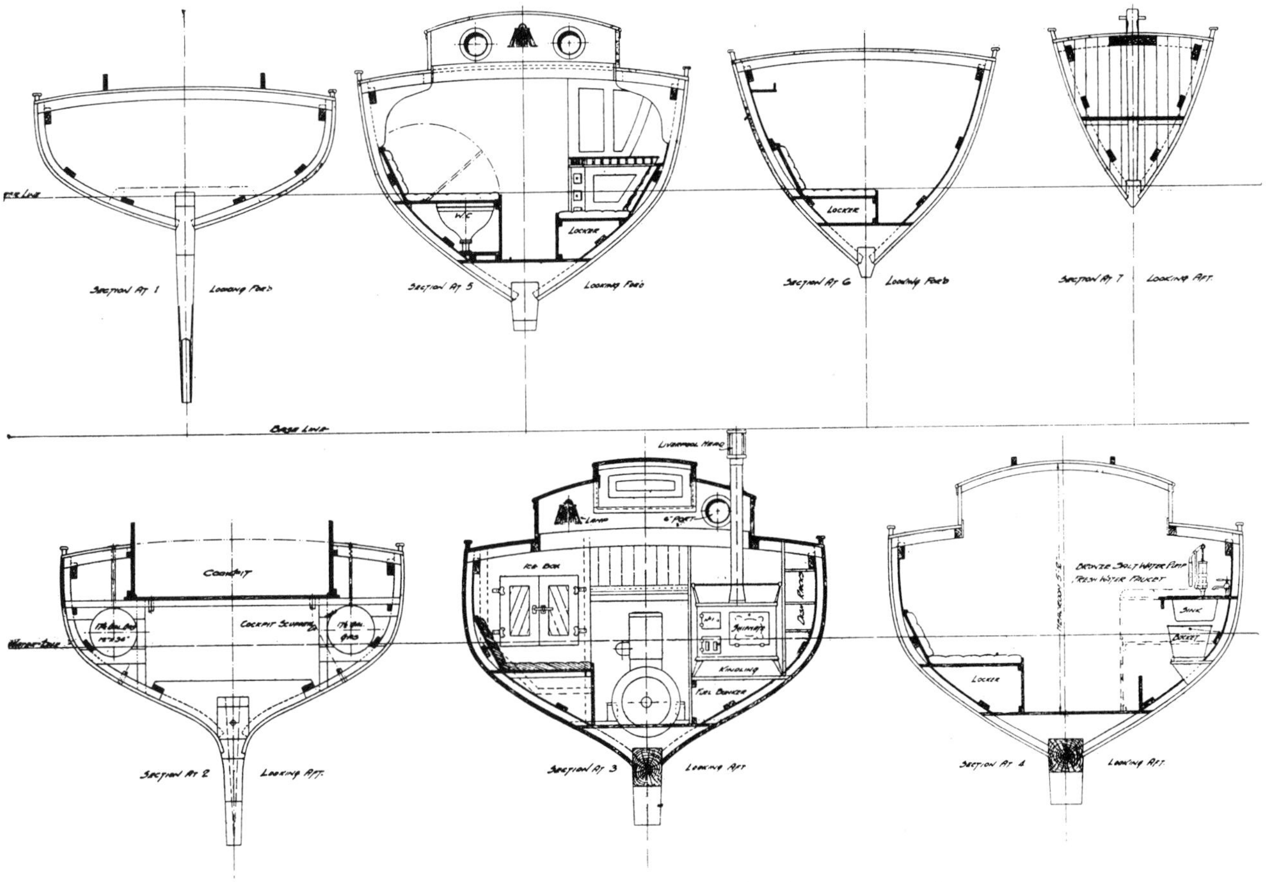

Sections of the West Wind. (The Rudder, *September 1921)*

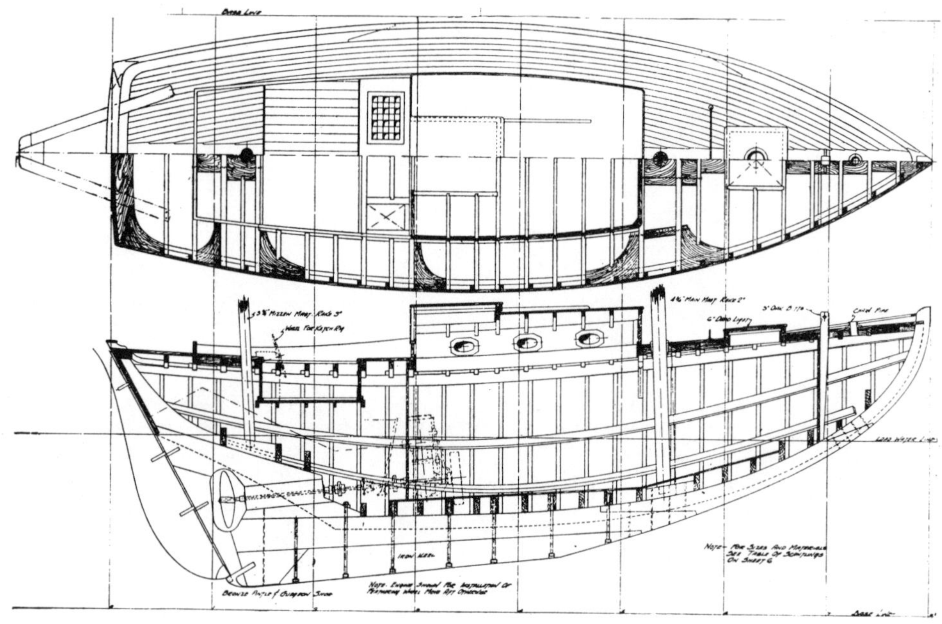

Construction plans of the West Wind. (The Rudder, *September 1921)*

out by extra-long battens. A neat trick, as long as you have a good sailmaker.

On the ketch, with her short booms, the lazyjacks double as topping lifts. Again, you'd want the mizzen reefing gear all rove off ready to go. You'd also want to put the mizzen gooseneck on a track so the boom could be raised out of harm's way when the sail is reefed.

As a ketch, the *West Wind* would go well under mainsail alone with a leading breeze or under jib and reefed mizzen on any point of sailing. For light weather you'd want a masthead, overlapping jib.

The steering wheel shown with the ketch rig in the construction plan probably makes more sense than the tiller shown in the outboard profile. With the unobstructed cockpit of the sloop rig, the tiller would be fine.

There's no place to stow a dinghy on deck when going offshore in a 24-footer. You'd want a deflatable dinghy or kayak that could stow on the stern or in the lazarette.

The weight of the little vessel's engine is nearly amidships. The machine is a single-cylinder, two-cycle, 7½-horsepower Mianus. She has two 17½-gallon gas tanks, one on each side under the deck in way of the cockpit. Her 18-gallon water tank is well forward and raised up under the deck to give a good gravity flow to the sink. Nice arrangement, but not the best place for all that weight (150 pounds for a full tank). Another neat arrangement with a price tag is the handy hatch in the bridge deck through which ice can be loaded into the icebox, the price tag being another deck opening that might let in a lot of water someday.

The *West Wind*'s snug cabin can get you all excited about cruising singlehanded or with a shipmate. She has a well-thought-out arrangement. For instance, there's always a place to sit to leeward whichever tack you're on. (Most layouts are fine in the harbor; it's the waves outside that separate the good ones from the lousy ones.)

The little vessel has 5 feet of headroom, which lets you get around the cabin easily, but to stand up straight you have to be in the open hatchway.

The stove is set athwartships where it's least likely to dump its fiery contents onto the cabin sole. It's well shielded from the companionway ladder. There is a water closet under the port bunk, but a bucket would be much handier offshore. She even has a bureau and a hanging locker up forward, and there is a good deal of stowage space in the engine room and under the cockpit, as well as in the lazarette.

When I think of sailing this fine little vessel, I see her at sea in a good breeze. (I know Mr. Beaufort didn't include a "good breeze" in his scale; I guess I mean fresh to strong.) I see her with single reefs all around, maybe making an overnight passage Down East across the Gulf of Maine is a smoky sou'wester. Or, wind on her starboard beam, scurrying along the bright blue sun-streaked Pacific troughs, gaining an offing from the Golden Gate to head south to Mexico. Or, maybe, running off under headsail alone before a sudden gale in the Mediterranean — me, you, even Mr. Cendoya himself — peering ahead anxiously, looking for a landfall on a Greek isle.

11/ The *Fair Wind*

Length on deck: 26 feet 5 inches
Length on waterline: 21 feet 6 inches
Beam: 9 feet 6 inches
Draft: 3 feet
Sail area: 349 square feet
Designer: William Atkin

It's curious that some of the best boating magazines — from the point of view of their readers — had rather short careers. *Skipper, Cruiser,* and *Fore an' Aft* are three that come to mind. *Fore an' Aft,* much under the influence of William Atkin, gave the cruising sailor plenty of food for thought in articles and designs during its few short years. Its back issues are still a rare treat.

They contain, for instance, the plans you see here of a small schooner designed more than half a century ago by Mr. Atkin himself. Several little vessels were built to the design, which Billy Atkin named *Fairwind.*

I am not one to quibble with Mr. Atkin, but having been an editor by trade, I do think the name of this little vessel should have been dignified by being written *Fair Wind.* It makes a lot more of the name, and I think the schooner deserves the added dignity.

So, hoping the late, great William Atkin wouldn't mind, I hereby change the name of his schooner from the *Fairwind* to the *Fair Wind.* After all, a fair wind is a major achievement and should be made the most of.

The *Fair Wind* has a skipjack type of hull, though her vee-bottomed sections are deeper than the true Chesapeake Bay skipjack.

The schooner is 26 feet 5 inches long on deck, with a waterline length of 21 feet 6 inches, a beam of 9 feet 6 inches, and a draft of 3 feet. Her sail area is 349 square feet. She carries 1,650 pounds of outside ballast.

The *Fair Wind* has fine bow and buttock lines; her entry is also quite fine. Her chine comes well out of water fore and aft to save her from looking clumsy.

With her considerable beam and flare, she'd sail quite upright. Stand up like a church, she would. No one could accuse her of real speed, but neither would she be a dog.

The schooner would be quite a good self-steerer. Her forefoot is not too deep; she has a long, straight keel with moderate draft and drag, and she has wide quarters. Do I hear rumblings of doubt that this hull shape would steer herself? Not to worry. My skipjack certainly did; and Captain Slocum made big claims in this department for his *Spray,* which, though round-bilged, had these same general characteristics.

I think the *Fair Wind* has a handsome profile, with her raked masts, curved longhead, raked transom, nicely steeved bowsprit, and booms set at a jaunty angle. Note the rake of her house set perpendicular to the masts, a vital feature of her good looks.

As usual, Billy Atkin provided his readers with plenty of construction details. I pass on a few to indicate that he didn't skimp on the schooner's scantlings.

William Atkin. (John Atkin)

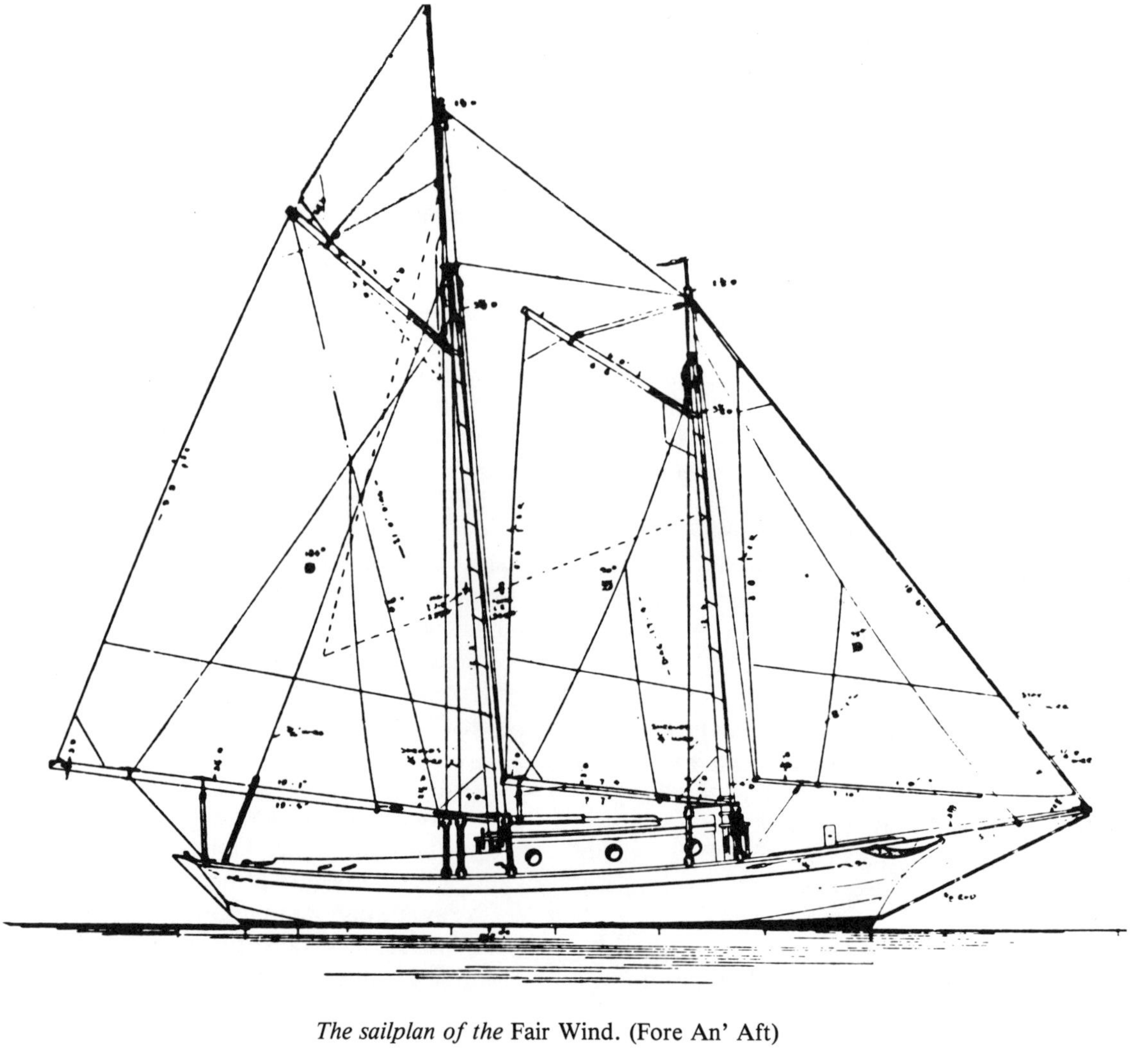

The sailplan of the Fair Wind. (Fore An' Aft)

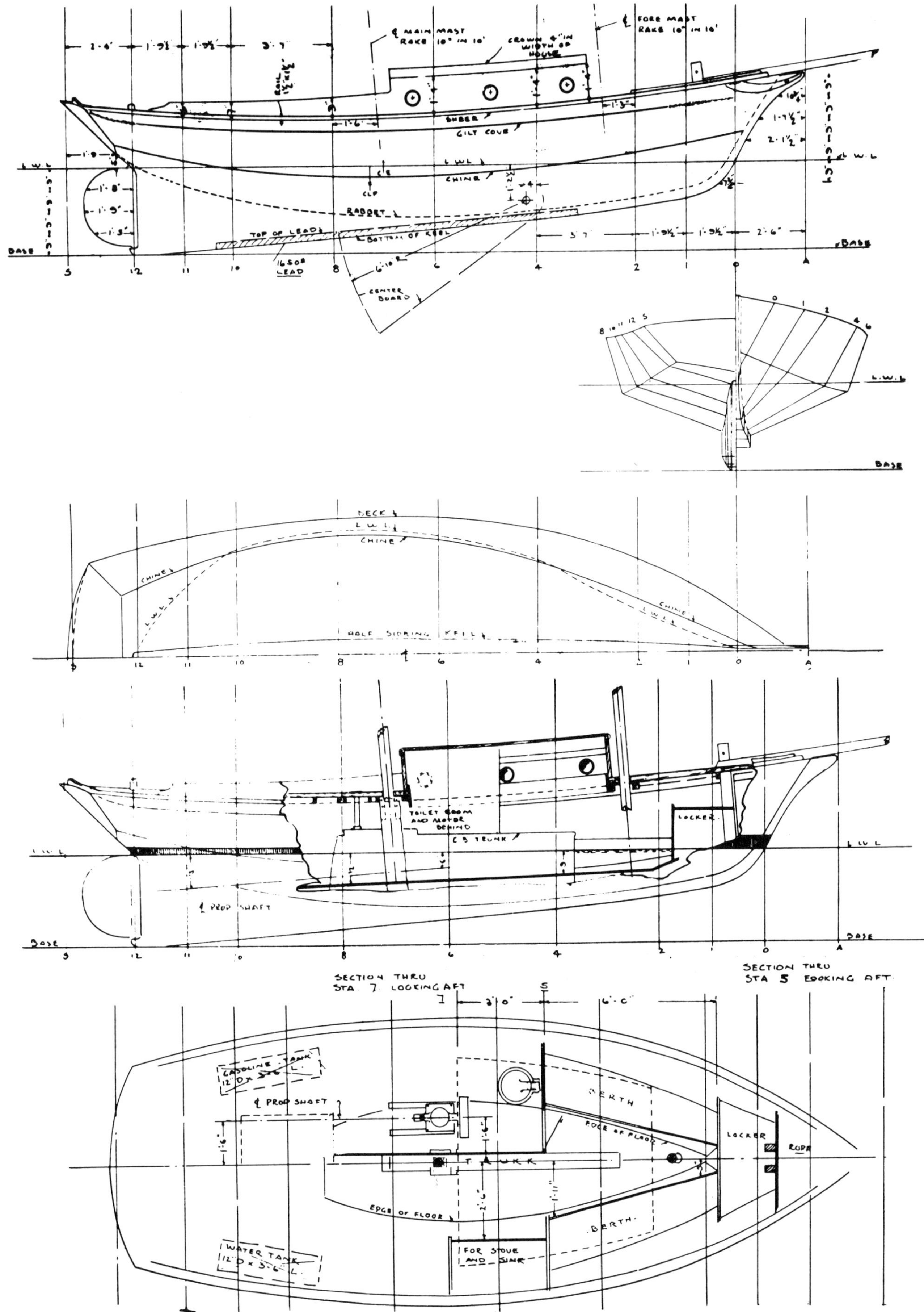

The lines and interior arrangement of the Fair Wind. (Fore An' Aft)

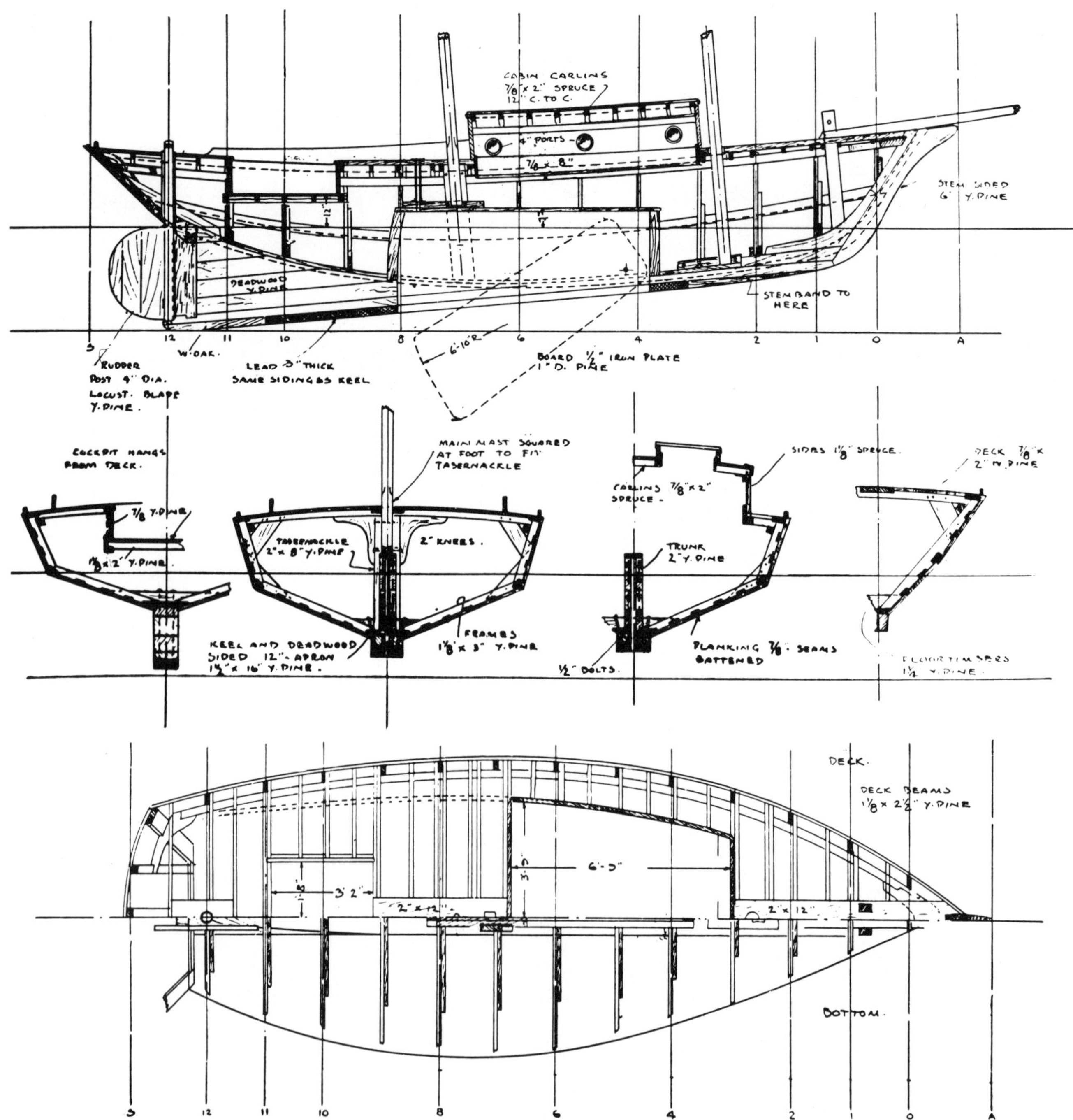

The Fair Wind*'s construction plans.* (Fore An' Aft)

The *Fair Wind*'s keel and deadwood are sided 12 inches. Her floors are 1¼-inch yellow pine. The centerboard trunk is 2-inch yellow pine. Frames, 1⅛-inch by 3-inch yellow pine. Planking finished to ⅞ inch with seams battened. Deck beams, 1⅛-inch by 2½-inch yellow pine. Deck, ⅞-inch pine. House sides, 1⅛-inch spruce. Carlins, ⅞ inch by 2 inches.

The mainmast steps on a tabernacle that straddles the centerboard trunk to bypass the trunk with the thrust of the mast, taking it right to the keel. The tabernacle is 2-inch by 8-inch yellow pine.

The *Fair Wind* has a fairly generous sail area, yet the rig has been kept reasonably low.

I like her ¾-length jib club. It can be self-tending, but it lets the sail set better than would a full-length club, for it allows a nice draft in the forward lower portion of the sail — a draft that would be somewhat spoiled by a full-length club.

I'd give her an overlapping foresail, a sail that would really bring her to life and would be well worth the bother of having to shift over when you tack.

Her big fisherman staysail would be her most popular sail on any kind of reach in moderate weather. Her tiny topsail is high enough to be a real help in light air.

When shortening down, she'd go well under the mainsail and jib. In a really hard breeze, she could scud along under foresail alone. I'd want a second deep reef in the mainsail.

Her backstays to the quarters tighten up the whole rig. The lazyjacks all round make sail handling a joy.

Her engine is off-center to port. The biggest drawback to this arrangement is that you couldn't use power and sail on the port tack if she were heeling much.

Her tanks are under the deck in way of the cockpit, gas to port and water to starboard. That's a nice big cockpit for a 26-foot boat.

The companionway is off-center to starboard, which allows a closed-in combination engine room and head to port. This combination makes better sense than having WC and engine each in its own tiny compartment: you have some breathing room whichever piece of machinery you happen to be operating.

You'd have table leaves on the forward end of the centerboard trunk and a folding galley seat on its starboard side. The headroom in the cabin is 4 feet 10 inches.

I think the little schooner would be a fine longshore cruiser for two sailors. Let's hear it for the *Fair Wind,* for Billy Atkin, and for the short-lived but valuable boating rag *Fore an' Aft.*

12/ The *Crystal*

Length on deck: 30 feet 6 inches
Length on waterline: 22 feet
Beam: 8 feet 6 inches
Draft: 4 feet 3 inches
Sail area: 479 square feet
Displacement: 5 tons
Designer: Fred Shepherd

There's no future in going ashore now, because we're just about to sail this nice little yawl, the *Crystal,* from our berth here behind the west breakwater at Stonington, Connecticut, down the beach to Point Judith, about 20 miles to the eastward in all, and it will be *down* today, because this smoky sou'wester obviously means business.

There'll be no trouble about getting "back," because this will be a sail that we visualize together, rather than actually go on. You'll come? Great! It's good that you brought your foul-weather gear; these imaginary trips sometimes get fairly realistic, and you never know but what we might have a squall before we get in.

Yes, this is an English boat. She was designed by Fred Shepherd some half century ago. Do you like her? I think she's a pretty little thing, and it will be fun to sail her.

She has nice wineglass sections, and her draft is exactly half her beam. This is a proportion that ought to give her an easy motion, but it's true that going to windward she'll make a bit of leeway. She'd need another foot of draft to hang on really well in a head sea.

Her waterlines and buttock lines are fairly full; she's quite powerful for a small boat.

I think her snubbed-up bow is saved by her short bowsprit, and certainly her graceful stern is not spoiled by her curving boomkin. She has a straight keel for hauling out or going on the hard.

Dimensions? The *Crystal* is 30 feet 6 inches long on deck, with a waterline length of 22 feet, a beam of 8 feet 6 inches, and a draft of 4 feet 3 inches. She displaces just under 5 tons and has 479 square feet of sail.

But we'd better belay all this talk and take advantage of this moderate southwest breeze. Set the mizzen, will you? while I bring her up to a short stay. Yes, sheet it right in flat for now. We've got plenty of room to leeward, so we might as well let her go straight astern with just the mizzen set while we wash the mud off the anchor, coil and lash the rode, and then lash the anchor on the bow, straight end of the stock up.

Rode's up and down. I'll catch a turn on the post. There, the surge broke it out; didn't even have to use the windlass, if you can call that dainty little thing a windlass.

Here she comes; hand me that swab, will you? Want to set the mainsail while I get this fo'c's'le head ready for sea? Peak it right up till you get some healthy wrinkles from peak to tack. I think we're going to have plenty of wind this afternoon to iron them out. Yes, isn't that an unusual peak halyard bridle? Kind of complicated, but it does spread the strain out well along the gaff.

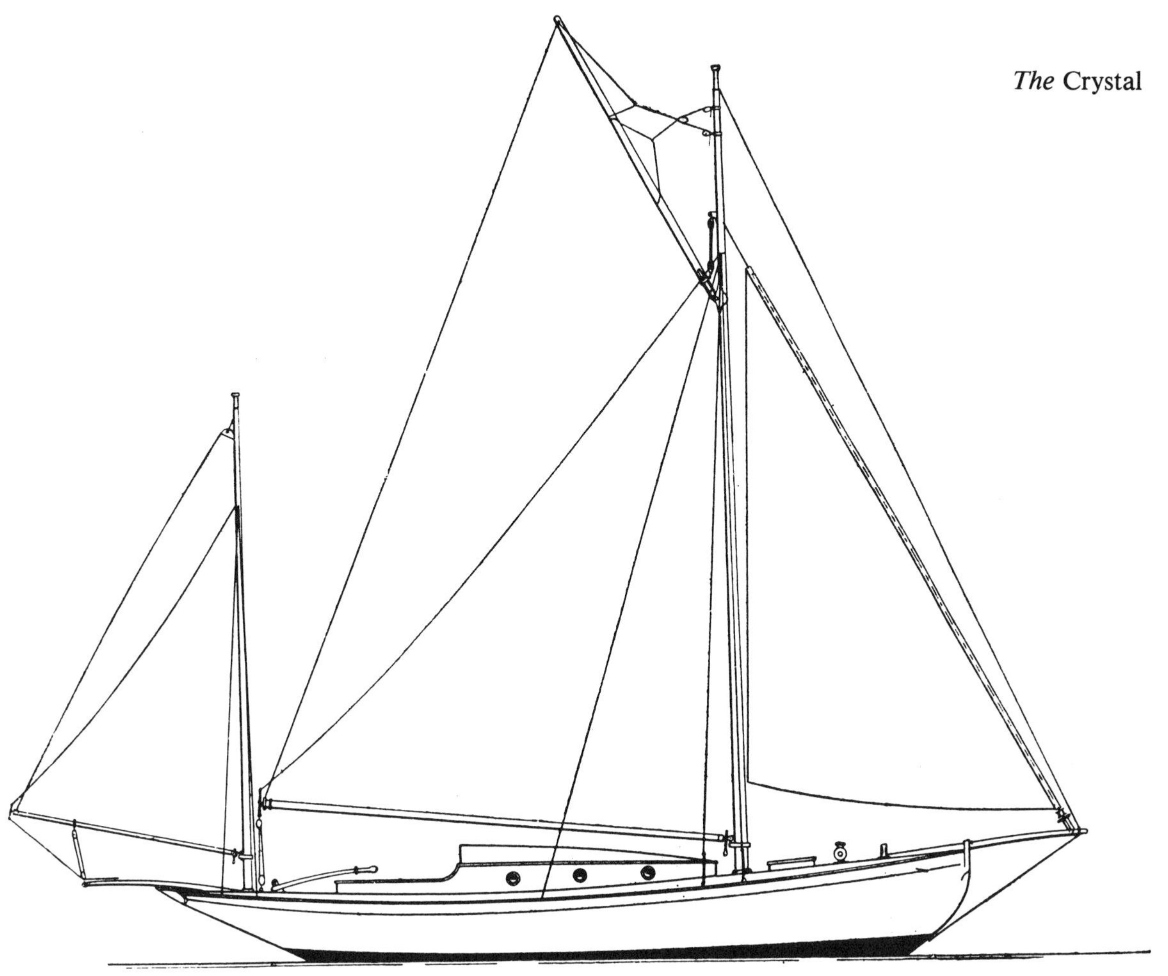

The Crystal*'s sailplan.* (Sailing, Seamanship and Yacht Construction *by Uffa Fox, reprinted by International Marine Publishing Company)*

Go ahead and take her. Just shove the tiller over to port and slack the mizzen sheet. I'll unroll that window shade of a jib and we'll be off on the starboard tack. That's the stuff; now straighten her out for the end of the breakwater and we'll see where she wants her mainsail.

Right you are, we need to strap her right in, and even so it looks as if we'll have to take a hitch to get around the east breakwater. Ah, feel her heel down and go! She's got about all the wind she wants already, doesn't she? Well, what do we care, we're in a handy yawl with a roller-reefing mainsail and a roller-furling jib. If it breezes up, we'll just roll some of this stuff away.

Now, watch that mainsail when I trim in this vang leading to the mizzen masthead. Look at that! Takes the twist right out of her, doesn't it? Magic presto.

I'd want a main trysail on this boat for really heavy going, because a close-reefed roller-reefing sail can get to be kind of a mess. Of course she'll go fine off the wind with jib-and-jigger; that's what we can do if it really blows today. I'd also want a storm jib to set up to the stemhead on a portable stay for a hard chance. I think there's a high-cut masthead overlapping jib down in the fo'c's'le someplace, but I doubt if we'll get a chance to try it.

You can go about as close to the breakwater as you want to before tacking, but I don't see anybody standing on the thing giving out prizes for coming close, so why don't we tack? I'll get the backstay and the jibsheet so just put her over anytime. Around we go. Kind of lumpy along here, so 5½ points off the wind is about all you can expect out of her. I don't doubt she'd do 5 in smooth water.

Look at those buoys leaning over out in the sound. Some ebb, huh? We'd best overstand a bit, 'cause it'll be setting us to leeward on the other tack.

That ought to be enough. Round we go. Should have it made now. She ought to fly right out through Watch Hill Passage with this tide under her. Not that she ain't going through the water pretty good too.

That's Napatree Point under the lee bow. Couple of old forts out there, built during the Spanish War. We

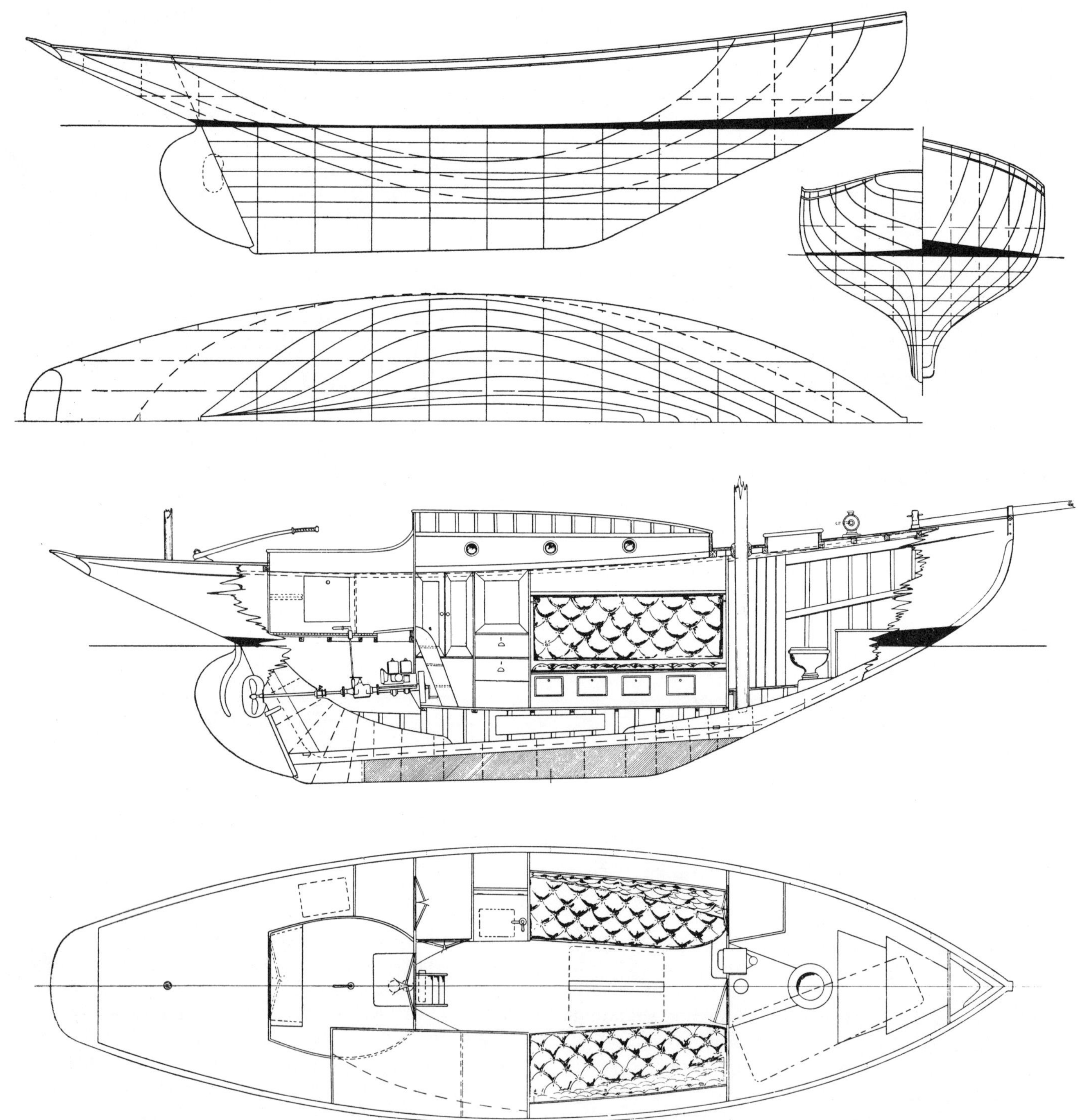

The lines and accommodations plans of the Crystal. (Sailing, Seamanship and Yacht Construction *by Uffa Fox, reprinted by International Marine Publishing Company)*

can go halfway between the point and the bell buoy off it, but let's hold her as high as we can and favor the buoy.

I like the *Crystal*'s narrow cabinhouse. Only 2 feet 9 inches it is, and leaves plenty wide decks of nearly 3 feet on each side.

A dinghy? Well, that's one nice thing about these mind's-eye trips; you don't have to bother with a tender. I agree; I hate to tow 'em. The best thing to do on this boat might be to raise the mizzen boom a bit and stow a 7-foot dinghy on the boomkin, using the mizzen boom for a boat derrick. I can see a nice cruising dinghy there with a high, curved bow shoved up between the mizzen mast and the shrouds one side and a broad transom squatting on the boomkin just forward of the mizzen sheet. She'd have a shallow centerboard and rudder, and a sprit rig that would make her fly in a favoring breeze. You'd row her to windward.

The cockpit is typically English — cramped. No wonder when Montague Dawson painted boats like this there were always a couple of guys sitting up on the house. But there's a nice seat for the helmsman, and you could put a folding canvas chair down in the forward part of the cockpit. That would be solid comfort with good protection. The cockpit floor is mighty close to the waterline, so the drains ought to be crossed and probably have plugs as well.

In harbor, with an awning over the after half of the main boom, there'd be room under it for a couple more folding chairs on deck either side of the tiller. Nice spot for tea.

What do you think the visibility is, maybe a couple of miles? No need for us to get farther off the beach than that anyway. Watch Hill Point to Point Judith is close enough to east, about 16 miles. Look at it break out there on the reefs. Quite a little sea running. We'll be feeling it as soon as we get by the lighthouse.

Now feel those seas lift in under her. She won't take long going down the beach today. Wind on the quarter and plenty of it. Why don't I stow the mizzen? Ought to make her steer a bit easier. Point Judith here we come!

You can get at the engine either through that hatch in the cockpit floor or from the cabin by taking away the ladder. It's a two-cylinder, hand-crank affair, very straightforward, and producer of one of the greatest sounds made.

Down below she has 6 feet of headroom under that narrow house, quite unusual for a little boat like this. The backs of the transoms in the saloon fold down to make bunks, revealing all sorts of stuff stowed behind them during the day, including, doubtless, the bedding. The forward ends of the transoms are narrow enough to make good seats, and they're near the stove. In the *Crystal,* there's always a good place to sit to leeward. And she has a fine cabin table. Why do so few modern boats this size have tables?

The galley is aft to port, and opposite it is a working surface that converts to a bunk. The water closet is in the fo'c's'le where it belongs, giving plenty of privacy and space.

All in all, the *Crystal* is a fine little cruising boat for two with room for the occasional guest or guests.

We're already at Weekapaug? Halfway to Point Jude. My, but look at her fly! It's breezing on. I think I'll roll down some mainsail before I relieve you.

Settle the throat halyard and crank a bit of sail onto the boom; then settle the peak a little and repeat. Kind of tedious to do by yourself, but there's no great rush and everything's under control. Inside of five minutes you've rolled away all you want to. There, that stops her shuddering down the seas quite so hard.

Can you see old Point Jude yet? Well, it won't be long. I'll take her if you want to drop below. Coffee? Wouldn't think of it, but a mug of tea would go down mighty good.

So the *Crystal* swings along, flying past the long stretches of sand punctuated by the occasional rocky point that is the shore between Watch Hill Point and Point Judith. The seas are starting to roll and spill a bit, plenty of big whitecaps everyplace you look. Unheeding, she tears away from them, around them, through and over them. Bright, hazy seascape, that smoky blue. Smoky sou'wester. Roll and go.

I think I see the land making out ahead. Yes, there's the lighthouse. We'll be able to see the breakwaters of the Harbor of Refuge in a minute. Let's anchor out there rather than bother going up inside to Galilee. I love it out there behind the breakwater with the spray flying up and over. Want to stock up that 50-pounder? The 35 would probably hold her, but it's really starting to whistle.

In she flashes through the hole in the wall, up she rounds in the sudden quiet behind the breakwater. Roll up the jib. Let go the main sheet and backstay. Run up the mizzen and sheet it flat. Yes, this'll do. Let go the best bower and give her plenty of scope as she settles back on her mizzen. Down with the mainsail and furl it.

And there's the lovely little *Crystal,* lying to a nice flat scope with her mizzen set, steady as a church and twice as safe, tucked in behind the breakwater at the Harbor of Refuge, Point Judith, Rhode Island.

Want to stay aboard a while longer? I do.

13/ The *Iris*

Length on deck: 36 feet
Length on waterline: 29 feet
Beam: 10 feet 3 inches
Draft: 5 feet 6 inches
Sail area: 666 square feet
Designer: Charles G. MacGregor

One of the most complete, well-made models I've seen is the 6-foot, 5-inch replica of the yawl *Iris,* built by her owner, John Martucci. He built it just the way his boat was built, with planking fastened to frames with countersunk screws concealed by wood plugs. Like the full-sized vessel, the model has an engine, anchor winch, stove, head, bilge pump, and electrical switches. All this stuff works on the model as well as it does on the *Iris* herself, maybe better.

This great model is now at the Mystic Seaport Museum, Mystic, Connecticut. Mr. Martucci built it in order to stay in touch with his vessel while she had to be laid up during World War II. He was used to staying in touch with his vessel; except for the war years, he kept her in commission year-round.

John Martucci was a good seaman. He served in the Italian Navy in World War I. He won the Cruising Club of America's Blue Water Medal in 1939 for an uneventful voyage in the *Iris* from Sheepshead Bay, Long Island, to Italy and back.

Charles G. MacGregor of Belknap and Paine in Boston designed the *Iris* for Mr. Martucci in 1938. George Chaisson built her at Swampscott, Massachusetts.

The *Iris* had only two owners until 1980, when the second one, Dr. Thomas J. Bridges, donated her to the Mystic Seaport. The Seaport sold her to Louis C. Joyce IV, of Cape May, New Jersey.

Mr. Joyce got himself a wholesome vsssel, with something of the fishing schooner look to her. Her husky, heavy hull is fine enough to have a good turn of speed.

She sits down in the water, yet has considerable freeboard: 3 feet amidships, and 4 feet 7 inches at the bow. She has a fairly deep forefoot and enough lateral plane to hang on quite well going to windward. There's a little hollow in the waterline forward and a little hollow to the garboards. She has a handsome stern with a well-raked and curved transom and plenty of tumblehome to the quarters.

The *Iris* is 36 feet long on deck, with a waterline length of 29 feet, a beam of 10 feet 3 inches, and a draft of 5 feet 6 inches. Her iron keel weighs 6,500 pounds, and she has another 2,500 pounds of lead inside ballast.

Her construction is rugged, but not unduly heavy. Her oak keel is 5¾ inches by 12½ inches. The frames are also oak, 1¼ inches by 1½ inches on 9-inch centers. Planking is 1⅛-inch cedar. Her vertical clamp is 1¾ inches by 4 inches, the horizontal shelf being 1¼ inches by 3½ inches, both of fir. She has full-length bilge stringers, 1½ inches by 4 inches. There are three extra-heavy, well-kneed deck beams in way of both masts.

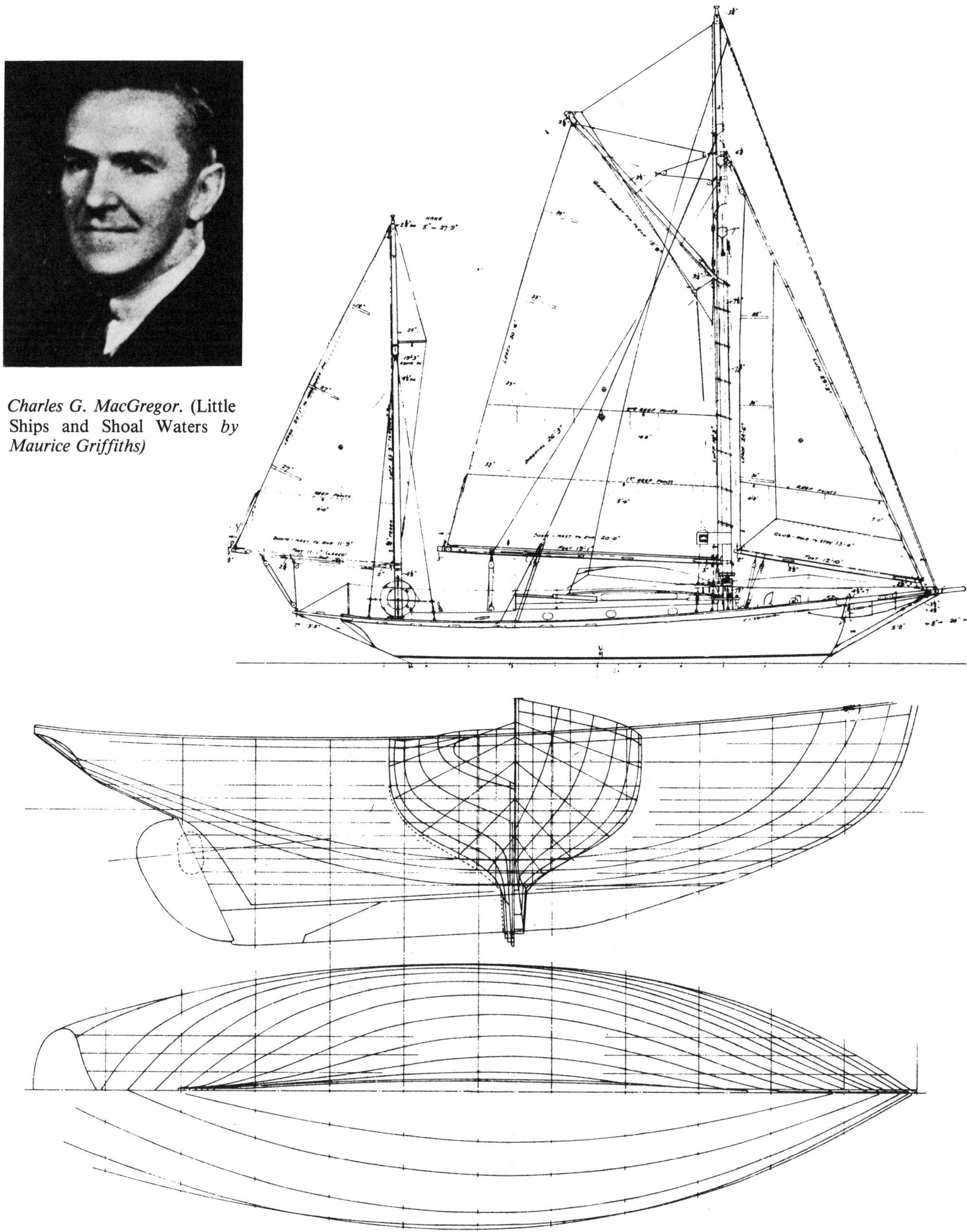

Charles G. MacGregor. (Little Ships and Shoal Waters *by Maurice Griffiths)*

The sailplan and lines of the Iris.

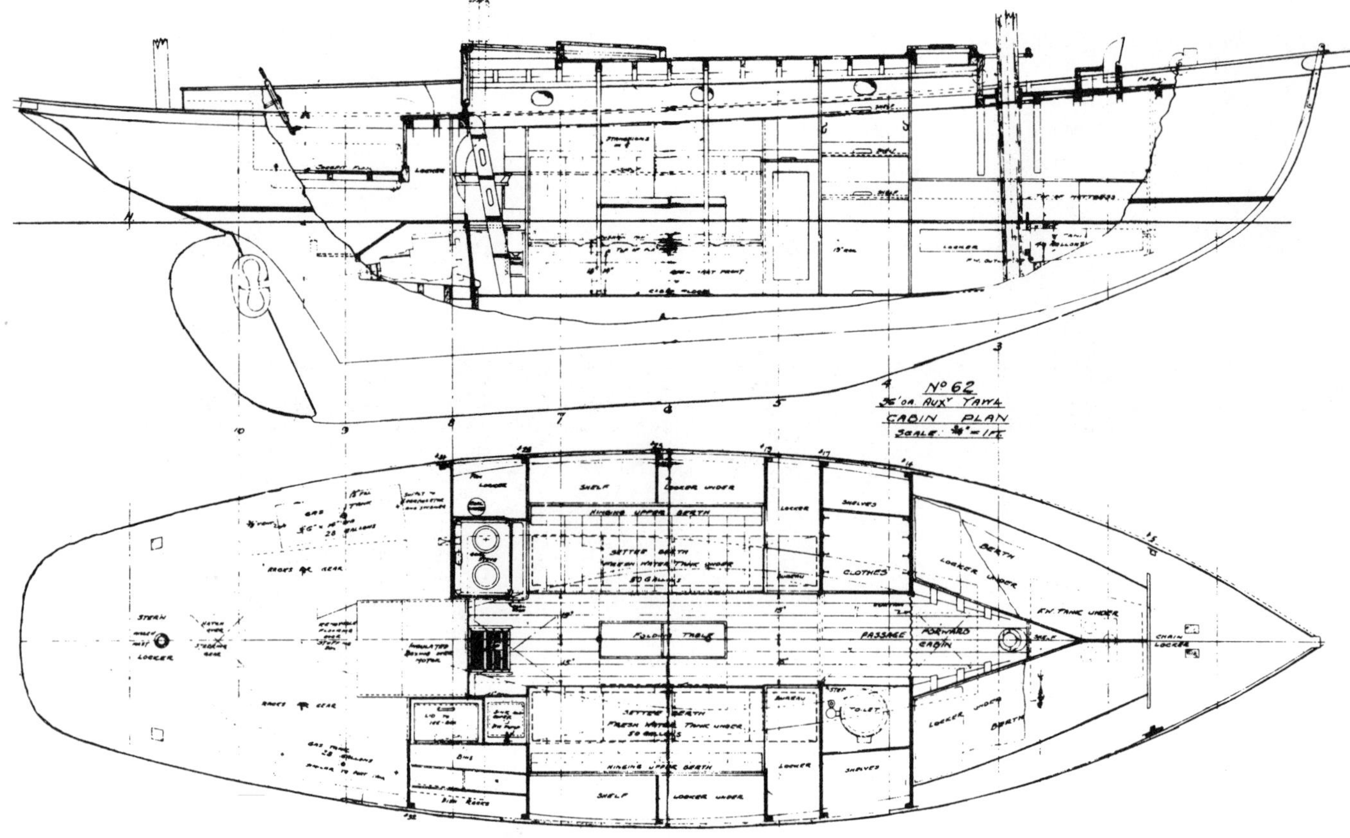

The interior arrangement of the Iris.

The deck is 1⅛-inch white pine, the planks being 2 inches wide. Her cabinhouse is 1⅜-inch pine.

The *Iris* has a moderate rig; her mainsail is well under 500 square feet. The total sail area is 666 square feet in the three lowers, with 378 in the mainsail, 129 in the mizzen, and 159 in the jib.

That squarish mainsail, not too long on the hoist but with plenty of mast above it for a good-sized working topsail (and its gaff vanged to the mizzen masthead) looks seamanlike to me. It would be a nice sail to watch. One of my correspondents put it very well: "No sail is so lovely as a four-sided sail."

The masthead is 41 feet 8 inches above the deck. The double bobstays make great good sense. You'd have a setup for the running backstays farther forward for short tacking.

I like the pinrail at the mainmast. I don't know about her removable boom gallows. I think I'd rather know that this handy structure would always be there.

The center of effort of the three working sails is almost directly below that of the mainsail; she'd balance nicely under mainsail alone or under jib-and-jigger. You'd start to shorten sail by reefing the mainsail, an easy chore with the sail in the middle of the boat. She has two deep reefs in the mainsail (I'd want a third) and reefs in both jib and mizzen. Note the reefing tackles all rove off on the mainsail's first reef and on the mizzen reef; she's businesslike. She'd probably need some mainsail to work to weather in a hard chance. Jib-and-jigger gives her only 288 square feet, probably not quite enough. This is the disadvantage of the yawl compared to the ketch.

The storm jib shown is about the same area as the reefed jib; it ought to be smaller. The sail sheets to the end of the jib club, a fine idea, since you can then use the four-part jib sheet to trim it. It would be even better to top the club right up and lash the clew of the storm jib to it. That would give you a really strong, easily controlled sheeting arrangement for heavy weather.

The *Iris* uses a modest jib topsail, though it is not shown on the sailplan. The big, masthead, overlapping jib shown would be a fine sail, though you couldn't tack with it, since the forestay and headstay are so close together.

Her lifelines give her a seagoing look. I'd want a swordfishing pulpit on that nice long bowsprit end.

She has an able-looking hull. (Mystic Seaport)

Her house is narrow, especially at the forward end, so she has plenty of deck space around the mast. The dinghy shown on top of the house is about 10½ feet long.

She has a big Dorade ventilator on the foredeck. There's a small hatch in the deck outboard of the after port corner of the house leading to a cylindrical coal chute. There's a hatch over the steering gear, an item it is good to be able to get at readily.

She has a windlass at the inboard end of the bowsprit. The ground tackle specified is a pair of Lawley anchors (of the yachtsman's pattern), one of 50 and one of 75 pounds. By the time she came to the Mystic Seaport, she was down to a pair of measly 20-pound Danforths.

The *Iris*'s engine is a 1956 Universal "Atomic" Four (quotation marks mine). She carries 56 gallons of fuel in two tanks. Water capacity, also in two tanks, is 90 gallons.

The yawl has a standard accommodation plan with the galley aft, saloon with two full-length transoms amidships, head and hanging locker next forward, and two bunks in the bow. Her relatively high freeboard allows headroom of 6 feet 3 inches under the house.

The galley stove is set athwartships so you can tend the fire even when sailing hard on the port tack. The stanchions for the cabin table run all the way to the overhead, providing great handholds when the vessel is lurching. There is plenty of storage space outboard of the transoms.

I think the *Iris* is a very wholesome cruising boat. Whether in the 36-foot or the 6-foot version, she's easy to admire.

14/ The *Saoirse*

Length on deck: 42 feet
Length on waterline: 37 feet 6 inches
Beam: 12 feet
Draft: 7 feet
Sail area: 700 square feet
Displacement: 24 tons
Designer: Conor O'Brien

The Gaelic word for freedom is *saoirse* [sheer'-shee]. This is the name Conor O'Brien gave to the cruising vessel he designed for himself in 1922, partly because he hoped she would give him personal freedom and partly to commemorate the establishment of the free state of Ireland. For the five years he owned her, the *Saoirse* brought him that peculiar mixture of freedom and responsibility that vessels bestow on their masters.

The *Saoirse* was built at Baltimore, not far from the Fastnet Rock on the southern tip of Ireland. She was designed for general cruising, not as a specialized ocean cruiser, but Mr. O'Brien made a round-the-world voyage in her from 1923 to 1925, sailing south from Ireland down the length of the Atlantic, then eastabout around the world in the Southern Ocean, and then up the Atlantic again, back to Dublin. In 1927 he took her in the Fastnet race, but she could not go to windward with the ocean racers in a gale and so dropped out.

The *Saoirse* has the lines of the European working craft, with her cod's head and mackerel tail. Her greatest beam is well forward. She has a nearly plumb bow, a deep forefoot, and a fine entry. There is considerable drag to her keel. Her sections are deep-bodied. Note the tumblehome at the transom.

Mr. O'Brien wrote:

> Of the technical details of the hull which that design represented I will say no more than that it had a fine generous midship section, calculated to give her all the stability required without any outside ballast, bows bluff above the waterline to keep her head up, narrow quarters to let her stern sink down; all very nicely proportioned except in relation to the quite inadequate length of 40 feet, for which I was asking the builders to tender. When I came to consider the cost of other things, apart from the mere hull and spars tendered for, I realized how foolish I had been to spoil the design for the sake of £50 or so; but by that time the construction was so far advanced that no alteration could be made; only the builders thought the stern looked so damnably ugly that they made more rake to the transom and gave me a present of 2 feet extra for the sake of their reputation.

Thus, as built, the *Saoirse* has a length on deck of 42 feet to go with her waterline length of 37 feet 6 inches, her beam of 12 feet, and her draft of 7 feet. The sail area of her original ketch rig is 1,210 square feet. She displaces 24 tons; her 8 tons of ballast is all inside in the form of scrap iron.

While the *Saoirse* was not fast to windward, neither did her owner and designer make any claims about her speed off the wind:

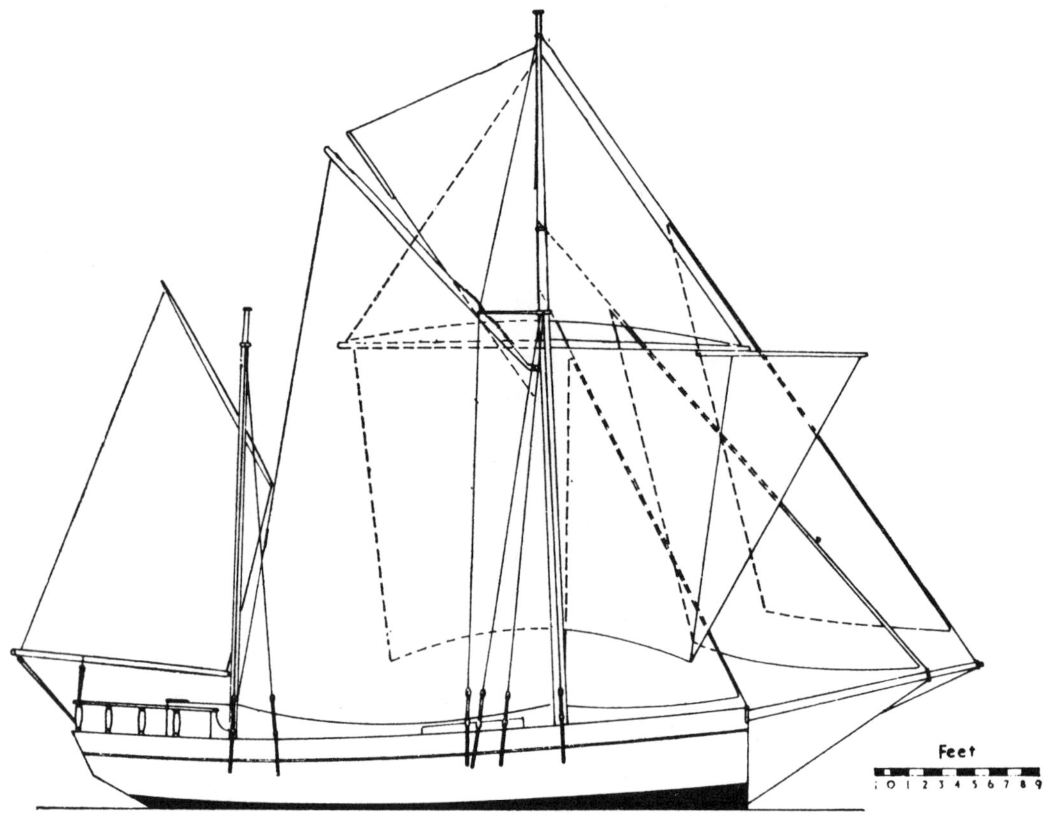

The original sailplan of the Saoirse. (Voyaging Under Sail *by Eric C. Hiscock)*

The Saoirse as rerigged to sail around the world. (Yachting, *August 1930)*

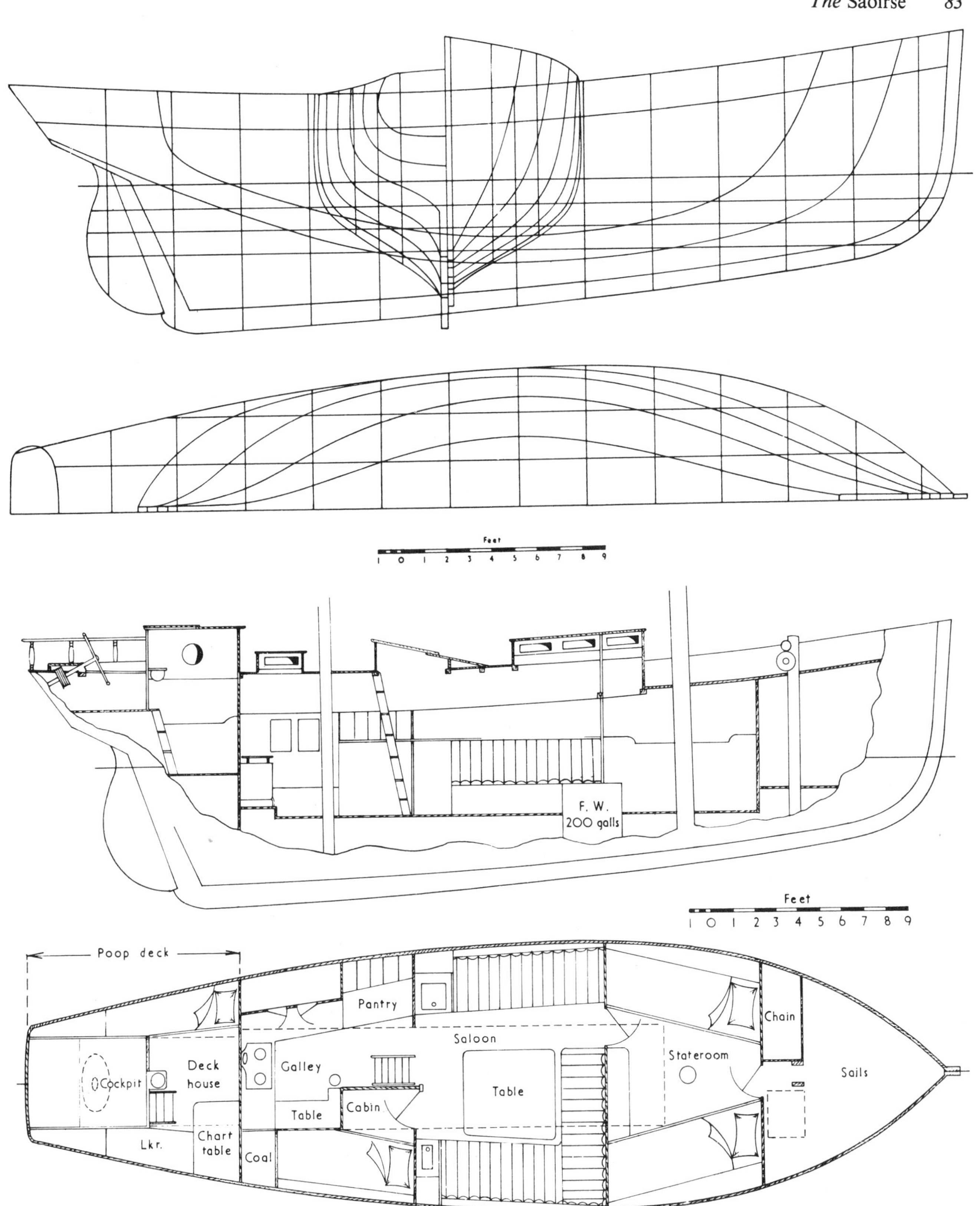

The lines and interior arrangement of the Saoirse. (Voyaging Under Sail *by Eric C. Hiscock)*

> I admit that *Saoirse* will not run very fast, however strong the breeze, but she has never yet been hove-to with a fair wind, and will accommodate in comfort the three men necessary to do justice to her, while, if one were indifferent to speed, she could be worked by oneself alone.

And:

> Though in smaller vessels it may not be possible to do anything but sleep, eat, and steer, on account of the motion, in *Saoirse* I was able to do even such delicate work as mending a clock.

The vessel's ketch rig has some unusual features: she has no main boom to thrash about in a calm at sea; her mizzen is a lugsail, like the one Joshua Slocum rigged on the transom of the *Spray;* she has a pole mainmast, which surprises me a bit, since Mr. O'Brien always sought practical repairability above elegance; and she has an extra-long bowsprit, so that something could really be made of the flying jib. Mr. O'Brien reported her to be a good self-steerer off the wind thanks to her far-ranging jibs to hold her head off. Conor O'Brien did, of course, vang his main gaff to the mizzen masthead. The mainsail has an area of 450 square feet.

On his sailplan, Mr. O'Brien drew in some square rig in dotted lines. He was thinking about an area of 500 square feet in a squaresail and two triangular raffees set above it. Or, the raffees could be set upside-down as studding sails! As William A. Robinson had done in the *Varua* (see *More Good Boats,* page 151), he added these squaresails to his ketch rig before his long voyage was half completed.

In 1927 Mr. O'Brien rerigged the *Saoirse* as a true square-rigger. "There was a certain difference of opinion on the part of those that saw her as to whether she was a topsail schooner or a brigantine," he wrote. At any rate, he gave her a fore course and a square foretopsail, a taller after mast on which he set a gunter mainsail, and nothing but staysails between the masts. He found that going aloft to furl the square topsail was easier than lowering his raffees to the deck. He wrote: "She makes a poor staysail schooner, and an indifferent brigantine; the masts are still too far apart, but it was the best I could afford, and anyway it's better than her ketch rig." And again: "Blessed is the handiness of the topsail schooner; I did not hit any traffic or any rocks, inward or outward; I did not scratch any paint while mooring or unmooring. I used to think I hated the necessary maneuvers, but now I pity those to whom the possession of an engine has made them unnecessary."

Instead of an engine, Conor O'Brien made himself a 21-foot yuloh, which gave him 1½ knots. (Curiously enough, that's just about the same speed a 10-foot yuloh gave my four-tonner.)

The *Saoirse*'s cockpit is high and secure on her stern, its sole being just about at the level of the main deck. Mr. O'Brien's idea for her steering wheel was that it should have a telescoping shaft so you could either sit down to it with the wheel in the aft position or stand up to it comfortably with the wheel extended forward nearly to the deckhouse. In the forward position, you could also sit in the off-center companionway to the deckhouse and steer in sheltered comfort.

That chart house is only one of the great features of the *Saoirse*'s layout. Its bunk and chart table are very handy to the helm, and there is a window in the forward bulkhead so you can see what's happening on the stove without going way below. Of his chart house Mr. O'Brien wrote: "I attribute a great deal of *Saoirse*'s success to it."

The vessel's galley is aft, a most unusual arrangement for a British craft of the time, in most of which cooking arrangements were relegated to a corner of the fo'c's'le.

Her master's cabin is handy to the main companionway, yet has privacy. Her big saloon has a nice L-shaped settee around the cabin table. There is an ample forward stateroom.

The *Saoirse* was still sailing in 1959, by then rigged as a gaff ketch with a marconi mizzen. She even had a main boom. I wonder what has become of her?

Conor O'Brien wrote a number of good books. He told the story of his circumnavigation in *Across Three Oceans.* He described the three major vessels he had owned in his book *From Three Yachts,* devoting 100 pages to the *Saoirse.* He presented his ideas on the practicalities of cruising in four small books: *The Small Ocean-Going Yacht; The Practical Man's Cruiser; Yacht Gear and Gadgets;* and *Deep Water Yacht Rig.*

In *Deep Water Yacht Rig,* Mr. O'Brien presented his design for a 55-foot, ideal ocean cruising yacht. It was based on the *Saoirse.* A vessel was built to this design for a Major Cyrus Strong at the yard of Tom Langdon in Florida. The prospective owner died before the interior work and fitting out had been completed. The hull sat for two years before a second owner had it towed to Annapolis, where he and his wife finished off the interior. Forced to sell her in order to stay solvent, they never got to sail her.

A third owner took her to Nova Scotia for fitting out, then sailed to Bermuda, surviving a hurricane that knocked her down once. Upon arrival, his wife made him sell the vessel.

A later owner, to whom I am indebted for what I know of her history, was J.H. Millar of Monaco. She was originally named the *Centurion* and later the *Aegean.*

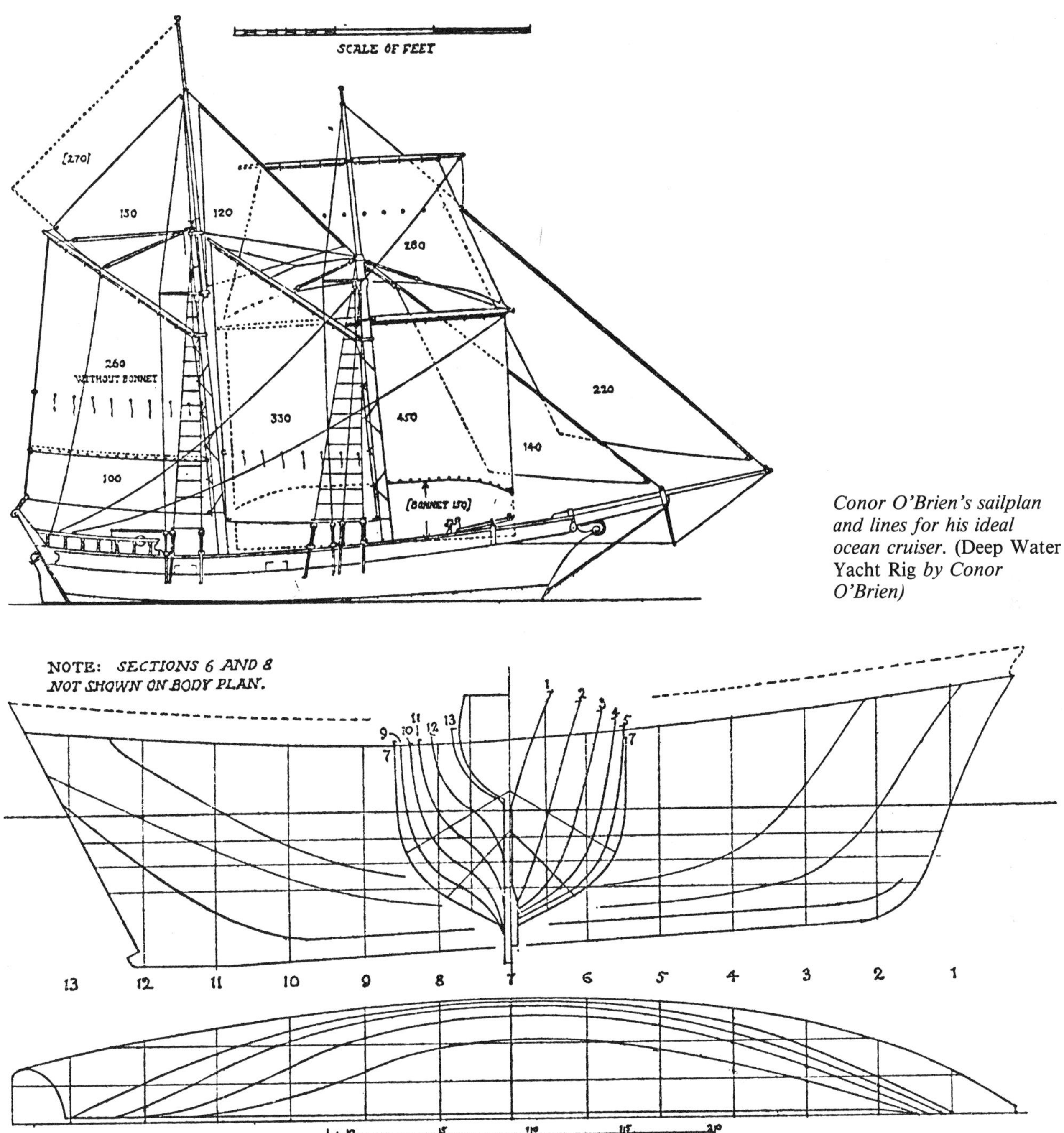

Conor O'Brien's sailplan and lines for his ideal ocean cruiser. (Deep Water Yacht Rig *by Conor O'Brien)*

Conor O'Brien's ideal ocean cruiser has a very deep forefoot but less drag to her keel than does the *Saoirse.* She has very old-fashioned, deep-bodied sections, but she is saved from being cumbersome by her narrowness and by her fine waterlines, particularly aft. Her narrow, almost dorylike transom reminds me of the stern William H. Hand put on his little ketch *Fundulus* (see *Good Boats,* p. 32).

The builders of the *Centurion,* like those of the *Saoirse,* couldn't stand to build her stern as designed. It is said that they added five feet to her overhang aft. This gave her a length on deck of 60 feet, to go with her waterline length of 48 feet, beam of 12 feet 6 inches, and draft of 8 feet.

Her rig is most interesting. She spreads 2,200 square feet of sail. She has no booms. Her big headsails are

The Centurion *on a reach. (J.H. Millar)*

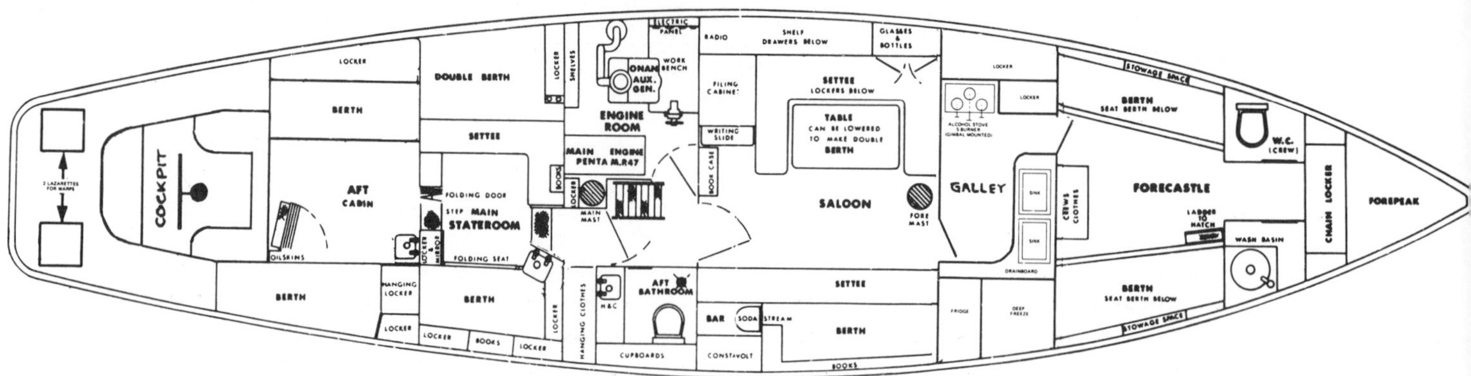

The arrangement plan of the Centurion. *(J.H. Millar)*

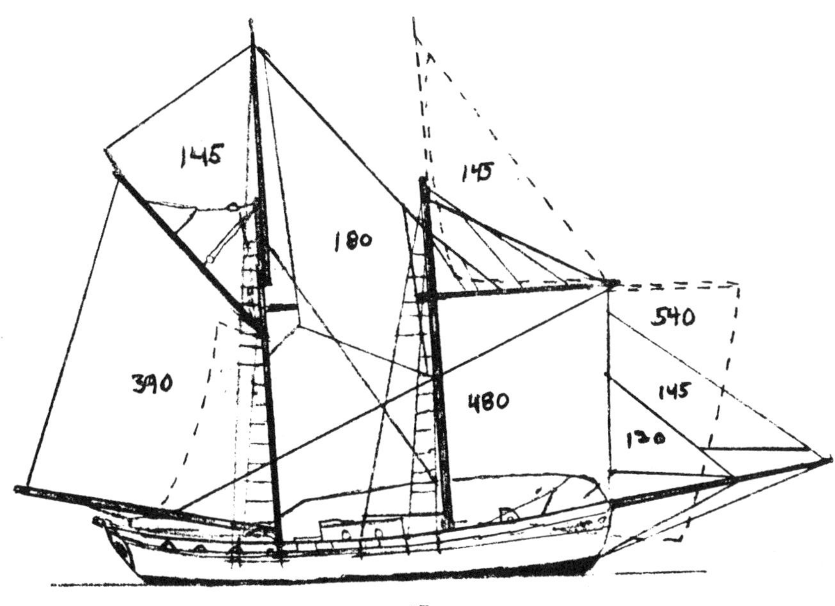

I couldn't resist O'Brienizing the Urrys' Cogge ketch.

tacked down away out forward to hold her head off when broad reaching.

Her squaresails have an area of 880 square feet; the course has a 150-square-foot bonnet that can be laced to its foot in light going, while the topsail can be reefed down to quite a small sail. That reefed fore topsail would be a fine sail in a gale in a big seaway, since it would be high enough to hold some wind with the vessel down in the trough. She'd be mighty handy when shortened down to her reefed fore topsail, jib, and reefed mainsail without its bonnet. Her big club main topsail adds an extra 120 square feet up where it will do the most good in a light air and on holidays.

Somewhere between the various rigs of the *Saoirse* and the rig of the *Centurion,* Conor O'Brien drew a "Working Sail Plan for a Yacht of 40 Feet Waterline." This was a sort of brigantine without a fore topmast, and the rig appealed to me so strongly that I couldn't resist trying it out on the hull of the Urry brothers' Cogge ketch (see *Good Boats,* page 4). I think when you combine the Urry brothers' thinking as to hull, stern windows, midships deckhouse, and so forth, with Conor O'Brien's ideas for a seagoing rig, you end up with a mighty romantic vessel. I wouldn't want to sail her in the Fastnet race, but I wouldn't mind setting off in her round the world.

15/ The *Aunt Sara*

Length on deck: 35 feet
Length on waterline: 28 feet 7 inches
Beam: 10 feet 10 inches
Draft: 4 feet
Sail area: 700 square feet
Designer: S.S. Crocker, Jr.

Like Gaul, Maurice Griffiths' book *Little Ships and Shoal Waters* is divided into three parts. The English editor, yacht designer, and writer gives you a little of everything: Part I is a treatise on how to design shoal-draft boats; Part II gives you 22 examples of the type; and Part III takes you on two cruises in boats that don't draw much.

The best of the 22 examples is Number 6, the *Aunt Sara,* designed a half century ago by S.S. Crocker Jr. Mr. Griffiths is a great admirer of Mr. Crocker's designs. He spent a weekend sailing in the *Aunt Sara* in New England waters as the guest of her owner, Lucius T. Hill, and succumbed to her charms. His caption for her photo is "Who wouldn't like to blow into an anchorage at her wheel?"

The *Aunt Sara* was built by F.D. Rolfe at Quincy, Massachusetts, in 1929. (Another boat was built to this design in 1933. This was the *Falcon,* built by Herman Lund at Erie, Pennsylvania, for Dr. E.P. Hussey of Buffalo, New York. The *Falcon* was given a ketch rig. And in 1935, a schooner-rigged sistership, the *L.F. Drake,* was built at Port Elizabeth, New Jersey, for S. Morton Chambers, who wrote me mentioning others, including one converted to a commercial fisherman in the Pacific Northwest.)

The *Aunt Sara* is 35 feet long on deck, with a waterline length of 28 feet 7 inches, a beam of 10 feet 10 inches, and a draft of 4 feet. Her sail area in the four lowers is 700 square feet.

Doesn't she have a handsome sheerline? It's just right.

Her forefoot is quite cut away for a boat with a clipper bow. Her transom stern with its outboard rudder is reminiscent of that of the Newfoundland jack schooners, but has more rake. It needs even more rake than it has, to my eye, to get rid of the chopped-off look of the jack schooners. Maurice Griffiths wrote, "It [the bow] needs, I know, a short counter stern to balance it . . .; and *Aunt Sara*'s broad transom, well rounded as it is, does not quite make the balance perfect." As I say, I think the *Aunt Sara* could get away with her nicely shaped transom with only a few degrees more rake. Besides looking better, such a stern would give her a bit more lift in a following sea.

She has very easy bow and buttock lines and ought to be reasonably fast off the wind.

To help *Aunt Sara* to windward, I'd give her a centerboard. A great invention, the centerboard. Imagine being able to increase your draft and lateral plane just when you need to as you come on the wind and then be able to go right back to that very moderate four feet of draft when sailing free or crossing a shallow place.

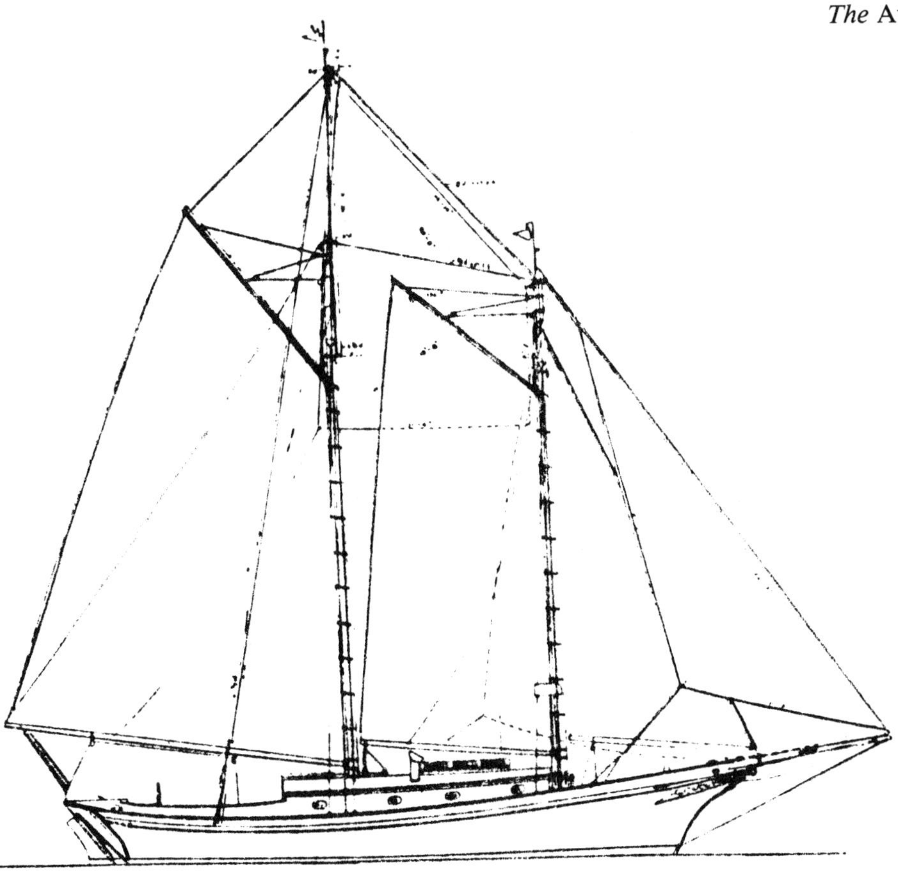

The sailplan of the schooner Aunt Sara. (Little Ships and Shoal Waters *by Maurice Griffiths)*

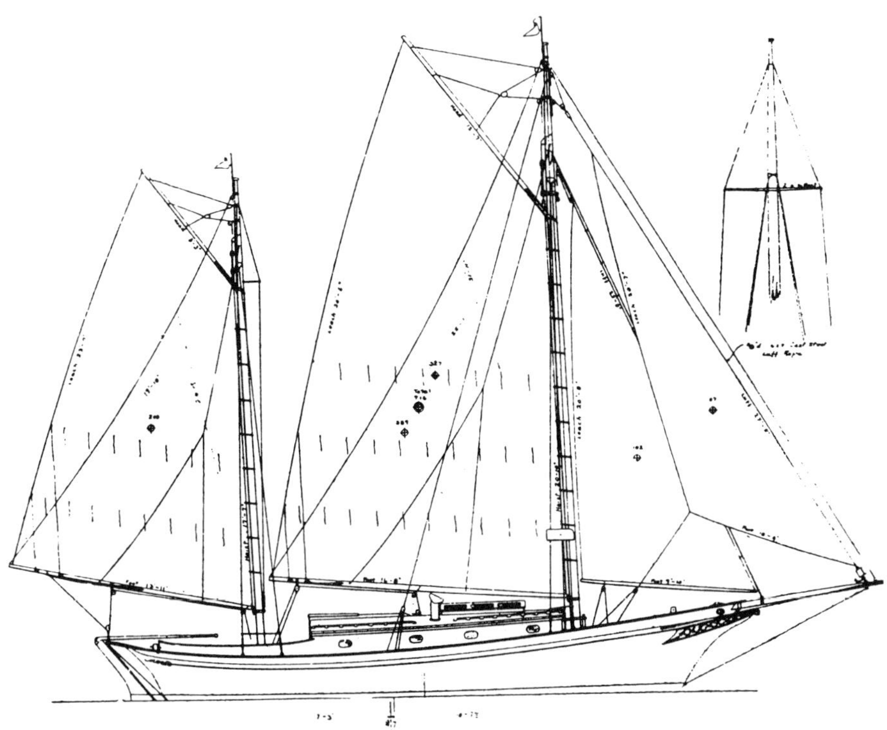

The sailplan of the ketch Falcon. (Little Ships and Shoal Waters *by Maurice Griffiths)*

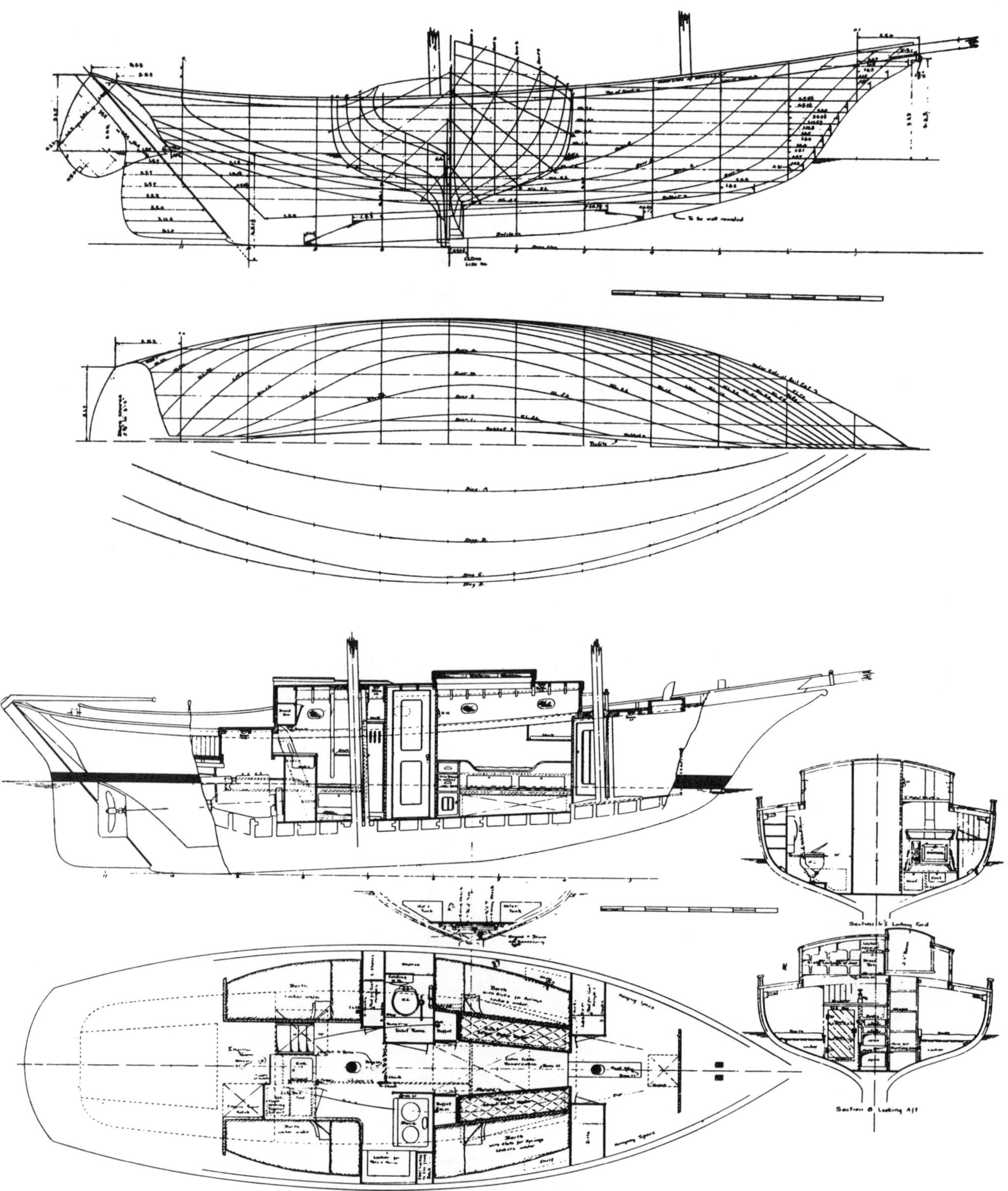

The Aunt Sara*'s lines and interior arrangement plans.* (Little Ships and Shoal Waters *by Maurice Griffiths)*

Why, it's almost magic. The Chinese were thinking when they developed the centerboard.

The *Aunt Sara* is beamy enough to sail fairly upright. She has a fine enough entrance not to have to punch a head sea twice before getting through it. She would have an extremely easy motion and be a very dry boat.

See her nice big rudder. Sam Crocker didn't skimp on the rudder. This boat would be some easy to steer under sail or power.

The single-topmast gaff-schooner rig looks well on her. Mr. Griffiths applauded this rig for American waters, but wrote, "We have to do far too much beating to windward around the English coast for a rig like this." This business that the English either have to beat dead to windward or run dead before it in their cutters, while we in America are allowed to reach merrily back and forth in our schooners may be more myth than fact. There is likely to be a lot of windward work in getting up to the westward from Down East, and even the English occasionally get a good chance along.

In any case, the *Aunt Sara*'s sailplan is well broken up, for ease of handling. You could shorten down by taking in the foresail, and you could heave-to under foresail alone. In the *Falcon,* with her ketch rig, you could shorten down by taking in the mizzen, and heave-to with mizzen and staysail. I'd rig her as a schooner myself. The schooner's light sails, her topsail and fisherman staysail, are up where they will catch the most breeze. I'd want a gallows frame on this boat with either rig.

The engine, under the bridge deck, is a Gray 4-40. The engine room is separate from the cabin and is entered through a hatch in the bridge deck. She has a 30-gallon water tank under each transom in the saloon.

The *Aunt Sara*'s arrangement is a good one for four people. Her forward bunks could actually be slept in with the boat working into a head sea, for they are moved aft out of the bow. The galley sink and icebox are right aft by the companionway; the galley stove is set athwartships so it may be tended and used on either tack.

My centerboard trunk would require moving the head to the fo'c's'le so there could be an unobstructed passage fore and aft on the port side of the trunk. (Where the head used to be, you could have a nice little chart table!) On the starboard side of the centerboard trunk you could have a fixed table connecting (dishwise) the galley with the saloon. Even with the head in the fo'c's'le, there is a lot of storage space up there.

How does she sail? Here's what Mr. Hill wrote to Mr. Griffiths:

> The worst weather we have been out in was a fifty-mile gale two summers ago in Buzzards Bay, which builds up a very steep sea. We carried the fore staysail and double-reefed main with three of us aboard, one of them a lady. We were entirely comfortable at all times and quite dry. No water came into the cockpit, although we ran dead before it for a time and expected that one of the short seas might break over the taffrail at any time. We were able to eat up to windward with this rig, although I wouldn't have wanted to claw off a lee shore under these same conditions in the middle of the night.
>
> I am sure of my wind velocity on this day, as I checked with the weather bureau the following morning. Also, getting into port I started up the engine, and it was necessary to run at almost full speed to hold our own.
>
> With a fresh to strong wind off-shore on the beam and all four lowers set she has logged 8 knots for two hours on end. This must be the maximum speed of this hull.
>
> In light airs *Aunt Sara* does surprisingly well. Her worst point of sailing, naturally, is to windward, and she will not approach the performance of the modern cutter rig. However, Mr. Crocker and I were working toward the so-called "motor-sailer" and were willing to sacrifice this point of sailing for the shoal draught and other features. Also, I am not a complete blue water sailor and confess to becoming thoroughly fed up after four or five hours banging into it.

The *Aunt Sara,* with her easy motion, her great carrying capacity, her easy steering, and her dryness in rough water, would make a fine offshore cruiser. Who wouldn't want to go looking for trade winds with her?

16/ The *Island Belle*

Length on deck: 59 feet
Length on waterline: 48 feet 6 inches
Beam: 12 feet
Draft: 3 feet 9 inches
Designer: Wirth M. Munroe

It would be nice to know the Truth about which designers of good boats had what kinds of influence on which other designers of good boats. Sometimes the influence of one designer on another is obvious; a number of designers got their start in the office of John G. Alden and couldn't help but be influenced by his ideas of what makes a good boat. Other times the influence is apparent, say, in the resemblance of the boats of a number of young designers to the designs of William Garden, for example. Yet it's difficult to know whether that resemblance is a matter of conscious copying, unconscious copying, or mere coincidence. Probably the young designers themselves don't always know.

This influence and adopting of ideas from designer to designer is a Very Good Thing. The whole premise of this series of books is that good boat designs of the past are worth study and emulation. If I were to try to design a boat, I would certainly keep firmly in mind the works of the Wizard of Bristol, Nathanael G. Herreshoff.

What got me going on this whole business of one designer influencing another is the *Island Belle,* a development of the Presto-type sharpie given the bow and stern of a whaleboat and a three-masted-schooner rig by her designer, Wirth M. Munroe.

It's not just that Wirth Munroe was the son of Commodore Ralph M. Munroe, the developer of the deep, ballasted, round-chined, flaring-sided sharpie that took its name from his *Presto* (see *Good Boats,* page 41), but also that Commodore Munroe and Nathanael Herreshoff became friendly with each other late in their lives and compared notes on boats. Then L. Francis Herreshoff, Nathanael's son, designed the *Marco Polo,* a double-ended, three-masted schooner the same size as the *Island Belle* at about the same time (just after World War II) that Wirth Munroe was designing the *Island Belle.* Probably coincidence, but, as I say, it would be nice to know the Truth.

At any rate, it's interesting to compare the *Island Belle* with the *Marco Polo* (see *More Good Boats,* page 164). The *Island Belle* is 59 feet long on deck (4 feet longer than the *Marco Polo),* with a waterline length of 48 feet 6 inches (3 inches less than the *Marco Polo);* a beam of 12 feet (2 feet more than the *Marco Polo);* and a draft of 3 feet 9 inches (1 foot 9 inches less than the *Marco Polo).* I don't have a displacement figure for the *Island Belle,* but she is undoubtedly lighter than the *Marco Polo.*

The *Island Belle* was designed for all-round cruising. Like the other Presto boats, she was to be a good gunkholer that would also be safe offshore in rough weather. The *Marco Polo* was designed specifically for

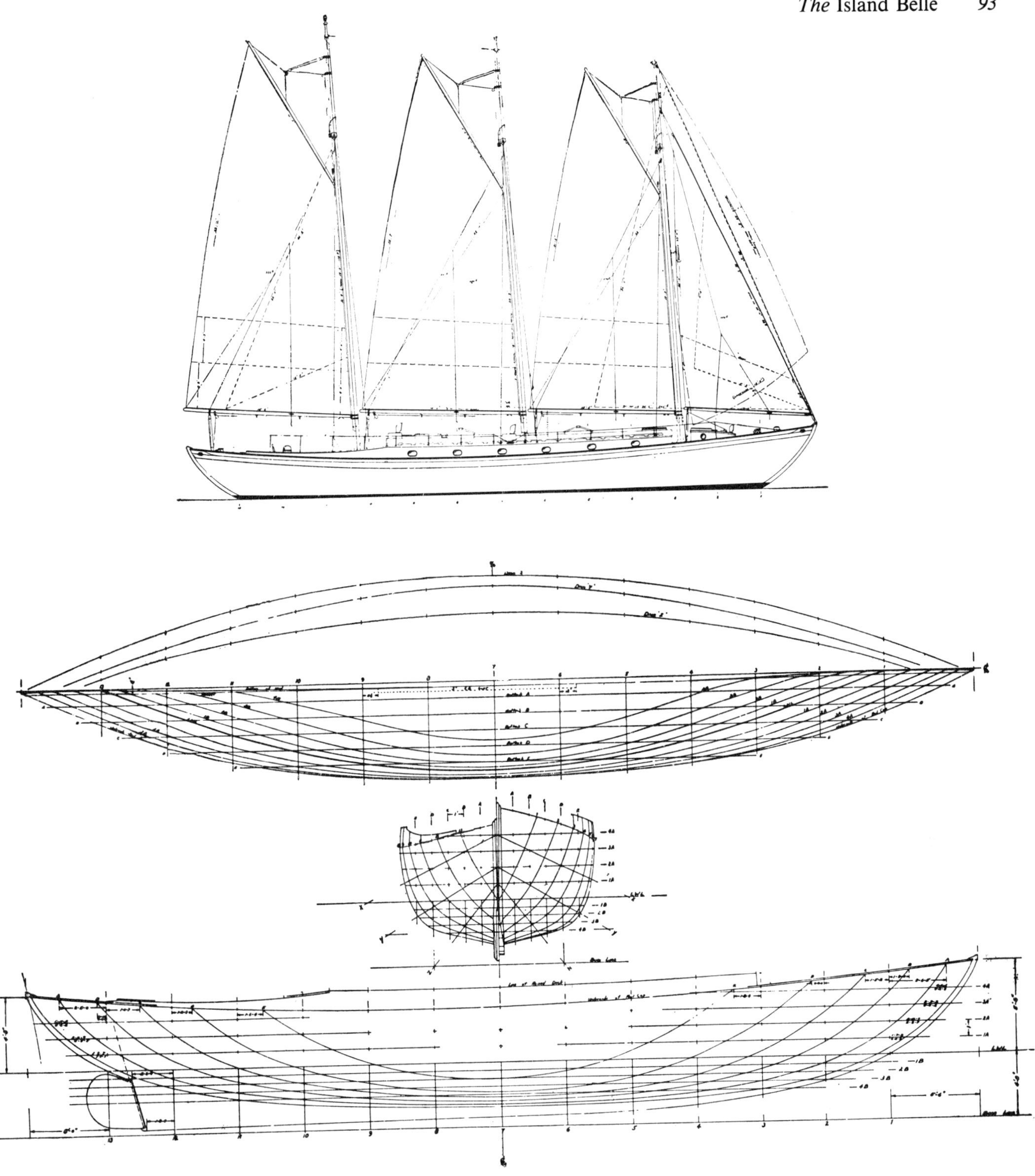

The Island Belle*'s sailplan and lines.* (The Rudder, *December 1947)*

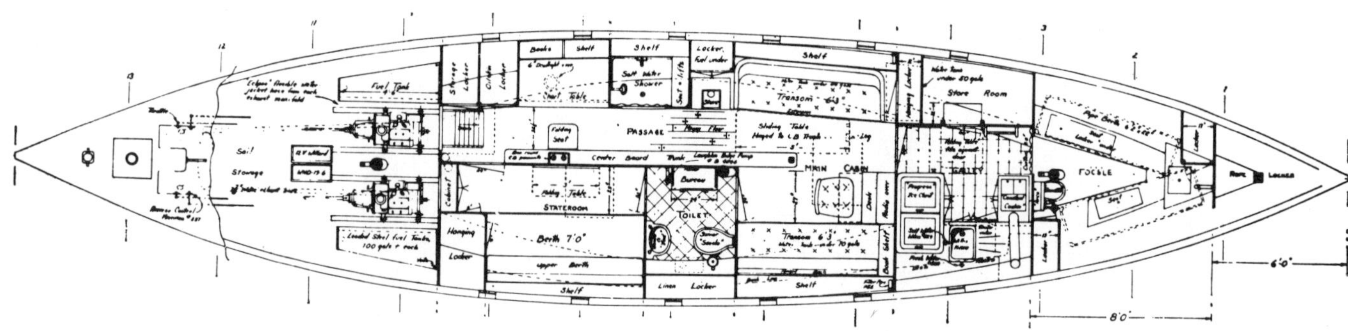

The Island Belle*'s cabin plan.* (The Rudder, *December 1947)*

Strutting along on the wind with her original rig.

long ocean passages. The *Marco Polo* has a big engine to help her on her way in light weather. The *Island Belle* would certainly sail faster than the *Marco Polo,* and the *Marco Polo* would be more seaworthy in a hard chance.

I do have to say two more things before we take a detailed look at the *Island Belle.* First, a big thank you to Joseph C. Dobler of Manhattan Beach, California, who put me on to Wirth Munroe's whaleboat-Presto-sharpie-tern-schooner in the first place; and, another big thank you to Dean A. Worcester of Crownsville, Maryland, who owned her for 21 years and wrote me many interesting details about her.

The *Island Belle* has the pretty profile of a whaleboat. Yet she is deeper and narrower than a whaleboat, with less flare and more freeboard than those open rowing and sailing beauties. Wirth Munroe's hull has very fine lines; she would reach her hull speed of close to 10 knots relatively easily.

Her high, slightly flaring topsides would give her stability once she begins to heel. One of her owners wanted to increase her stability for offshore racing; so, under Wirth Munroe's direction, he shifted her ballast from inside to outside. This gave her a keel that increased her draft to 4 feet 6 inches. Her designer felt the change improved the vessel.

She originally had a big centerboard just off-center to port, so the trunk avoided the mainmast (and probably jammed stones, should she take the bottom). Her rudder is protected by the keel; I'd want it a bit longer for maneuverability.

The three-masted rig keeps the sailplan low (to go with what is, after all, a fairly tender hull) and the sails small. The area of the mizzen is but 333 square feet. She'd have a good turn of speed despite her moderate, much-divided sail area, thanks to her fast hull.

Of course the divided rig means you have four sheets to trim every time you head up or off, or if the wind shifts. And you have ten spars to keep varnished. If you like varnishing spars (as I do), you'll love the *Island Belle.*

Her tall mastheads give a good lead to the peak halyards and allow the sails to be well peaked-up, yet have their gaffs clear the springstays between the mastheads (the springstays don't show in the sailplan, but they were part of the design and were rigged on the vessel).

When she got her keel, the *Island Belle* was given a marconi mizzen with a permanent backstay leading down to a boomkin. She also got a bowsprit. And the shape of her gaff sails was changed, increasing the lengths of the luffs and thus squaring the gaffs more. This change would have been disastrous without vangs. Wirth Munroe did not approve of these modifications to the rig.

John Moll's drawing shows her modified rig.

Her tall mastheads would allow a pair of big fisherman staysails, each with a club at the peak of the sail to extend the head, Tancook whaler style. Just imagine her flying along on a reach in a light breeze with those babies set! She'd turn a few heads, wouldn't she?

I'd prefer her two headstays to be side by side for ease in shifting jibs, and particularly for ease in tacking with the overlapping jib.

She has lazyjacks all around, which makes great good sense.

When shortening down in the *Island Belle,* you'd take in the mainsail first. If it blew harder, you'd find she would balance under foresail and mainsail. Dean Worcester liked to sail her under mizzen and forestaysail in heavy weather. She'd heave-to, like a two-masted schooner, under foresail alone. Or, she could reach or run like a scalded cat under storm jib and mizzen trysail.

Her raised deck gives her a strong hull and a lot of unbroken deck space, and will keep her relatively dry. The secret to good looks with a raised deck is to keep the bow higher than the deck, and the stern at least as high. That way, the hull dominates the raised deck rather than vice versa. You'd want the *Island Belle*'s raised deck protected by higher lifelines than are shown. Think of all the boats you could stow up on there; I visualize at least a peapod (with a little double-paddle canoe tucked inside) and a sailing dinghy.

There's a lazarette way in the stern reached by a deck hatch. Sails stow beneath the cockpit sole (that's where we'll put those fisherman staysails).

Her engines straddle the mizzenmast. She originally had a pair of Kermath 2-113s, each turning an 18-by-16-inch feathering wheel. It's hard to argue with the reliability given a vessel by two engines. And if you want to drive her with both sail and power, you have the nicety of a lee propeller well submerged.

She has two 100-gallon fuel tanks outboard of the engines. She carries 190 gallons of fresh water: 140 in a pair of 70-gallon tanks, one under each transom in the saloon; and 50 in a tank in the galley on the port side.

When you come down the main companionway, there is an oilskin locker handy to port. In the passageway leading forward there's a big chart table, with its seat folding off the centerboard trunk, and a 6-inch deadlight in the overhead right above it. Next comes a saltwater shower and a heating stove; I'd want some sort of connection between these two appliances.

To starboard is a double stateroom with 7-foot lower and upper berths and a folding table. The head connects to both stateroom and saloon and has its own little bureau.

In the saloon there is a nice desk and chair and a hinged sliding table attached to the port side of the centerboard trunk.

The galley has a big storeroom to port with a hinged table off its door. There is a ladder so you can go out the galley hatch, or at least climb up for a breath of fresh air and a look around before the coffee boils.

The fo'c's'le has its own head and two pipe berths.

For some reason, I visualize the *Island Belle* running off in fairly thick weather in Ipswich Bay north of Cape Ann before a moderate gale from the northeast. She's under foresail alone and making knots, and her people are keeping what Frank Bullen in *The Cruise of the Cachalot* called a "brilliant lookout," for they know that if they get a sounding of 20 feet before they see the bell buoy marking the entrance to the Essex River, they'll have to haul their wind, work her offshore round Cape Ann, and feel their way into Gloucester. They wouldn't sound their way in on a lee shore in this weather if they didn't have plenty of confidence in the vessel's ability to beat back out.

But it's not all that thick, and soon after a sounding of 25 feet, a wet, oilskinned arm is raised toward the "horizon" ahead, and, sure enough, there's the big buoy, clanging and swaying, fine on the starboard bow.

Then it's just a matter of picking a way in past the buoys that mark the shifting channel, running in past the tower on Two Penny Loaf, reaching the welcome calm of Essex Bay, and jibing up the river with, fortunately the last of the flood. When the final twist of the stream has been followed, she's eased alongside, docklines are made fast and hauled taut, and the crew tumbles below to see about a fire in the stove, some dry clothes, and maybe even a toast to the vessel.

Dean Worcester wrote: "This boat is exceptionally well balanced under many combinations of sail and sails herself admirably. She is easy to single hand, and my wife and I would take her most anywhere without additional crew. We cruised from Maine to Key West, always with great confidence in her sea kindliness."

The *Island Belle,* long since renamed the *Rebel,* was going strong until just recently. A boatyard fire in 1983 destroyed her.

17/ A Pinky

Length on deck: 43 feet
Length on waterline: 39 feet 4 inches
Beam: 14 feet
Draft: 6 feet 9 inches
Sail area: 1,200 square feet
Designer: Howard Chapelle

Join us on board a 43-foot pinky schooner taking advantage of an easterly breeze — complete with fog and rain — to run to the westward offshore in the Gulf of Maine. We left Yarmouth, Nova Scotia, yesterday, intending to call at Grand Manan, but with the poor visibility and the gentle breeze sending us along heading the way we wanted to go, decided to hold on in the usual attempt to outwit the prevailing sou'wester.

We have just relieved the watch and are still buttoning our sou'westers against the wet misery. The lucky dogs who have tumbled below to a hot stove told us over their shoulders that they heard the Bull Rock whistler 25 minutes ago even if they couldn't see it. Judging by the way the ground swell from the southeast is heaping up under the weather quarter making her roll as we run before it, we must be on the Guptill Ground, which would be just about right.

So just fly down like a sea gull to our wallowing little vessel. This is all mind's-eye stuff, but bring your oilies anyway, and I hope you don't get seasick.

Tell you what. Let's strap that foresail and jib right in tight; they're not doing much this far off the wind anyway, and maybe they'll stop us from rolling so much in this nasty seaway. Just take the slack out of that vang on the fore gaff, will you? It makes up on the pinrail in the starboard main rigging. There, that's better.

I haven't had a pinky on these pages since Howard Chapelle's own *Glad Tidings* sailed across pages 98 through 101 of *Good Boats*. I gave you a brief history of the pinky type then, and, of course, Mr. Chapelle himself has written about pinkies at some length in two of his books, *American Sailing Craft* and *The American Fishing Schooners,* so suffice it to say here that the pinky is a 19th-century double-ender with distinctive built-up bulwarks at the stern, developed for fishing in the waters through which we are sailing this yacht replica today. Howard Chapelle designed this vessel a half century ago, basing her closely on an Eastport pinky of about 1850.

He gave this pinky slightly finer ends than the Eastport model had and increased the drag of the keel slightly so that she draws 3 inches more water than did her ancestor. Our pinky replica is 43 feet long on deck, with a waterline length of 39 feet 4 inches, a beam of 14 feet, and a draft of 6 feet 9 inches.

Mr. Chapelle also eliminated the gammon head knee at the stem, which gave the Eastport pinky's bow the concave "clipper" profile. This simplification seems to go well with the replacement of the Eastport pinky's gaff mainsail, main topmast, and main topsail by a mere leg-o'-mutton mainsail.

Did you catch a little whiff of drier air just then?

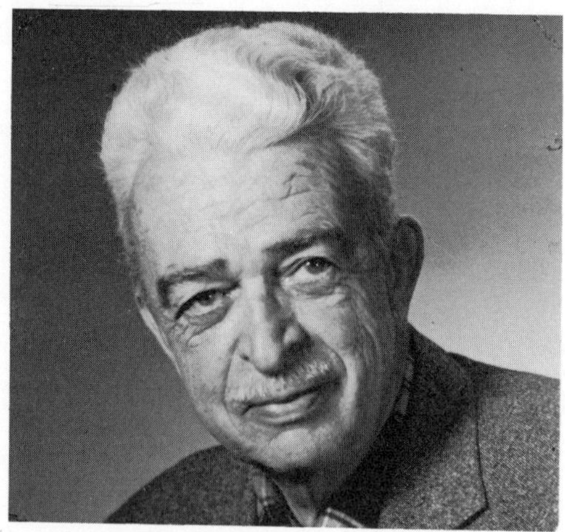

Howard I. Chapelle.

Probably my wishful thinking. Sure wish this drizzle would stop. But take her for a bit while I drop down and tap the glass. My, but look at it jump up! Wonder what's going on around here. Guess we'll just have to wait and see.

I think our pinky has a pretty profile with her stout bowsprit, slanting sternpost, high stern bulwarks, and well-raked masts. She's certainly a compact and rugged vessel and well deserves her reputation for seaworthiness.

Don't you like her easy motion? Even when it was kind of rough back there, she didn't throw us around much.

Everything about her is moderate, the only bulges in her dimensions being in her beam, displacement, and sail area, all of which are generous. She's not really fast, as you can see, but she will turn in good average speeds and can keep going endlessly in bad conditions. Of course we mustn't drive her in an attempt for speed, for she's not overly stiff, and she can be knocked down if you don't take sail off in a real breeze. These old-fashioned heavy vessels are kind of deceptive that way; they seem able to take anything, and they are if you shorten them down, but feats of sail-carrying in a breeze can be dangerous, because this type of craft isn't strong on ultimate stability.

Watch it. Don't let her jibe. I think this wind is coming around a bit. Better head her up some while I get that backstay forward. Yes, the breeze is backing right around. Let's jibe her over now. That's the stuff. Let her come back to west and I'll set up the new backstay. It feels distinctly colder, doesn't it? At least the damned rain has stopped.

It's good that she has plenty of sail to keep her moving along in a gentle breeze like this. Doesn't that big mainsail do some pushing, though? And her tall mainmast gives her a certain majesty that no working pinky had.

Her mainsail has 750 square feet; the foresail, 300; and the jib, 150, for a total of 1,200 square feet. There's a fisherman staysail in the forepeak that adds another 225 square feet.

Did you notice that all her standing rigging is doubled up? A good idea. There are two headstays, two bobstays, two stays between the mastheads (the horizontal one leads to the point of attachment of the main lower shroud), and two pairs of shrouds on each mast. We've moved the preventer backstays in on deck; they used to make up way out on the tombstone, if you can believe it.

The track on the mainmast is heavy, and we keep it well greased. The hauling end of the halyard goes aloft, made fast to the topmost slide for a downhaul.

She has plenty of parts to the mainsheet, and it's rigged double-ended, with a come-along on one side. The main halyard is double-ended too, with a jig one side. With this gear, you can set the mainsail just the way you want it without breaking your back.

We put a third reef in the mainsail and a second reef in the foresail, and you'll notice we keep the clew earings all rove off on the mainsail, because the boom is so long. There's a main trysail down below, too, a tiny, strong one. Yes, leading the vang on the fore gaff though a block on the mainmast instead of down to the deck was our idea. It works like a charm.

Her jib is nearly as much a light sail as is her fisherman staysail. It's sort of an afterthought; the pinky's ancestor, the Chebacco boat, had no jib. Pinkies love the combination of foresail and close-reefed mainsail with no jib in heavy weather.

The lazyjacks on the jib? That's a trick we imported from the Chesapeake Bay.

Oyyyy! Feel that blast! Luff her right up! I'll let the jib fly so her head will come up. Now for that main downhaul. Slack out the topping lift, off goes the halyard, and down she comes on the run. There, no more mainsail, and none too soon, either: this wind has some real weight in it. I'm going to get the jib off her too.

There. Let's let her jog along under the foresail and take stock. Cripes, it's a small gale already! Clearing off, though. Right out of the northwest.

What's that low piece of real estate up to windward? Yes, it is land, and see the lighthouse? Must be Machias Seal.

I wonder if we shouldn't head in. This looks like a

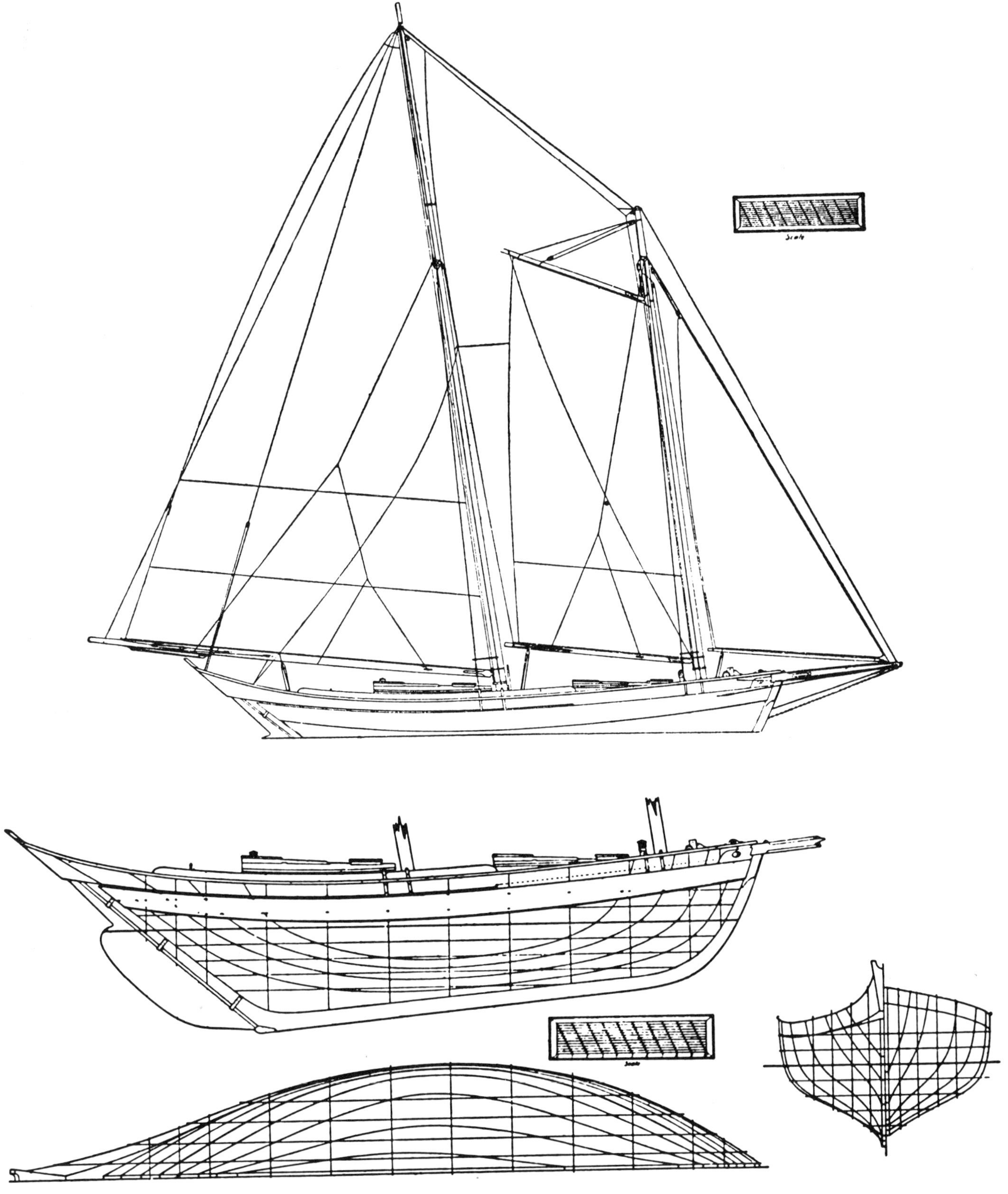

The pinky yacht's sailplan and lines. (American Sailing Craft *by Howard I. Chapelle)*

real gale, and it's going to get rough out here. Why don't I rouse out the other watch and see if they wouldn't like to put a close-reefed mainsail on this vessel and beat into Cutler.

So up they came, muttering their sleepy grumbles but laying into the third reef earing with a will and helping to tie off the points. Up went the triple-reefed mainsail, a modest little sail. But even that proved too much, for she boiled along dipping even the washboards under occasionally. So it was jog again and pull down the first reef in the foresail.

This she liked, and now the pinky came into her own, lifting into the rising sea, throwing her spray, and making her way to windward, put about on the port tack and laying in for the mainland. As the other watch went below, we told them not to worry: the land was less than 15 miles away and it didn't look as if we'd be too far to leeward of Cutler when we reached it.

The pinky carries a little 12-foot peapod on deck, either athwartships abaft the forward house or fore-and-aft with one gunwale atop the house.

She steers with a big tiller, and we've put a bench for the helmsman right across the deck, like the one they had in the French pilot cutter *Jolie Brise.* Works great.

The head is back in the pink stern, a very sanitary arrangement.

Down in the after cabin she has two bunks outboard of transoms, a good stove, a table, and plenty of lockers. Amidships there is a generous hold, lending the vessel versatility. In the forward cabin is the galley at its after end, with a U-shaped settee around a table forward.

There is a strong watertight bulkhead between the forward cabin and the forepeak, just abaft the foremast. We heard a sad-but-true story a while back of a vessel of about this size and construction that sank in the North Sea in broad daylight, after hitting a container lost overboard from a ship and floating just awash. It's stories like this that make you build bulkheads.

And so Mr. Chapelle's pinky worked her way inshore against the rising gale, gaining ever-smoother water. In under the lee of Long Point, we put her about and worked her up the shore, driving along in a flat sea and easing her through the worst of the gusts coming off the hills.

She shot in past Little River, flew into the wind, and settled back on her anchor in Cutler. Down came the sails. Mighty good to be in.

As long as you've come this far, come on below and help us drink a toast to the vessel. I think that down here someplace is a bottle of Mount Gay rum.

18/ The *Saxonia*

Length on deck: 34 feet 6 inches
Draft: 4 feet 9 inches

All maritime activity in Essex, on the east coast of England, marches to the tune of the tide. It's a low, flat coast twined with rivers and creeks that depend on high water for their navigability and studded with offshore sands that, at low water, can be dangerous lee shores or fine breakwaters according to which side of them you are on.

The bawley *Saxonia* (could there be a better name for a stout British vessel?) has her mooring far enough down Pyefleet Creek off the Essex river Colne so that she can come and go even at low water. Yet all of us sailing in her one fine fall day were keenly aware of the tide, for we fairly flew down the river with the ebb and, on returning, crept back in over it.

The owner and master of the *Saxonia* is Christopher Kerrison, managing director of the Colne Oyster Fishery Company and also an entrepreneur in Scottish oysters. After the severe winter of 1962 wiped out the Colne oyster fishery, it was Chris Kerrison who revived it.

Chris bought the *Saxonia* in 1966 to dredge oysters in the Colne. She had been built over a three-year period from 1929 to 1932 by Aldous Ltd. at Brightlingsea, near the mouth of the river. The Aldous yard, one of the biggest and best known in the area, built a great many local fishing vessels and more bawleys than any other yard. The yard is but a memory now. The *Saxonia* was built as a motor bawley but with a hull modeled very much along the lines of her sailing ancestors. She was rigged with mainsail and forestaysail — foresail in England — as steadying sails. She's 34 feet 6 inches long on deck and draws 4 feet 9 inches.

Sometime in her career she had a wheelhouse added. She worked out of Leigh, around the corner on the north side of the Thames Estuary, until the early Fifties. Chris Kerrison kept her dredging in the Colne until 1977, when she and another motor bawley were replaced by a steel catamaran.

Chris laid up the *Saxonia* for a year, for he had decided to rig her up as a sailing bawley and use her to fish for fun. He put the traditional bawley rig into her. He replaced her big old three-cylinder, 44-horsepower Lister with a much smaller auxiliary plant, a 30-horsepower Yanmar diesel turning a Hundested variable pitch propeller.

Chris was nice enough to include me in a "day out" on the water in the *Saxonia.* John Leather, who is a most knowledgeable maritime historian of the region and has other marine talents too numerous to mention, was on board. So was Francois, a French oysterman. These experts were interested to learn a bit about our Chesapeake Bay skipjacks, still dredging oysters under sail.

The gear on a bawley is heavy. We got underway

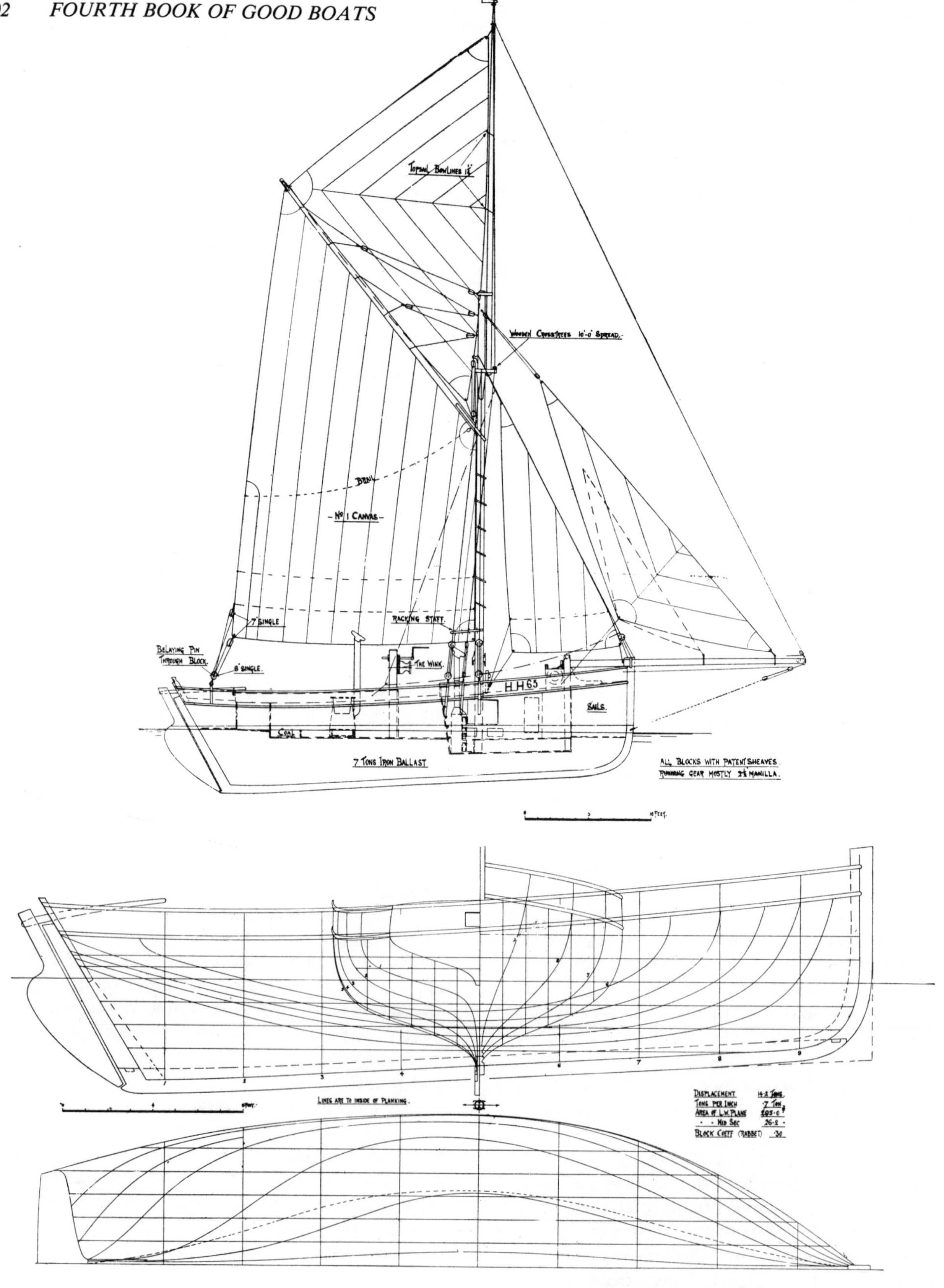

The sailplan and lines of William Maxwell Blake's typical bawley. (Yachting, *October 1931)*

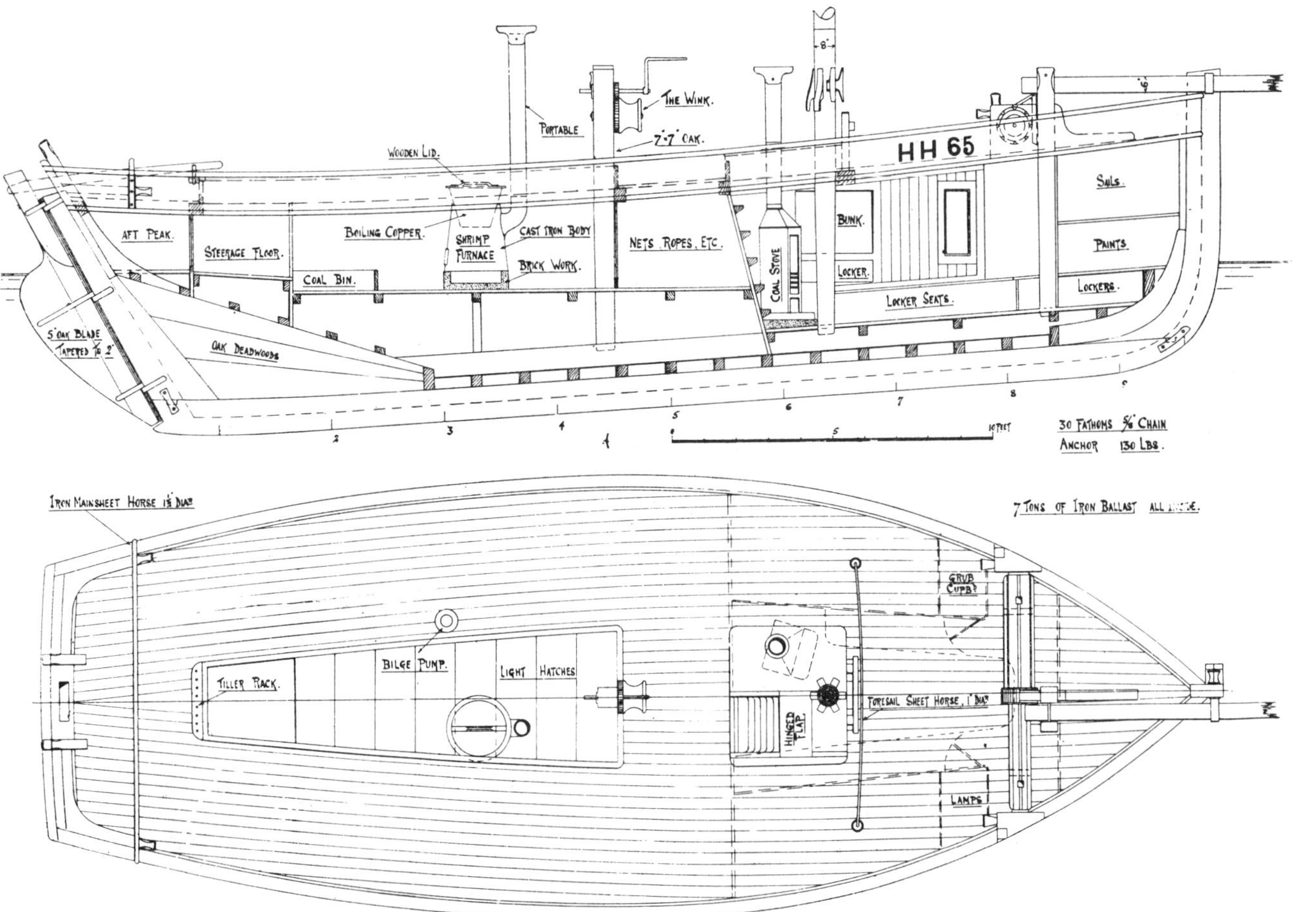

Interior and deck plans of the Blake bawley. (Yachting, *October 1931)*

under sail, and hoisting the mainsail was definitely a two-man job, one on each halyard. She has a long, heavy gaff.

Once the mainsail was standing to Chris's satisfaction, we set a small jib flying on the bowsprit traveler, pulled well out the long, level spar. This sail ensured that she would pay off smartly once the mooring was let go. And so it did. Chris squared her off on a broad reach before the fresh breeze, and then we ran up the foresail.

She ran along easily and comfortably, and not too slowly, either. As we got out of the river the breeze eased off to moderate, and then she wanted a bit more sail, but we were just enjoying the vessel and her East Anglian surroundings, not driving her for market.

The bawley is descended from the Peter boat, a smaller type of similarly rigged fishing craft referred to in records as early as 1540, according to John Leather, our history mentor. The Peter boat evolved into the larger, somewhat finer-lined bawley in the mid-19th century.

The bawley was a localized craft. Leigh and Harwich (forty miles northeast of Leigh along the Essex coast) were the principal ports from which they worked. In the heyday of bawleys in the late 19th century, a hundred worked from Leigh, and 60 from Harwich.

In 1850, John told us, the master of the Leigh bawley *Secret* installed a boiler in his vessel and boiled his catch of shrimps right on board, so that when he landed them they were all ready for market. He added value to his catch, started a move to put coal furnaces and shrimp boilers in every bawley, and may even have given the type its name. Chris Kerrison keeps the original copper shrimp boiler in the *Saxonia.*

By the turn of the century, bawleys were being built up to 42 feet long on deck. Construction was heavy and cheap, with sawn oak frames, pitch pine bottom planking, and pine topsides and decks. Iron ballast was carried all inside, ceiled over in the bilge.

Fifty years ago, William Maxwell Blake studied the bawley type and made a set of drawings of a composite bawley incorporating typical features. It is his plans that are reproduced here.

The Blake hypothetical bawley has a length on deck

of 37 feet, length on the waterline of 35 feet 3 inches, a beam of 13 feet, and a draft of 4 feet 10 inches. She displaces 14.2 tons and carries 7 tons of ballast. Her sail area is 875 square feet.

Studying her lines, you can see that her ability to sail comes from her fine entry, easy bow lines, and long run. Her hull lines exude steadiness. She's heavy and beamy. She has easy bilges and picks up bearing everywhere as she heels. A mighty comfortable sea boat.

Bawleys were used primarily for shrimping, but also did other kinds of fishing as opportunities presented. Trawling for shrimp was summer work, the season running from May to September.

During the other months of the year, a good many bawleys went after whelks, which are big, edible snails. The men would set a 40-fathom trot line (at least that's what a Chesapeake Bay crabber would call it) anchored and buoyed at each end and baited with mashed crabs. They'd leave the line down from 20 minutes to an hour, pull it up, pick off the whelks that had attached themselves to the bait, and toss them into nets hung over the side to clean. The whelks were sold live and brought three shillings a bushel in 1930.

Bawleys, like other types of East Coast fishing boats, took part in the festivities of the many-faceted annual regatta days, racing for prize money.

John Leather was instrumental in having reprinted in 1979 a delightful — at times, hilarious — book about a bawley, her irrepressible skipper, and her amazed owner. The book, *Gotty and the Guv'nor,* was written by Arthur E. Copping in 1907, and is great reading.

As we reached along outside Mersea Island, along came a big spritsail barge, beating up to meet us. We fell in with her, tacked, and brought the *Saxonia* up close-hauled to parallel the barge and see what we could do with her. But for the lack of fish in our hold and cargo in the barge's, it could have been a scene from 100 years ago.

Chris triced up the loose foot of our mainsail, so we'd have an unobstructed view of the barge abeam to leeward. She was under mainsail, foresail, topsail, and mizzen. Careful as I was at the tiller, the barge out-pointed us a little, nor did she fall back. As we approached the mouth of the river, the barge began to brail in some sails and lower and furl others. Soon she had nothing set at all, yet her pace never slackened. I stopped worrying.

The *Saxonia* seems much bigger than her 34-foot length. This is due to her heavy displacement, acreage of clear deck space, and her deep bulwarks. You steer her from a standing room, a wonderful arrangement. You can stand up to get a good pull on her big tiller, you are well protected, and your eye level is favorable for seeing over bulwarks and under sails.

The bawley rig is a specialized form of the English cutter. The lower mast is short, the topmast, tall. Topmasts were often struck or left ashore in winter. Tackles for handling the trawl gear were often set up as preventer backstays to help the rig stand going to and fro in heavy weather.

A 35-footer would have 17½ feet of bowsprit outboard. The bowsprit ran out to starboard of the stemhead and was rigged naked, with only a running bobstay.

A distinctive feature of the rig is the boomless mainsail, which means the clew of the sail has to be kept inboard so the sheet can stretch the foot tight on the wind. So the sail has a short foot and, with the long gaff, a vertical leech. You get plenty of twist in the sail, and I found myself muttering sacrilegious mutterings about vangs on board the *Saxonia.*

On a 35-footer, sail areas might be: mainsail, 500 square feet; topsail, 200; foresail, 95; and working jib, 115, for a total of 910 square feet.

One reason for the boomless mainsail is that a boom is not always the best of companions when you're working on deck. Another is that the boomless sail allows you to work running gear that can quickly change the sail's area, to keep trawling speed steady as the strength of the breeze changes. Bawleys always had a tack tackle or "truss," so the tack of the sail could be triced up in a twinkling to reduce its area. There was also a brail halfway up the leech so the sail could be partially or wholly gathered to the mast at that point. Often a topsail would be kept set over a half-brailed or trussed mainsail. Sometimes the first shallow reef would be tied in and the sail left standing high to keep the deck extra clear for working.

The mainsheet consists of a double block on a traveler and two single blocks on the sail, one at the clew cringle and one at the cringle for the first reef. The sheet belays on a pin through the double block. When you reef, you move each of the single sheet blocks up one cringle.

Running before it in a light breeze, the bawleymen would often pole the mainsail out. They always stowed the sail with the end of the gaff right on deck to one side with the throat of the furled sail hoisted partway up the mast so the gaff would fit inboard. This looks strange to an American who is in the habit of going round his decks at anchor topping up booms to jaunty angles, but there is no denying it's a seamanlike stow.

In light weather the bawleys could and did set good-sized jibs, huge jib topsails called spinnakers, and balloon foresails.

The bawley's rig is versatile. (Gotty and the Guv'nor *by A.E. Copping)*

On the *Saxonia* the mainsail seemed very drafty, but it did seem to stand all right going to windward. I suppose she'd do a bit better on the wind with a slightly flatter sail. Chris and John agreed that there aren't many people around today to cut a good mainsail for a bawley.

The boomless mainsail was certainly well behaved, even running dead before it. I thought jibing was child's play compared to shifting over a sail with a long, heavy boom. Yes, the two big, heavy sheet blocks on the sail do fly across the vessel when you jibe and do thrash about when you tack, but they're well aft, so you'd have to be absent-minded to go back there and get hit. Those blocks aren't troublesome, yet you don't want to forget they're there.

The long gaff and rather low-slung peak halyards put a very heavy strain on the lower masthead of a bawley. When the *Saxonia* was rigged for sailing, the head of her lower mast was tapered in too much, so it won't quite stand the gaff, as one might say. "When we're racing, we don't dare look aloft," Chris said. He has since put a new mast in her.

I wouldn't want to have to go out on the *Saxonia*'s bowsprit in a seaway. It looks like barren territory to an American used to shrouds, foot ropes, nets, and even longhead rails. But if you have to, you can bring this bowsprit in to you. At the mooring, the bobstay is let go and triced up under the spar, so it won't foul the mooring pendant. Before you get underway, you take the bobstay tackle to the big, wooden-barrel windlass and put a real strain on it, so the bowsprit will know it's not supposed to wander.

The foresail sheet has a bowline in the lee rigging. When tacking, we held it there to weather for half a jiffy, so there'd be no question of her head going round. The jibsheets belay well forward in the lee waterways. As she came majestically round, we could flatten the new sheet in nicely by hand before the sail really started to pull.

Our barge rival's propeller urged her into the river ahead of us, where she found a berth and swung to an anchor in the ebb. We beat in after her against it making neither fast nor disappointing progress. The *Saxonia* is not close-winded of course, in modern terms, but if you give her a half point to work with, she'll get you there in fine style. With her little jib in the moderate breeze, she had a fairly strong weather helm.

The *Saxonia* would be a wonderful vessel to sail in a big breeze and sea, but of course shortening her down would take some muscle and a bit of time.

When the bawleys were trawling for shrimp, they used to work four nets at once. This technique changed in favor of towing one big beam trawl. Edgar J. March described the beam shrimp trawl the bawleys used in

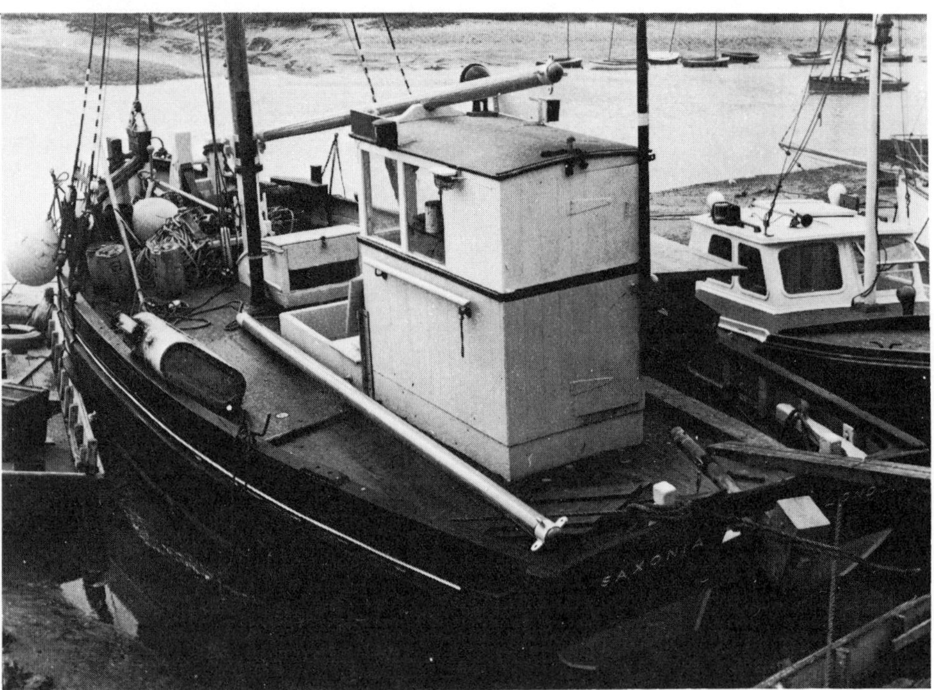

The Saxonia *before she acquired her traditional sailing rig.*

their heyday as having a 21-foot beam weighted with iron heads of 65 pounds each. The warp was 56 fathoms of 3-inch rope.

The bawleymen used a small telltale dredge, which they hauled at short intervals to see if shrimps were about.

All the hauling was done by hand from a midships winch mounted on the "wink," a 7-inch-square oak post standing above the deck and stepped on the keelson.

The cast iron furnace, held in a brick structure, topped by its copper boiler, held a place of honor just abaft the wink. Shrimps were shaken out of the net, sieved and sorted, boiled, dried, and packed into baskets. The bawleymen would trawl all day and then come in and put their baskets of shrimp on the evening train to the London market. It was the extension of railroads into Essex in the 1860s that enabled many East Coast fisheries to expand distribution beyond local markets. With long days and short nights, the crews of the bawleys lived on board all week and went home only at the weekend.

Chris Kerrison wants to try the *Saxonia* as a shrimp trawler, going back to the old way of using multiple nets. He'll start with a pair of 12-foot beam trawls boomed out from the mast. It should be an interesting experiment.

The bawleys usually had a fo'c's'le for four, the chief amenity thereof being a coal stove. The *Saxonia*'s fo'c's'le is plain and simple, with lots of room in all directions but the vertical.

In 1897, a 40-foot bawley complete with all gear cost £100. By 1912, this cost had risen to £400. Mr. March recorded that a new mast for a bawley at that time cost seven pounds, four shillings, with a 10-shilling allowance for the old mast. By 1930, the cost of a bawley had risen to £800. Chris Kerrison paid £1,700 for the *Saxonia* in 1966.

Now the *Saxonia*'s master has the fun of sailing her like the bawleys of old. And this he did, standing over to Pyefleet Creek to work her up to her mooring.

The jib came off easily. We eased the halyard and, with all the wind out of the sail, gathered in the clew and hauled the tack in. I don't know though. I'm probably too provincial about it, but in a real breeze, give me a jib hanked to a stay and a stout downhaul.

Chris made his mooring, in amongst those of some yachts, under power. I didn't blame him. If you got into a lash-up with a bawley among moored yachts, you could run up quite a bill in a short time: most of the things she'd hit, she'd sink. But we hit nothing at all and even got ashore dry shod, quite an accomplishment in itself on the muddy shores of Essex. We'd had a great "day out."

19/ The *Terns*

TERN III
Length on deck: 53 feet
Length on waterline: 44 feet
Beam: 12 feet 3 inches
Draft: 7 feet 6 inches
Sail area: 1,200 square feet
Displacement: 31.7 tons
Designer: Claud Worth

TERN IV
Length on deck: 62 feet
Length on waterline: 49 feet
Beam: 13 feet 6 inches
Draft: 8 feet
Sail area: 1,500 square feet
Displacement: 18 tons
Designer: Claud Worth

The British eye surgeon Claud Worth took his yachting very seriously, and in the early years of this century expounded his views about boats in magazine articles and books.

Dr. Worth sailed in and owned a number of vessels, and was always a careful observer of hull shape, construction, rig, and fittings; and of how they all worked together at sea. He developed his own ideas about what was best. (Two of Claud Worth's boats have appeared previously in this series: the 42-foot Fife ketch *Maud* in *Good Boats,* and the 39-foot Stowe yawl *Tern II* in *More Good Boats.)*

In the fourth edition of his book *Yacht Cruising,* Dr. Worth wrote in 1934:

> Some years ago I began trying to plan a cruising yacht which should combine the good points of all the vessels I knew and should be equally suited for home cruising or for an ocean voyage . . . . At first the quest for the ideal was undertaken merely for amusement. But by about 1912 the plans seemed so perfect that the vessel simply had to be built. I sent the "lines" to my old friend the late Mr. Albert Strange who redrew them for me on tracing cloth.

The "lines" alluded to became those of the fine cutter *Tern III.* It would be most interesting to know just how much Albert Strange changed Claud Worth's lines. My guess is, not much.

Dr. Worth continued,

> The qualities sought in designing a vessel which may be at sea for days or even weeks at a time were — easy motion, so that the crew may not be unduly tired and may be able to get regular meals. She must be able to lie-to safely and certainly in bad weather. She must run safely and steadily before any sea in which it is reasonable for a good vessel to run at all. For coasting voyages she must be weatherly and able to carry her way in a short steep sea, for it is hateful to be hung up by head winds. She must be handy and easily managed by a very small crew. She must be very strongly built of durable materials. She must have good accommodation and ample room for stores and gear. She must be as fast as is compatible with these requirements. And she must be a good-looking vessel . . . .

Dr. Worth added, "To fulfill these conditions, the vessel must be moderate in every way." And that is just what the *Tern III* is: a "moderated" English cutter. Her stem is curved a bit instead of being plumb, her counter is not too long, her forefoot has been cut away a bit, her beam is not too narrow, and her draft is not too deep. She is still a fine-lined vessel. She has a sharp entrance. Dr. Worth described her as having a "small counter well tucked up." Her bilges are quite slack, and she sits deep in the water.

The *Tern III* is 53 feet long on deck, with a waterline length of 44 feet, a beam of 12 feet 3 inches, and a draft

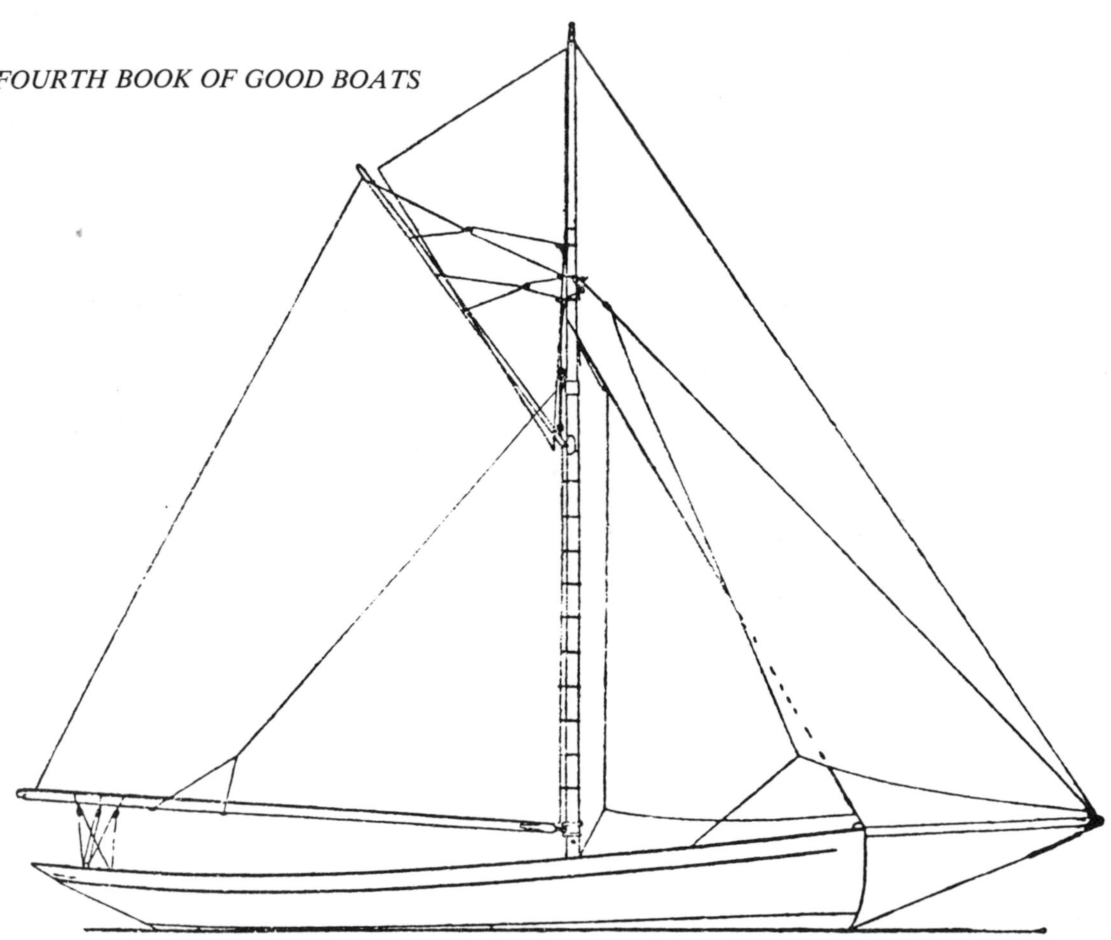

The sailplan of the Tern III. (Yacht Cruising *by Claud Worth)*

of 7 feet 6 inches. She displaces 31.7 tons and has 13.4 tons of ballast, 8 tons inside and 5.4 tons outside.

Her sail area in the three lowers is about 1,200 square feet, with about 750 square feet of that in the mainsail.

The *Tern III* was built by the Whitstable Shipping Company; she was launched on May 13, 1914.

All the wood in the hull except for the topside planking and the deck is oak, "old seasoned, autumn-cut Kent oak . . . . It was beautiful wood, very white, heavy and close-grained . . . ."

Her keelson is 7 inches by 7 inches. The floors are sided 5 inches and spaced 16 inches apart. The frames are sided 2¾ inches and molded 4½ inches at the heels and 3 inches at the heads. All her frames are double. They are spaced on 16-inch centers. Her shelf is 5 inches by 4 inches. Her bilge stringers are 6 inches by 3 inches. Her bottom planking is 1½-inch oak; the topsides are planked with teak. Her planking is fastened with 5/16-inch-square copper nails clenched over rings.

She has lead ballast cemented between her floors amidships, and all the other bays between her floors are filled with cement. Before being cemented, the wood was treated with hot tar and pitch.

Her deck is double-planked with 1⅜-inch pitch pine topped with a layer of ¼-inch silver spruce, the latter fastened down with 30,000 1-inch brass nails. "This deck was an experiment. It was perfectly successful, but I should not repeat it in a new vessel, for a layed deck of Rangoon teak is better."

In 1921 the vessel's bottom was sheathed with 16-ounce copper. "Ruberoid" was put on under it and then a layer of "thin felt impregnated with bitumen."

The theme of moderation carried out in the hull of the *Tern III* is repeated in her rig. Her bowsprit is not too long or too low, her boom is not too long, and her rig is not too tall.

Her mast is a solid stick of Norway spruce 9 inches in diameter. The main boom is hollow, 7½ inches in diameter, and the hollow gaff is 5½ inches in diameter. She has a solid Norway spruce bowsprit of 6½-inch diameter extending 15 feet outboard.

Her tapered hollow topmast fits over the lower mast, but Dr. Worth later concluded that a normal fidded topmast would have been better. He also concluded that the rig was a bit *too* moderate; he wrote that he wished he'd made the lower mast two feet taller.

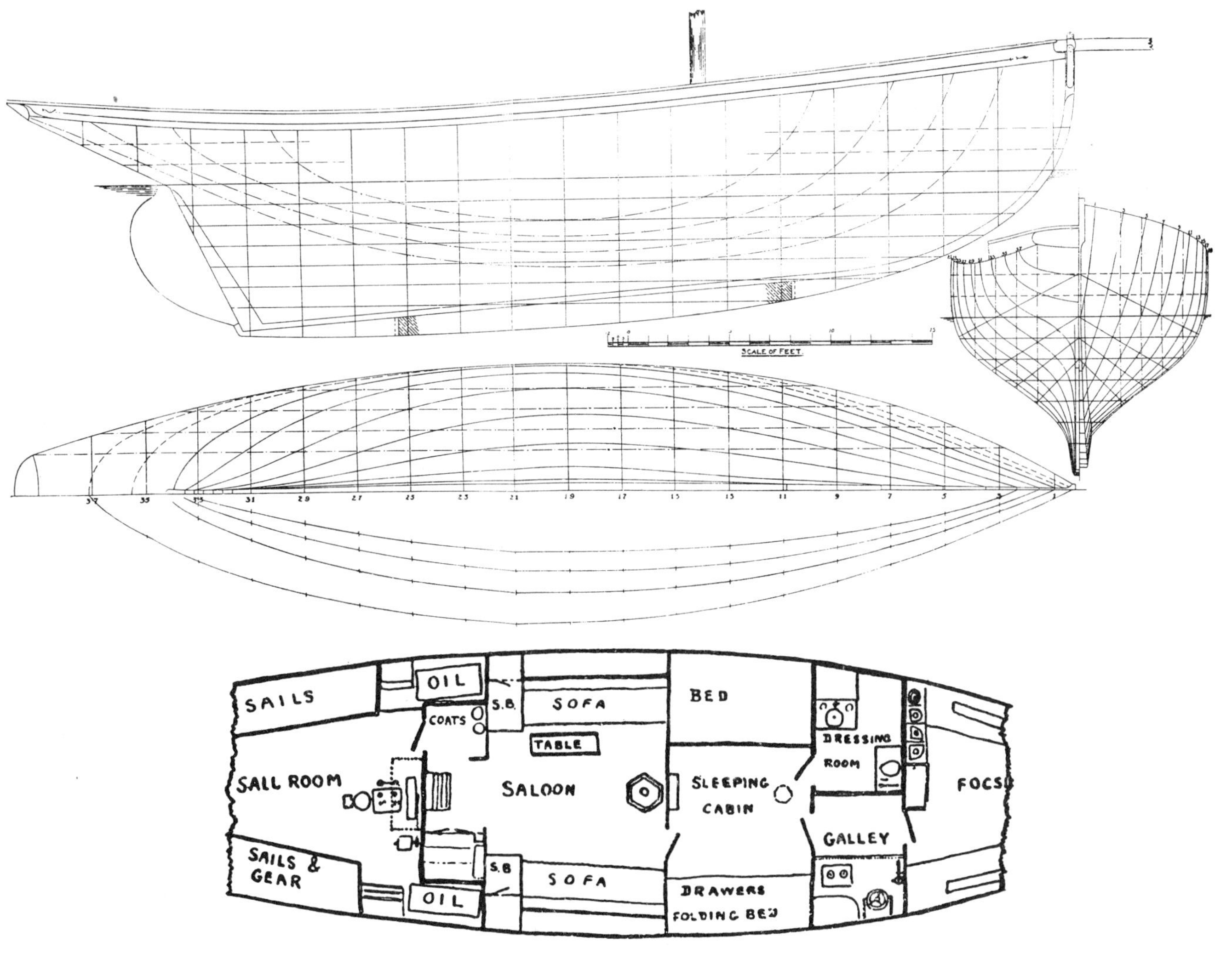

The lines and a sketch of the interior arrangement of the Tern III. (Yacht Cruising *by Claud Worth)*

Her shrouds set up to channels, which give a better spread to the rigging and keep the decks clear in way of the mast. Her running backstays both set up 5 feet abaft the mast when working to windward, and the weather one is brought back to the quarter when she is on a long board or a reach.

The leech of her mainsail is led aft enough by the length of her boom so that the sail will set nice and flat on the wind. She has a six-part mainsheet. There are three deep reefs in the mainsail. "It will be blowing hard if we have to use the second reef." Dr. Worth used the anchor windlass to heave down the reefing pendant on the leech of his mainsail.

Her foresail is self-tending, the clew being far enough forward of the mast so that the sail can still be loose-footed. She had, of course, a balloon foresail. "With a moderate wind a point free we usually set the balloon foresail."

Her topsail is a thimble-header, which is lighter and easier to set than a jackyard or club topsail.

The *Tern III* has a completely separate rig — except for her mast — for winter sailing. All the sails are a bit smaller and heavier, and her winter main boom is fitted with roller-reefing gear.

Tucked away back aft, she has a 13-horsepower Kelvin paraffin (kerosene) motor. She carries 60 gallons of the fuel. The propeller is off-center on the starboard quarter. She has a separate generator. "The vessel is fitted throughout with electric light." Modern stuff in 1914.

"A little sunk deckhouse-companion with comfortable sitting room for two people" provides shelter for the watch on a nasty night or a good place to curl up in port without missing anything.

Down below, her saloon looks most comfortable. The backs of the transoms turn down to form berths.

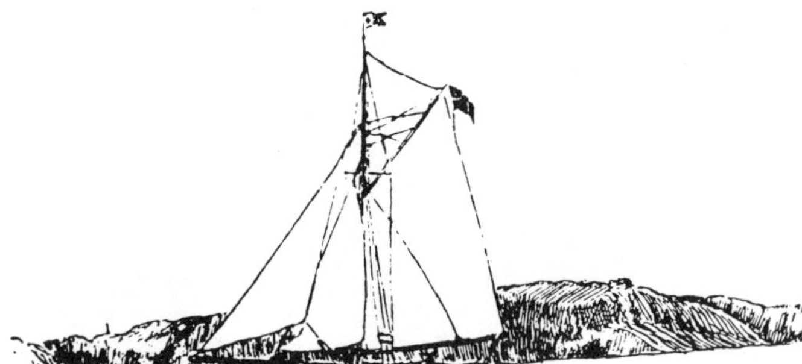

A sketch of the Tern III *by Dr. Worth.* (Yacht Navigation and Voyaging *by Claud Worth)*

There's a hexagonal stove up against the forward bulkhead. Forward, in the "sleeping cabin," the "bed" is 6½ feet long by 4 feet wide. There's a big chart drawer under it.

Her galley looks a bit cramped and is far enough forward to give the cook a pretty good elevator ride in a big head sea. Plenty of room in there for all kinds of spare gear that would be really accessible instead of being buried under something else.

The Worths cruised extensively in the *Tern II* during her first decade, except for the hiatus of World War I years. She crossed the Channel to the Continent, went north to Scotland, south to Spain, and all the way up to the Orkneys. Some of these cruises are recounted in *Yacht Cruising.*

When Mrs. Worth wanted a separate bedroom, Dr. Worth had to get a bigger boat. The situation gave him the opportunity to design and have built another fine vessel and to refine further his ideal cruiser. It is interesting to compare the *Tern IV* with the *Tern III* to see the minor changes that Dr. Worth considered improvements. Busy with his practice, the good doctor designed the boat over a year's time chiefly between the hours of 5 and 8 a.m.

The *Tern IV* was built by Philip and Son, Dartmouth, over a period of 14 months. Dr. Worth thought she should have taken only 10 months to build, but the yard said the extra time was justified because he was so hard to please in matters of materials and workmanship. At any rate, the *Tern IV* was launched in the fall of 1924. She was described fully in Claud Worth's next book, *Yacht Navigation and Voyaging,* published in 1927.

She is 62 feet long on deck, with a waterline length of 49 feet, a beam of 13 feet 6 inches, and a draft of 8 feet. She has 18 tons of lead ballast, 13 outside and five inside.

Her sail area in the four lowers is about 1,500 square feet, with about 950 square feet in the mainsail. Her mizzen has only 120 square feet.

The *Tern IV* has proportionately less freeboard than her predecessor, and the finer lines generally — particularly in her run — of the longer hull. She has slightly harder bilges, more hollow to the garboards, a more cut-away forefoot, and a bit more overhand forward. These changes all removed the *Tern IV* a bit further from her traditional plank-on-edge ancestors, doubtless to her advantage.

Dr. Worth made two changes in the construction of the new vessel: the heels of her frames were let into the keel and bolted through it athwartships; and her floors were made of galvanized steel, because oak crooks of sufficient quality couldn't be found. The *Tern IV* was planked with teak except for her garboard strake and the next strake, which were of American elm. Her hull was coppered. She had a teak deck.

Her rig, like that of her predecessor, was really that of a snug cutter. Dr. Worth wanted to keep the mainsail down to a reasonable size, so he drew his sailplan with the main boom ending well inboard of the boat's stern. People objected to the looks of this sailplan, so he added the mizzen as an afterthought. It would be handy for keeping her head to wind either when lying to or at anchor.

The winter rig of the *Tern IV* consisted of a slightly smaller self-tending foresail and a mainsail of the same hoist and foot as the summer sail, but with a head and gaff only two-thirds as long. With these two sails set, Dr. Worth said, she would turn to windward like a dinghy.

The *Tern IV* was fitted with a squaresail. The yard was hoisted on a jackstay, which in turn was hoisted up the forestay by the foresail halyard. The yard had braces but no lifts. Dr. Worth admitted that it chafed a good deal on the forestay.

The fittings for the *Tern IV* — her windlass, bilge pump, boat davits, mainsheet buffer, and staysail horse — were all designed by Dr. Worth and were specially made to his exact specifications of the finest materials available. "The fore sheet-horse, with traveler [translation: fore staysail traveler with ring], is of rustless steel and was made by the Wilkinson Sword Company from material supplied by Messrs. Firth of Sheffield." She carried three anchors, a 150-pound best bower, an 85-pound kedge, and a 115-pound spare anchor stowed below.

The *Tern IV* had a Gleniffer four-cylinder,

The sailplan and lines of the Tern IV. (Yacht Navigation and Voyaging *by Claud Worth)*

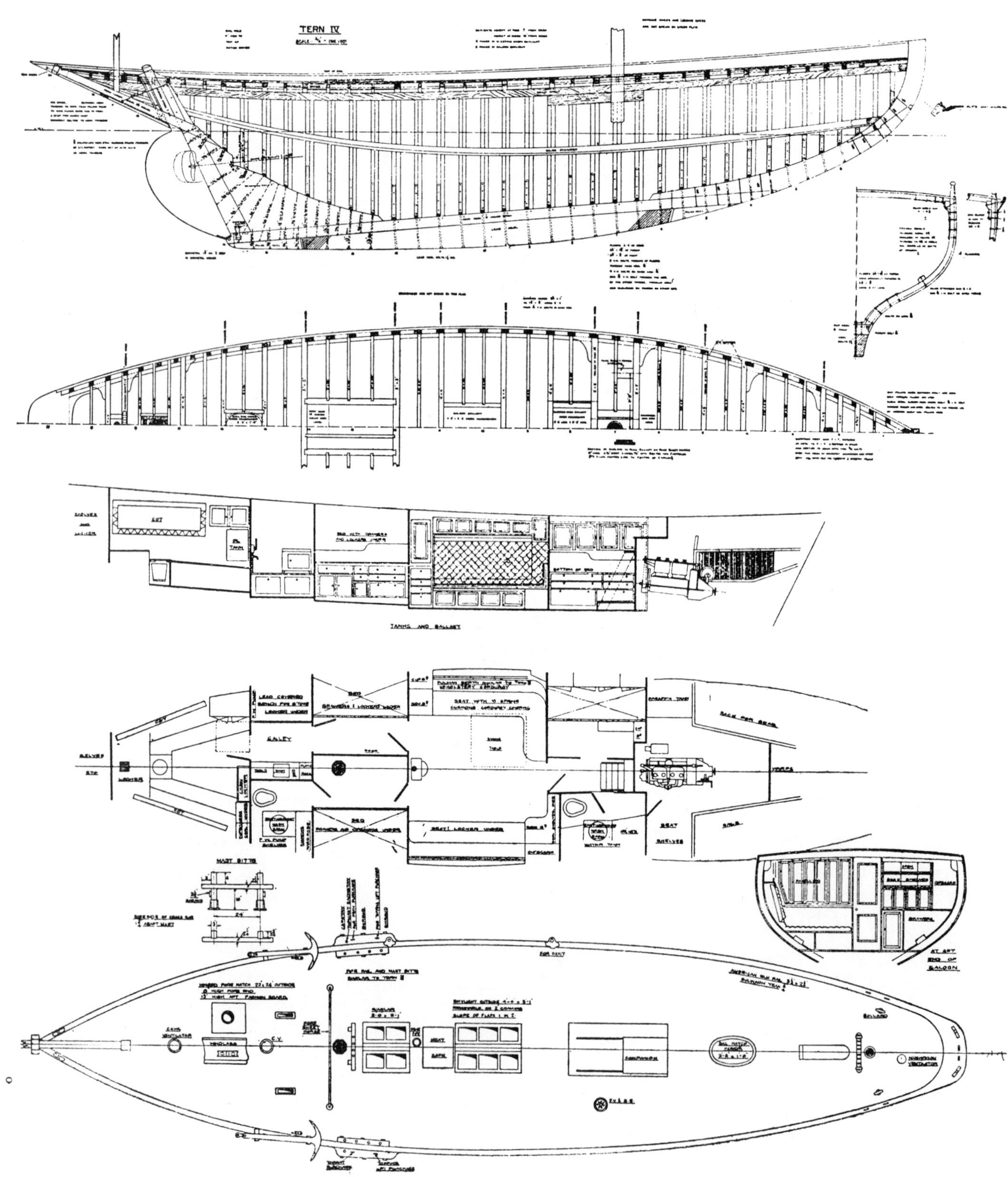

The construction, accommodations, and deck plans of the Tern IV. (Yacht Navigation and Voyaging *by Claud Worth)*

The Tern IV *at sea.* (Yacht Navigation and Voyaging *by Claud Worth)*

24-horsepower, paraffin engine. Dr. Worth said the machine provided much more power than he needed.

She carried a 14-foot sailing dinghy on deck with a smaller boat stowed inside it. Nice stuff.

Below, the additional stateroom and washroom were added at the foot of the companionway. She has an open coal stove in the saloon. There's a big bin for dry stores beneath the galley floor.

As in all Dr. Worth's yachts, the details were worked out to a nicety:

> The teak binnacle with brass hood carries a transparent spirit compass at a height of 2 feet above the deck where fortunately it has no deviation. A door in the aft side of the binnacle gives access to the electric light and switch. A diaphragm with shutter enables the helmsman to regulate the intensity of illumination of the compass card or to mask it entirely. A bell-push inside the binnacle rings a bell in the fo'c's'le. Here also the log slate and pencil are kept. By opening this door the helmsman gets sufficient light to read the orders or to enter his notes.
>
> During a cruise a teak chest fits in its place on deck forward of the deckhouse-companion. It contains two square white glazed earthenware jars, which were specially made for the yacht, each capable of holding 60 or 70 pounds of meat.

The Worths continued their cruising in the *Tern IV.* They sailed her to Spain and to the Azores. Returning to England from the Azores in 1926, the *Tern IV* sailed 1,020 miles in five days.

The *Tern IV* is still going strong. I'm not positive, but I believe the same statement may be made about the *Tern III.*

20/ A Big Schooner

Length on deck: 87 feet
Length on waterline: 70 feet
Beam: 22 feet 9 inches
Draft: 9 feet
Sail area: 2,500 square feet
Designer: Ralph E. Winslow

When I was young, I always wanted to be a sea gull. It seemed to me that gulls led a great, free, seagoing life, and I always thought it would be wonderful to be able to fly all over the world watching good boats sail in all weathers.

I would, of course, have been one of your Jonathan Livingston types of gulls, not a dump-picker. Power dives during gales at sea, daring swoops just out of reach of huge breakers crashing against granite cliffs. That sort of thing.

Now that I'm "grown-up," I want to be an albatross. *Diomedea exulans,* the wandering albatross. Weight, 27 pounds; wingspan, 12 feet. Wings just under 6 inches wide, a high enough aspect ratio to make a modern racing sailor jealous.

Of course most of my travels will have to be in the Roaring Forties, but I take heart that a few of my species have made it across the doldrums to the windy latitudes of the north.

Want to join me for a little soaring and good-boat-watching? We just crossed the intersection of 45 degrees south and 35 degrees west in the South Atlantic. (Heading south for the old breeding grounds on South Georgia.) Fresh northwest breeze on the starboard tailfeathers. Glide down to leeward, losing altitude but gaining speed rapidly. Pick, as a pull-out point, the back of a steep sea and whip up off its deflected air, wheeling into the wind. Climb to 60 feet before the near-stall makes us turn and again trade altitude for speed. If we play the forces right, we can do this for hours without a wing beat.

But there's a speck of sail down yonder to leeward, so let's tack downwind and see what she is. (It's too bad we albatrosses are a bit nearsighted in air — the better to see fish underwater.)

Appears to be gaff-rigged with some size to her. A schooner, look, going our way on a broad reach under four lowers. Isn't she a handsome vessel? Let's ride the dirty air off that big mainsail and watch her go for a while.

Why, I do believe she's the schooner Ralph E. Winslow designed in 1921 for Alexander Smith of New York City. That's her all right. Built that year by the Vineyard Shipbuilding Company at Milford, Delaware. (Some memory we albatrosses have.)

Mr. Smith wanted a full-powered vessel, but one that could sail, including to windward without power if need be. He admired the cut-down auxiliary fishing schooners working out of Gloucester and asked Mr. Winslow to design him a vessel along their lines. Said he wanted a little ship that could "go anywhere anytime." Brave talk, but words old ocean can blow away. It looks as if Mr. Smith got himself an able vessel, though.

I think she's big enough so that that high deckhouse

Ralph E. Winslow. (The Rudder, *May 1945)*

amidships doesn't detract too much from her good looks. I grant you her foresail, with its bottom cut off to clear the open bridge atop the deckhouse, looks a bit strange, but I do think it's a practical concept that works.

Let's make a short dive underwater alongside and see what her lines are like. Say, she's rolling right along, isn't she? Went by faster than I thought she would. She certainly is a full-bodied, burdensome vessel. Fairly short run, I thought. Moderate draft. Now let's get back to riding that slant off her mainsail.

Doesn't she have a nice, springy sheer? I like her high bow; she must have freeboard forward of nearly a wingspan; looks like about 10½ feet.

I'd say her dimensions are: length on deck, 87 feet; length on the waterline, 70 feet; beam, 22 feet 9 inches; and draft, 9 feet.

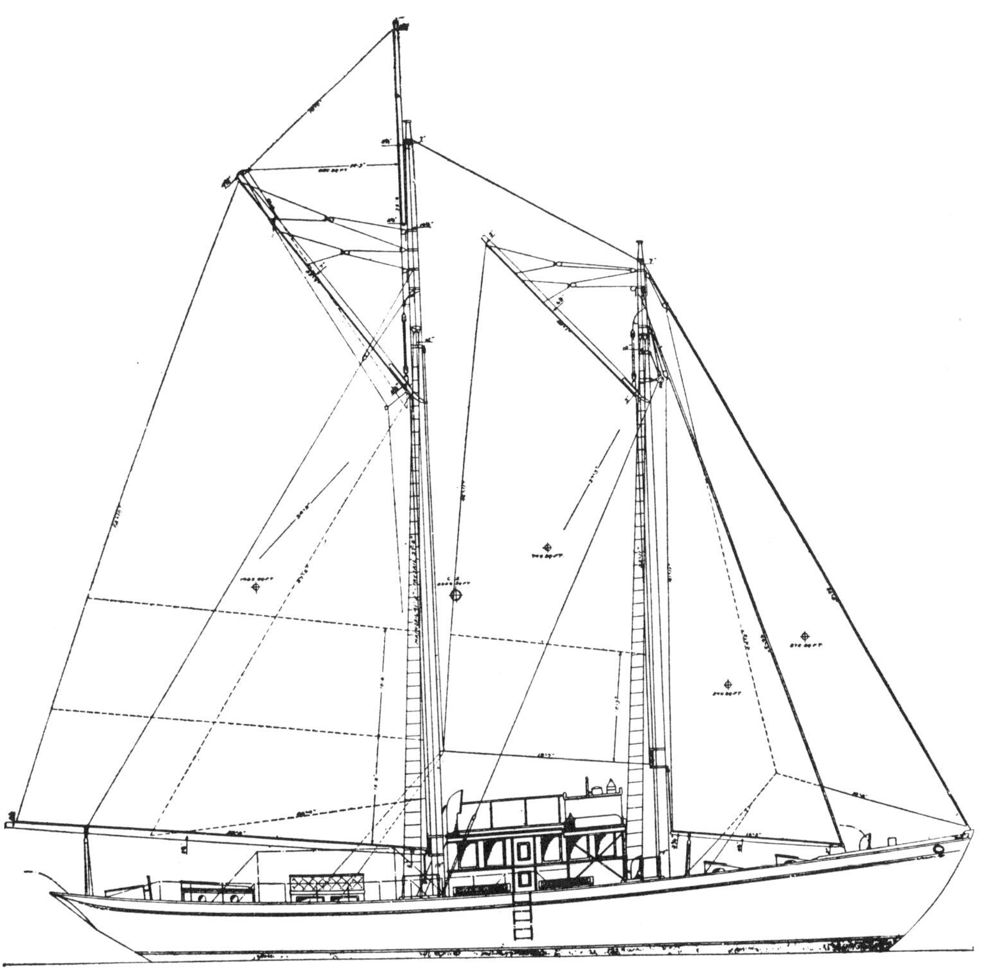

The sailplan of the Winslow schooner. (The Rudder, *July 1921)*

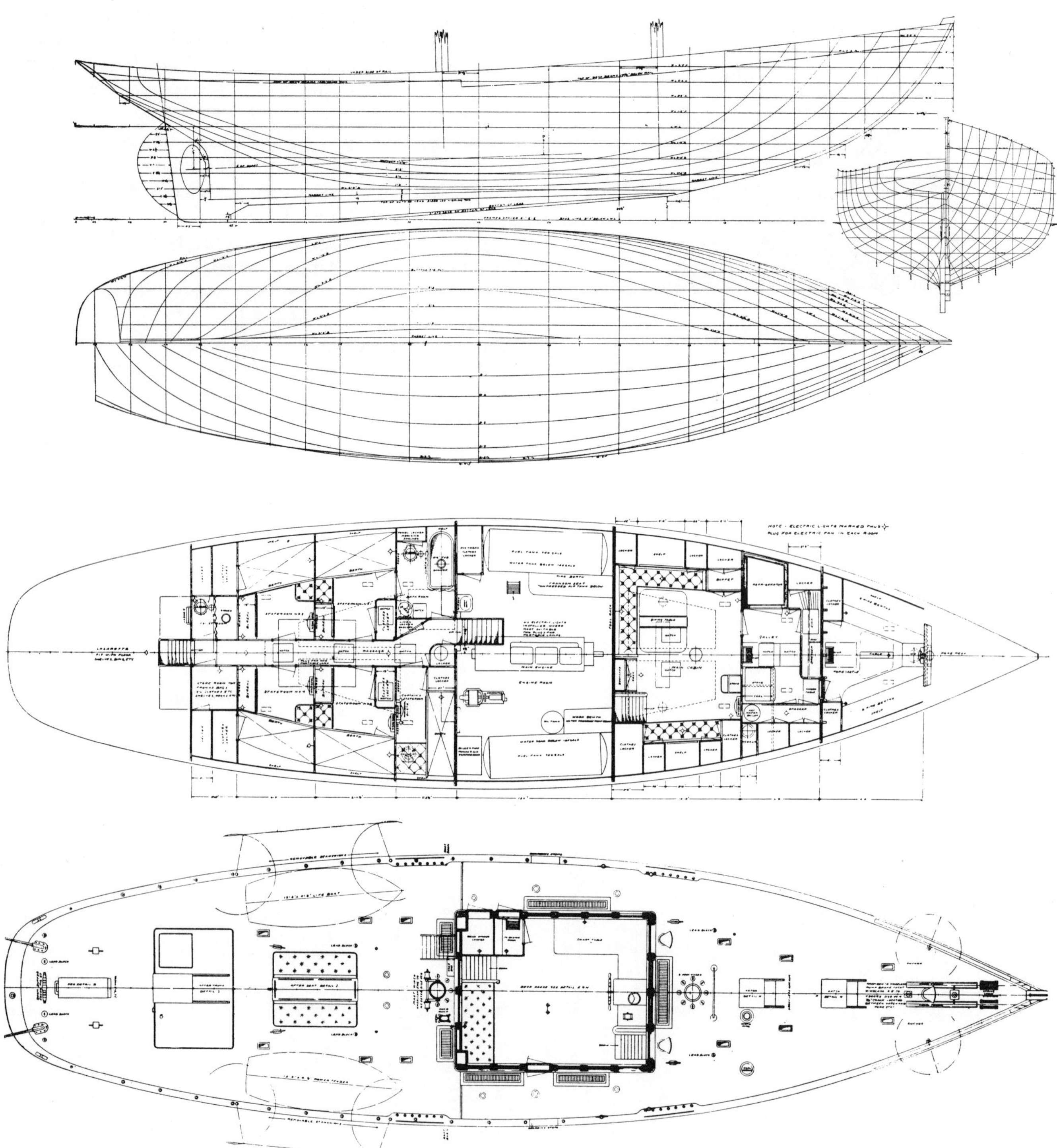

The lines, accommodations, and deck plans of the Winslow schooner. (The Rudder, *July 1921)*

Her hull and rig remind me a lot of Donald B. MacMillan's schooner the *Bowdoin,* designed by William H. Hand Jr., the same year Winslow turned out this vessel. The *Bowdoin* is the same length on deck, two feet shorter on the waterline, has 2½ feet less beam and half a foot more draft. Both vessels have about 2,500 square feet of sail in their knockabout rigs.

Construction? The keel of the Winslow schooner is 12-inch-by-12-inch oak, the keelson being yellow pine of the same scantling. Frames are white oak, 10 inches by 10 inches, on 21-inch centers. Planking is 2¾-inch stuff.

Oh, ho! Feel that wind shift? It's going to haul right around to the southwest and breeze up. Look there, now even the humans are sensing the change. Here come some more of them tumbling on deck to flatten in the sails and shorten her down. They must have been here before. They're taking the mainsail right off her and setting the main trysail, ready for the coming gale. Now the jib comes down too. They're getting a bit carried away with shortening down, aren't they? My goodness, if they're not reefing the foresail. I guess they want to get her all snugged down before the snow flies. That slowed her down some, but she'll have breeze enough before long.

I don't know about that loose-footed foresail. I think I'd want a boom on it, sheeting to a high traveler. I also think I'd want a preventer backstay on the mainmast for heavy weather.

What looks at first glance like a preventer backstay on the foremast is really a brace to the yard she crosses. I suppose a squaresail on the foremast is not a bad idea; there are probably plenty of times when you'd want to trade that aborted foresail for it. I should think they'd forget about that main topsail. Its yard must be a big, clumsy thing to struggle aloft and get down again without its braining somebody. I'd want a big fisherman staysail and a balloon jib for her, wouldn't you?

They've got plenty of places to steer from: in the wheelhouse, up on the open bridge, or back aft. Up on top of the deckhouse, they've got enough height of eye to see about five miles to the horizon. Kind of ironic, isn't it? We've got the height to see a long way, but not the eyes; they've got the eyes, especially with those big black things they hold up sometimes, but not the height.

There is room on deck aft for two boats, and the ones she's carrying look to be 13½ feet long. Notice the low break in the deck just forward of the mainmast.

Those are nice seats either side of the big skylight. The hatch in the after port corner of the trunk cabin just forward of the wheel leads down into a big lazarette.

If I were those humans, always worrying about getting in the water by mistake, I'd carry her lifelines all the way forward to the bow.

Her ground tackle, all stowed away out here, consists of a pair of 350-pound anchors with ¾-inch chain. She also carries a handy 150-pound stockless anchor with a manila rode.

Isn't her big wheelhouse glorious? Huge chart table, big settee, and all the comforts of home. Great place to watch her go from behind glass.

The floor of the deckhouse is right at main deck level; the entry is through the doorway on the starboard side.

In the after port corner of the deckhouse, there is inside and outside entry to the huge engine room beneath the house. She is powered with a six-cylinder, 125-horsepower Winton engine, swinging a two-bladed wheel with a diameter of 50 inches and a pitch of 32 inches. Makes 8 knots under power. There's a separate generator set in the engine room and a big electric pump, which will pump the bilge, wash the deck, flush the sanitary tank, or put pressure on a fire hose. Her two 750-gallon fuel tanks are also in the engine room, and there's a big workbench, to say nothing of a pipe berth for the engineer.

The saloon is forward of the engine room, and it looks plenty comfortable with its L-shaped settee around the big table, and its stove and desk.

Aft of the engine room are five single staterooms (four big enough for doubles) and two washrooms, one with tub and one with shower.

Up forward are a big galley and a four-person fo'c's'le, each with its own hatch to the deck. She sure is roomy.

And look at her now. Forging ahead through some mighty fierce snow squalls, even for down here, shouldering her way just beautifully through a rapidly building sea. The waves are starting to spill and break with great regularity, but she's easing along in great shape and only taking spray on deck. If this keeps up, though, they'll want to shorten down further to just the reefed foresail and then she'll be able to stand a lot, with her head tucked under her wing, so to speak.

Maybe we'd best let her go on her way and do that very thing until this gale blows out.

21/ The *Albatross,* Brigantine

Length on deck: 89 feet 9 inches
Length on waterline: 72 feet
Beam: 21 feet 6 inches
Draft: 10 feet 6 inches
Sail area: 4,000 square feet
Displacement: 126.6 tons
Designer: Henry Gruber

Thanks to Uffa Fox's wonderful drawings of the 90-foot brigantine *Albatross* in his *Second Book,* I have had the privilege of "chasing away before the wind," as he would have said, under square rig. The *Albatross* was designed a half-century ago by Henry Gruber; when he included her design in his book, Uffa Fox first put her plans down in exquisite detail on his own drafting board, as he did for all the vessels that sailed across his pages.

My square-rigger work was done in my mind's eye, of course; the *Albatross* (this is not the brigantine *Albatross* that foundered in the Gulf of Mexico some years back) was never, to my knowledge, built. She has taken me a good many miles over the years, nonetheless, for she is indeed a handsome vessel, what with her clipper bow and well-steeved bowsprit, scrollwork forward and aft, well-raked mainmast, and four yards crossed on the foremast. Why, even her radio antenna, stretched between her trucks, looks exactly right. Everything about this vessel was proportioned beautifully by Henry Gruber.

The *Albatross* has the lines of an old-fashioned sailing ship refined to those of a yacht. Her clipper bow has considerable overhang and a perfect, reversed curve. She has a fairly long counter stern. Her sheerline is fair, with just enough action. She has a deep forefoot and hollow entrance and a long keel with little drag. There's plenty of tumblehome to her topsides, and her garboards are well hollowed-out.

The *Albatross* is 89 feet 9 inches long on deck, with a waterline length of 72 feet, a beam of 21 feet 6 inches, and a draft of 10 feet 6 inches. She displaces 126.6 tons, of which 38.3 tons is ballast, 2.6 tons of it inside for trimming. Her sail area is 4,000 square feet.

She has an auxiliary engine of 100 horsepower that drives her at 7¾ knots. Her interesting speed-horsepower curve illustrates the usual law of diminishing returns:

8 h.p.	gives	3 knots
17 h.p.	gives	4 knots
28 h.p.	gives	5 knots
45 h.p.	gives	6 knots
66 h.p.	gives	7 knots
118 h.p.	gives	8 knots
218 h.p.	gives	9 knots
303 h.p.	gives	10 knots

Despite the fineness of her hull, the *Albatross* is big enough to carry her moderate rig relatively upright and steadily, a must for a square-rigger requiring you to go aloft regularly to furl or loose sail.

She needs a few hands lounging around on deck ready

Above: *Henry A. Gruber on board the* Bluenose. (Uffa Fox's Second Book *by Uffa Fox, reprinted by International Marine Publishing Company)* **Below:** *The sailplan of the* Albatross. (Uffa Fox's Second Book *by Uffa Fox)*

4 8 12 16 20 24 28
SCALE FEET
SCALE METRES

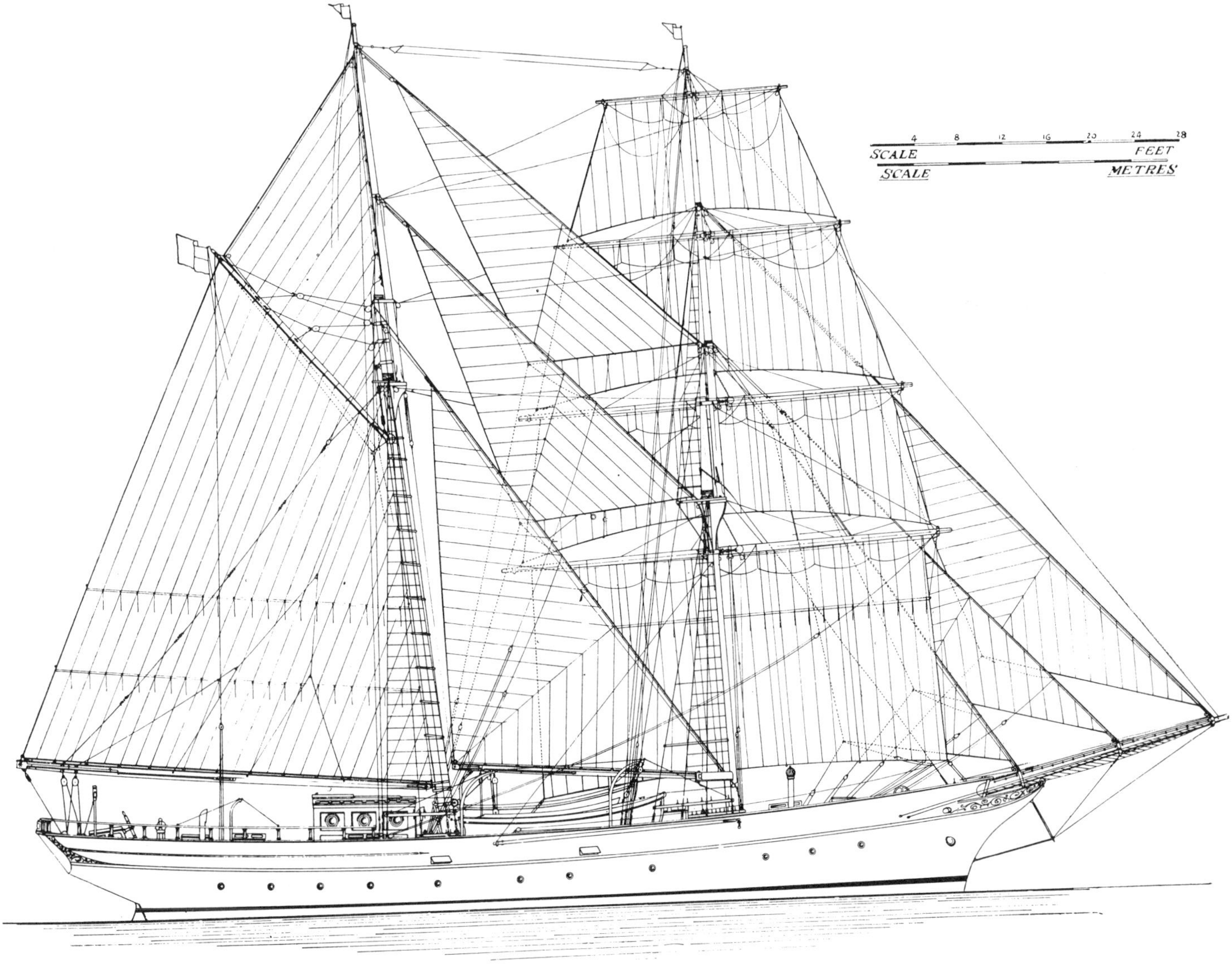

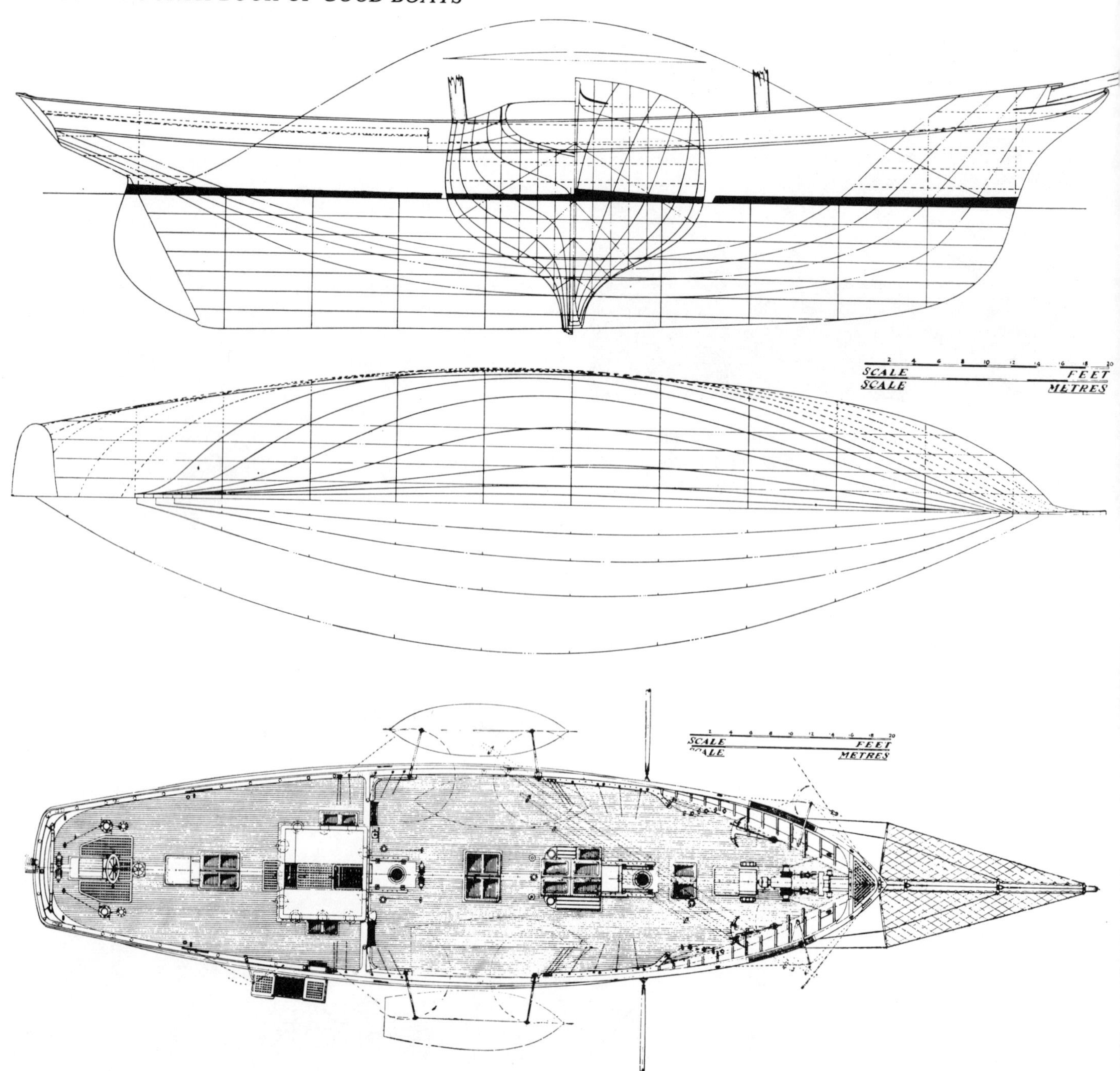

The lines and deck plan of the Albatross. (Uffa Fox's Second Book *by Uffa Fox, International Marine Publishing Company)*

to jump-to when it's time to put her about under full sail. There are four yards to brace round once their backed sails have shoved her head well through the wind, to say nothing of the foresail tack and sheet to shift and the sheets of three headsails and two main staysails to tend. All this running rigging, as well as the halyards and downhauls of her fore-and-aft sails and the halyards, sheets, clew lines, and bunt lines of her squaresails, belay on pinrails in way of the masts at waist height where you can put some weight on them. There is sufficient sailorizing in a vessel like this to satisfy even the hardest case.

Her yards can be braced to within 32 degrees of the centerline, so she could certainly sail within six points of

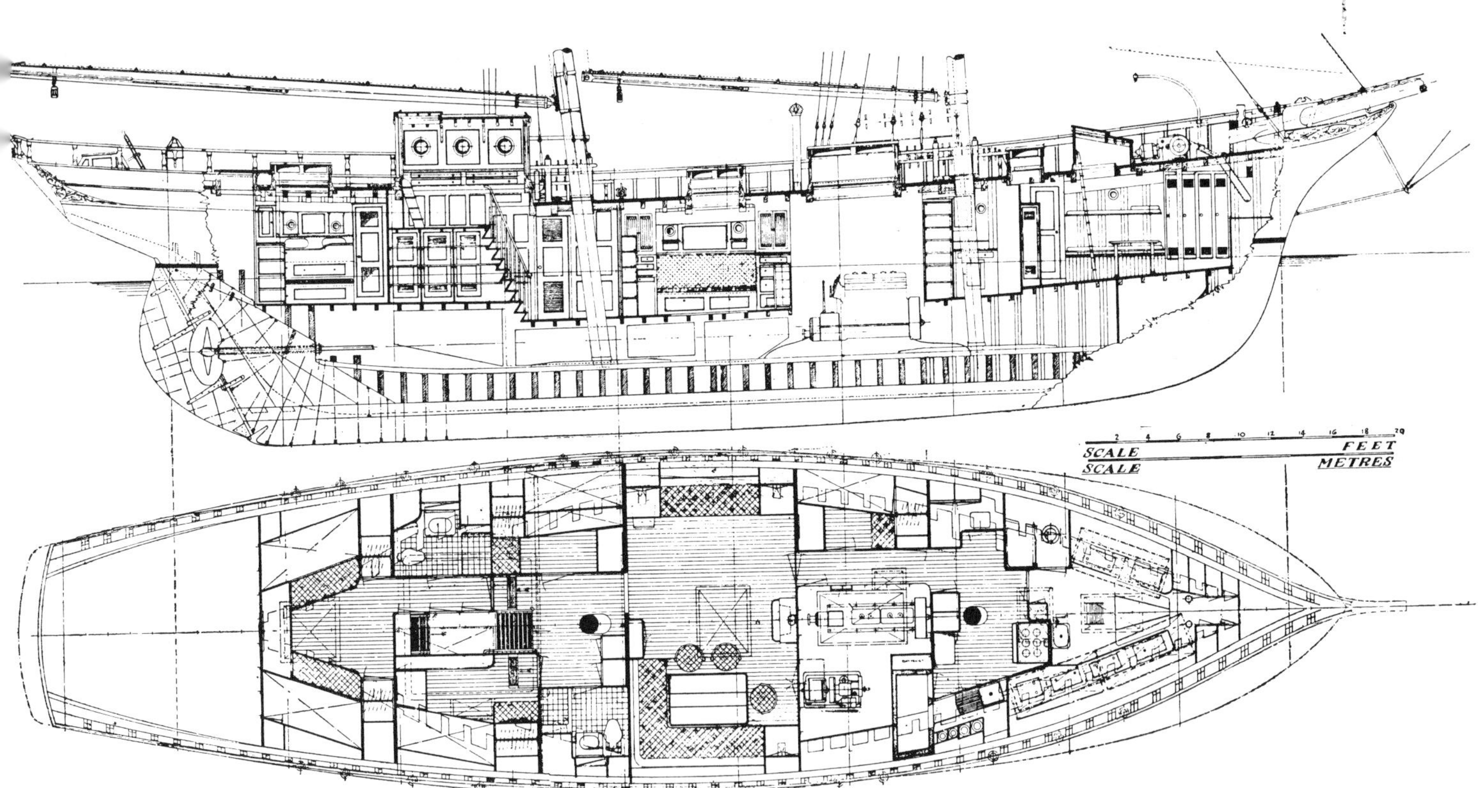

The interior arrangement plans of the Albatross. (Uffa Fox's Second Book *by Uffa Fox, reprinted by International Marine Publishing Company)*

the wind, and closer in steady conditions. Her yards are hollow to save 30 percent of their weight aloft.

To simplify her sparring a bit, she has a spike bowsprit (no jibboom) and a pole fore topmast (no fore topgallant mast).

Her fore course may be reefed, though with double topsails, that would seldom be necessary. Her lower topsail is a fine heavy-weather sail; it's very modest in area, yet is high enough not to get becalmed in the trough of a big seaway, so it will help keep her reasonably steady.

Note the vang on her main gaff made up to a three-part tackle on the quarter and the baggywrinkle on the main topping lift to keep the big sail from chafing too much.

The great thing about her rig, of course, is those squaresails. How fine to watch that mighty pyramid pulling her along off the wind; or, how grand to stand aft at her wheel, working her to windward all you dare, aware of the swing and dip of her high bowsprit end but watching like a hawk the luffs, out to weather, of those four trapezoids.

The end of her bowsprit is 15 feet above the water. I can't look at that bowsprit netting without thinking of lying in it, all care washed away by the rolling roar of the bow wave as she plunges to wet her martingale.

Her bow is a most seamanlike place, with its windlass, anchor davits, flaring bulwarks, and grating right forward at the rail. All she lacks is catheads. Aft there is a nice monkeyrail round her raised quarterdeck.

She can carry big boats in her waist, the ones shown being an 18-foot whaleboat and an 18-foot launch. Plenty of times they could be carried outboard, slung from their davits to clear the deck. In port they would lie to boat booms, port and starboard, held by lifts to the fore top. There's a davit on the starboard quarter for hoisting up the after end of a real accommodation ladder. All this big-ship stuff is plenty of fun to fool around with.

Her sunken deckhouse — lovely place — has a big chart table to port and a settee to starboard. It's nice to get into a port of call that may have been your objective for days or weeks and have a place to leave the harbor chart, with its marks of navigation — perhaps indicating an anxious approach — spread out during your stay to remind you of the accomplishment of bringing her in safely.

Down below she has a big saloon amidships; it's 11 feet long and takes the full 20-foot beam of the ship. Complete with fireplace.

Aft are three staterooms and two bathrooms. There's a door into the engine room from the forward passage,

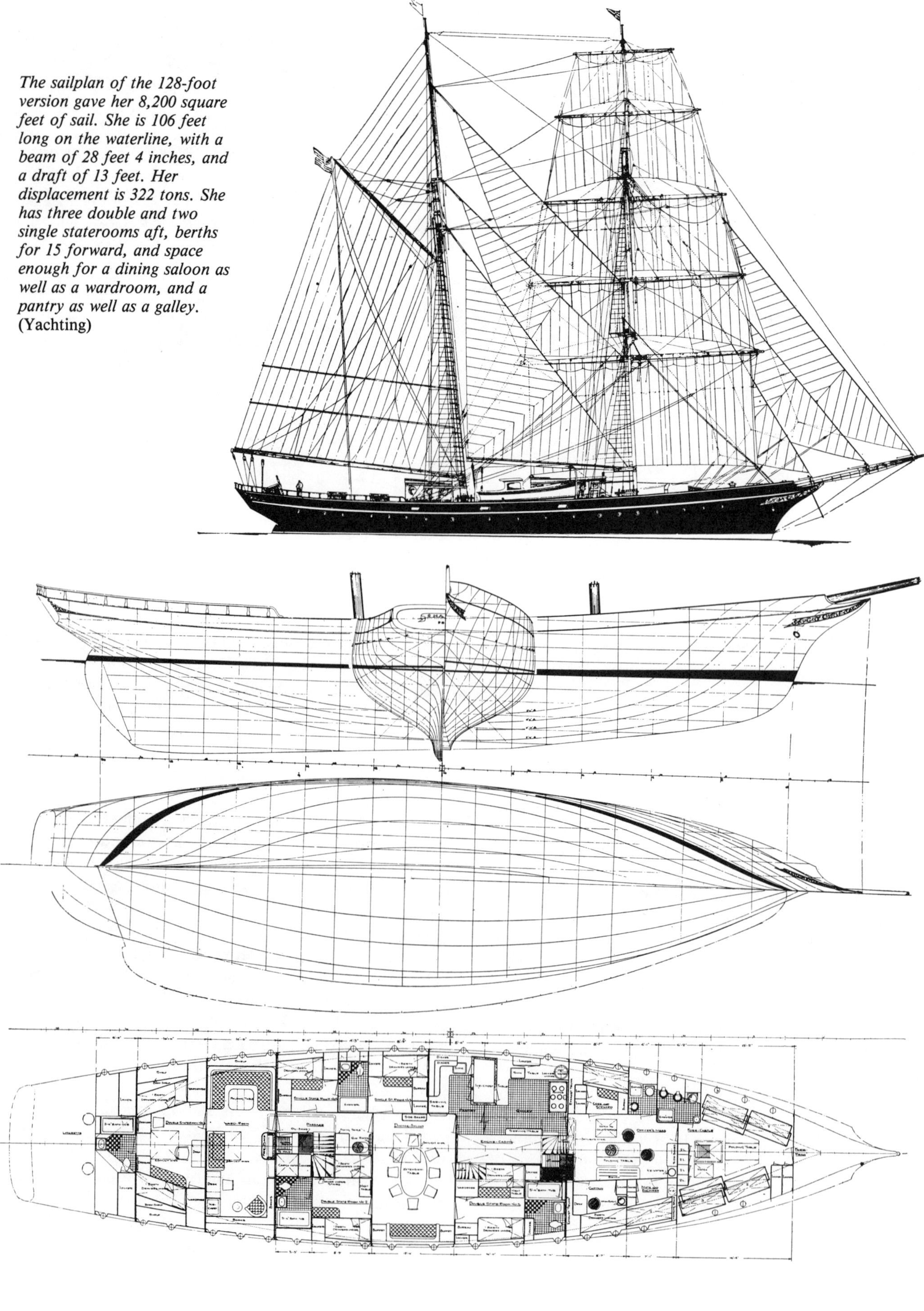

The sailplan of the 128-foot version gave her 8,200 square feet of sail. She is 106 feet long on the waterline, with a beam of 28 feet 4 inches, and a draft of 13 feet. Her displacement is 322 tons. She has three double and two single staterooms aft, berths for 15 forward, and space enough for a dining saloon as well as a wardroom, and a pantry as well as a galley. (Yachting)

an engine room that has plenty of space and light to help you work on the big machine or the separate generating set.

The full-width galley surrounds the foremast. There's a separate captain's cabin and a fo'c's'le for six with its own washroom.

Some romantic dreamship, I say. Henry Gruber designed a bigger version, too, a 128-footer with the same delicate proportions as the *Albatross*. Nor, I believe, was she built.

No matter. They make fine vessels for vicarious voyages. Right now I'm perched on the upper topsail yard of the *Albatross,* nearly 60 feet above the water, watching for a coral atoll to darken the horizon with its expected fringe of palm trees.

22/ The *Retreat*

Length on deck: 18 feet
Length on waterline: 14 feet
Beam: 7 feet
Draft: 5 inches
Displacement: 1 ton
Designer: William Atkin

One of my favorite boats to watch, growing up on the Pawcatuck River, was the handsomest little 30-foot western-rigged dragger you'd ever want to see. Her owner, when I knew her, had taken her over as pretty much of a wreck from his father and had rebuilt her completely into a fine, serviceable vessel. The old boat had been named for the son who later saved her from dying — she was called the *Bobby D.* — which seemed fair enough. She lived in the cove next to ours, so we could see her moving majestically down the river plenty of times.

I lost track of the *Bobby D.* for some years and feared she'd been sold away. Then one fall she showed up again in the tiny, secluded cove right off our cove, where she tied up for the winter. She was acting as tender to a houseboat alongside, a nice 20-foot scow with a well-proportioned dwelling on it. The two vessels were round the corner where you couldn't see them except from a certain angle, and they were snuggled right up against the shore. Some fun, it looked like.

William Atkin had a similar experience of seeing a fine little houseboat in an idyllic setting in a cove on Long Island, which inspired him to design a similar vessel for *Motor Boating* magazine. The design jumped off the page at me when, with these visions of the *Bobby D.*'s charge somewhere in the back of my mind, I was thumbing through a copy of *40 Designs for Postwar Boats* (Volume 20 in *Motor Boating*'s Ideal Series, published in 1944), kindly loaned to me for an entirely different purpose by Mr. R.G. Bailey of North Fort Myers, Florida.

Billy Atkin's inspiration had been named the *Retreat,* so that's what he named his design, which he also labeled a "shantyboat deluxe." *Retreat* is a good name for a vessel to be so used. A minister friend of mine calls his cruising boat the *Retreat.* When you call him up in the summer with some burning theological question, the person at the church who answers the phone says, "Oh, I'm afraid the minister's not here. He's on *Retreat.*"

I see Mr. Atkin's *Retreat* moored in a quiet cove on a lake, long bow and stern lines to trees ashore keeping her just out of reach of the lily pads. There are dragon flies, a straw hat, and shimmering water.

Of course she could be a river vessel, drifting her lazy way toward the sea, maybe with somebody helping her along a bit standing up on the front porch pushing on a pair of sweeps, and maybe even with a mate doing a bit of towing with a pulling boat.

Not to worry. We're not starting an imaginary river voyage. You can read a great account of a real one in Harlan Hubbard's book *Shantyboat: A River Way of Life,* published in 1953 and reprinted in 1977 by the

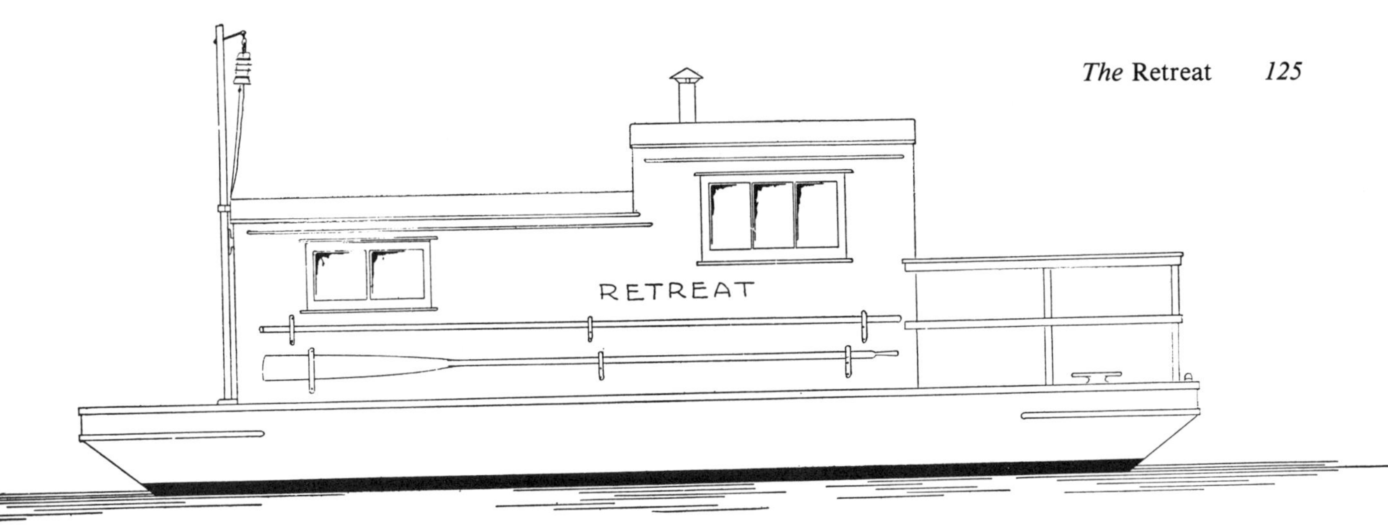

The outboard profile of the Retreat. (40 Designs for Postwar Boats *by William W. Atkin)*

University Press of Kentucky. Harlan and Anna Hubbard spent seven years easing down the Ohio and Mississippi Rivers from Brent, Kentucky, to New Orleans.

Billy Atkin envisioned moving the shantyboat *Retreat* over land if necessary to reach a particular watery objective:

> Fact is it would be no trick at all to fix a pair of automobile wheels each side at the middle point of the over-all length, making a trailer that at the same time would be a houseboat. Axle would not be required nor springs. Two front knuckles from a heavy car welded to suitable plates could be through bolted to the sides; then removed after the trailer had been wheeled down into the water.

My usual comments about the pretty curves in a boat's hull don't seem to apply to the *Retreat*. But she does have a snug, practical look, doesn't she?

The shantyboat is 18 feet long on deck, 14 feet on the bottom, with a beam of 7 feet and a draft of 5 inches, depending on loading. The depth of the hull is 2 feet, so if she drew 5 inches, she'd have left a freeboard of 1 foot 7 inches. She'd displace just about a ton, without books.

Mr. Atkin recommended keeping the scantlings of this shantyboat reasonably light. He specified side and bottom planking of ¾-inch white cedar, with end planking of a heavier wood, such as yellow pine or white oak. Chines to be ¾ inch by 1½ inches; frames, ¾ inch by 2 inches; and doubling pieces where the ends join the bottom, 1½ inches by 4 inches — all white oak.

He suggested 1½-inch by 1¾-inch oak stringers to stiffen the bottom. Shelf, ¾-inch by 2¾-inch fir. Deck beams, ¾-inch by 2-inch fir. Deck, two layers of ¼-inch plywood, covered with canvas. (I suppose it would be tempting to build the whole vessel out of plywood today and use plenty of the high-class sealants.) Cabin floor, ¾-inch tongue-and-groove fir, laid right on the stringers.

Studs for the house, 1⅛-inch by 1¾-inch fir. House sides and ends, ½-inch Homosote. Housetop beams, ¾ inch by 2 inches. Housetop, ¼-inch plywood, canvas covered.

The designer estimated the cost of all materials for this vessel — in 1944 — to be $200. She'd be relatively cheap to build today.

And she's so simple with most everything square that most any of us can visualize ourselves building this little home afloat. Well, at least I can visualize myself painting her: red copper bottom, dark green hull and house with black and dark red trim. You wouldn't want her to stand out too much against the shore.

Her front porch (complete with porch railing) is 4 feet 6 inches long. The back porch is only 2 feet 6 inches long. I think I'd have to extend the back porch a bit; you need room for a good chair back there out of the wind when anchored by the bow.

You can tippy-toe round the outside of the house on the narrow side decks holding onto the grab rails under the eaves. There's a 10-foot oar and a 10-foot pole stowed in brackets on each side of the house.

If you were doing much moving and anchoring, you'd want heavy ground tackle handled by an anchor davit at each end of the vessel. Once her anchors were down, you wouldn't want to have to come outside for anything.

You could anchor her bow and stern or plant her with an anchor off either bow with the rodes crossed to keep her from sailing around. You could let her lie to an endless line run through blocks on two anchors so you could shift her position at will without disturbing the

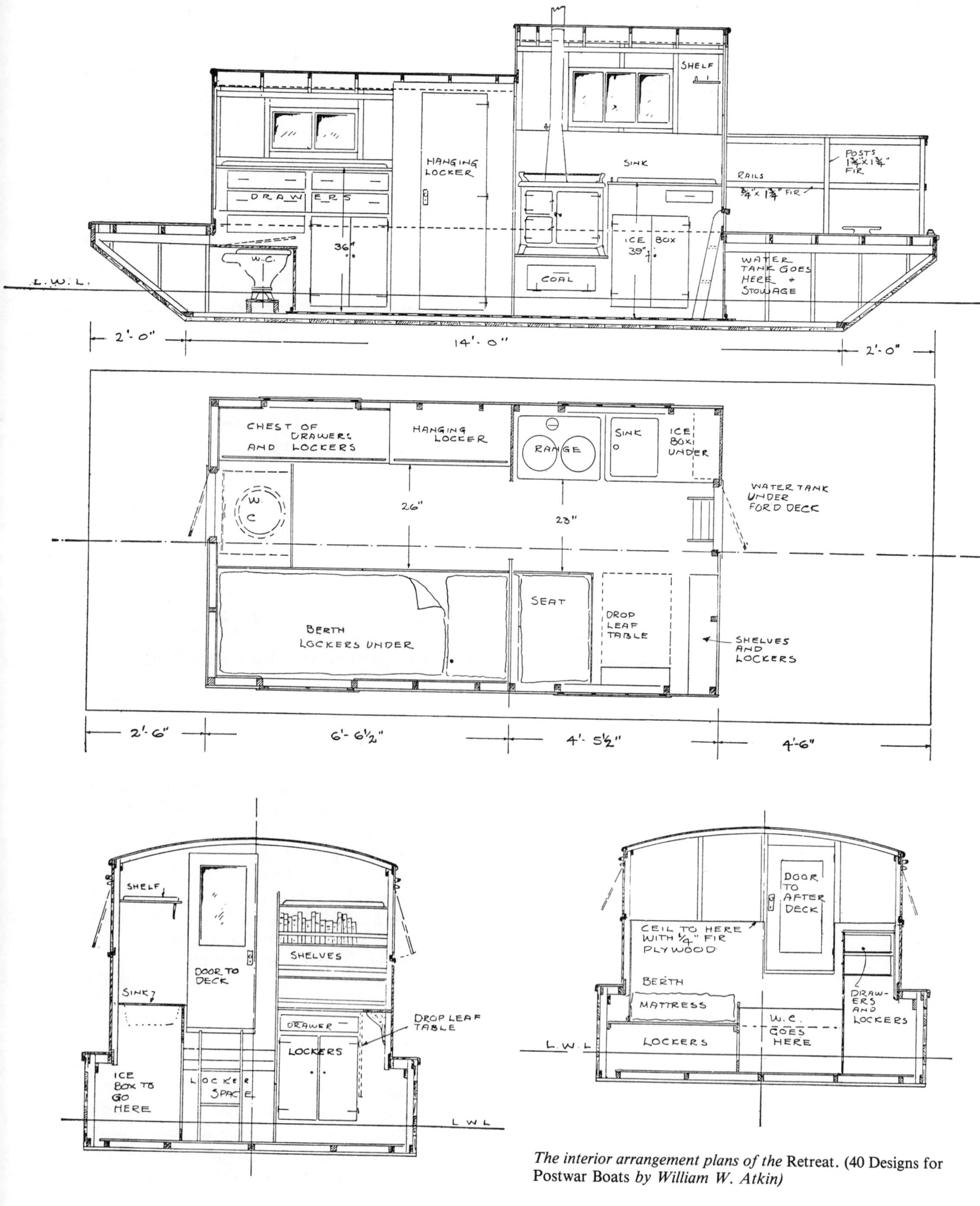

The interior arrangement plans of the Retreat. (40 Designs for Postwar Boats *by William W. Atkin)*

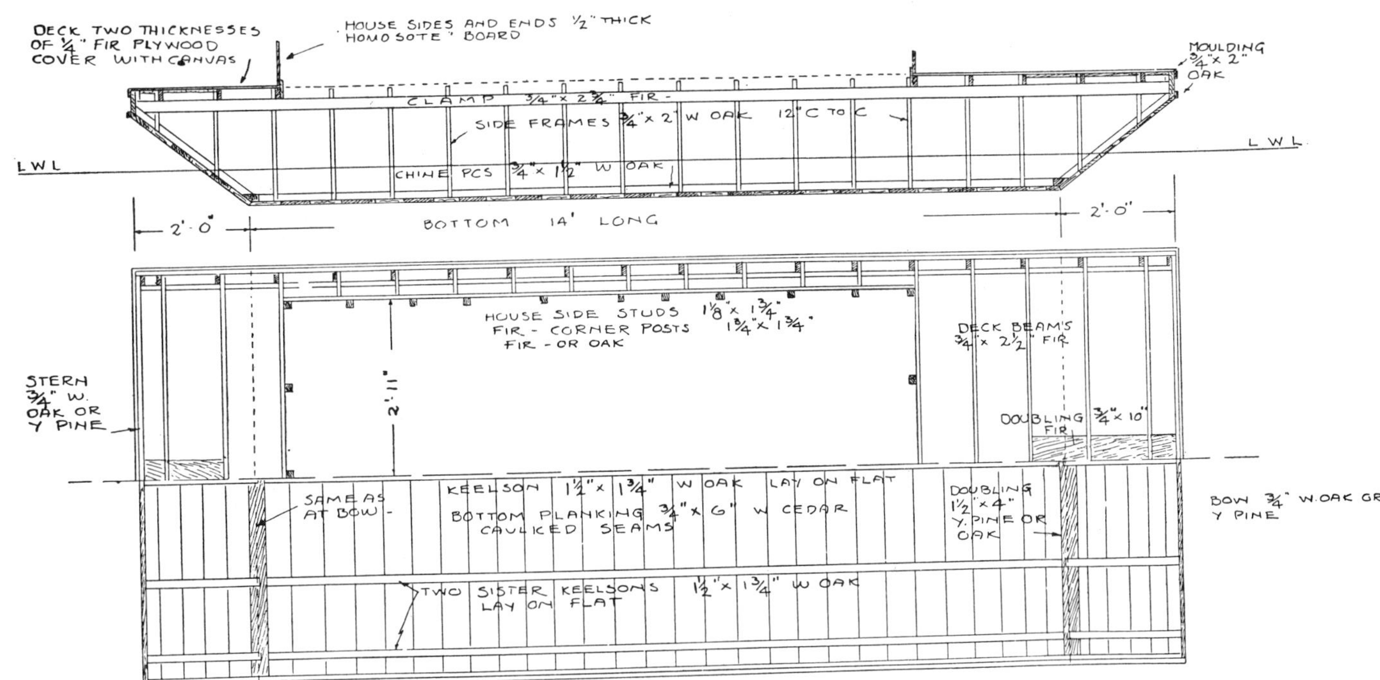

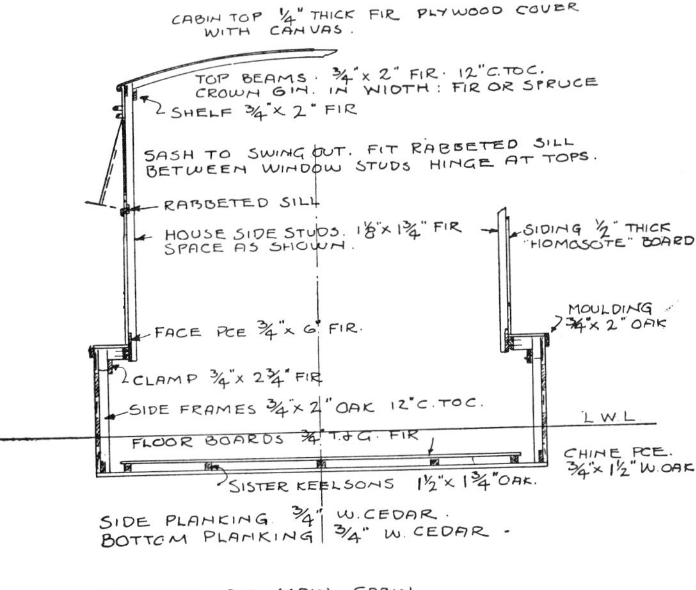

The construction drawings of the Retreat. (40 Designs for Postwar Boats *by William W. Atkin)*

ground tackle. Pull her out of the cove a ways or back in as whim and weather might dictate. She could be tied up to one or more stakes.

At any rate, her mast is for holding up her riding light. How about beefing up the spar so it would take the topping lift of a long gangplank, lowered ashore like that of a Mississippi River boat? So strengthened, the spar could also support poles rigged out athwartships to hold the boats clear on a calm night.

You could be fancy and have a nice sailing dinghy. Join Arthur Ransome's *Swallows and Amazons* for a bit of adventuring. Or, you could be sporty and have a fast sliding-seat rowing boat. I see flat-bottomed boats of handsome line tending the *Retreat.* Skiffs and punts with oversize sculling notches. Of course there could be a power tender, anything from a simple yawlboat to a real vessel like the *Bobby D.*

But for all her easy, slow mobility, this boat conjures up, perhaps more than any other image, visions of long quiet times in her innards. Many who see the *Retreat* will concentrate their attention on her cabin.

Everything in it is within easy reach. Mr. Atkin shows you the bare essentials of a layout, but 10 years of living on board would doubtless produce many special little arrangements.

Harlan Hubbard wrote:

> The many problems of space arrangement which came up were like puzzles to work out, and often the solution was an ingenious one. Nothing is arbitrary or merely decorative. This shell which we built, or which grew around us, has become as efficient as that of the river mussel, and has almost as little waste space. A visitor

does not see how intensively the space is developed. Many innocent objects have unexpected uses, and our guests require some training and instruction in living with us. We sometimes think of our boat in the hands of a stranger. He would come upon puzzling contraptions and unexpected compartments one after another. The boat would fall apart with some of its secrets undiscovered.

The heart of the *Retreat* seems to be her iron range. You'd carry coal for it, but you'd gather and burn driftwood. She'd have kerosene lamps, with a mantle lantern for reading.

In the high part of the house there is 6 feet of headroom, and in the sleeping part, 4 feet 10 inches. The windows, hinged at the top, open out, You'd have sticks for different amounts of air.

The water tank is under the front porch. I'd want a roof over the back porch for rainy days. I suppose it's inevitable that canisters of bottled gas would find their way back there? Anyway, the back porch would be the base for the morning swim.

Some fine vessel, I call her. A good place to watch the early morning mists rising off the still water and the moonlight sparkling off the ripples of the night wind. Make sail in the skiff; reach out across the moon path and then reach back for that riding light showing where the little houseboat lies.

23/ The Boston Whaler

Length on deck: 13 feet 4 inches
Beam: 5 feet 5 inches
Draft: 6 inches
Displacement: 340 pounds
Designer: C. Raymond Hunt

Frank Hall said he had an interesting new workboat at his yard down the river, so of course we had to go see it. At first, the thing looked rather nondescript.

I was about to tell Frank I thought she looked like a plastic bathtub, but decided not to when I saw how happy he was with his new boat. He jumped into her and walked along the wide gunwale holding his arms out for balance. She only heeled a couple of inches. He said she was really handy for all sorts of jobs around the yard.

Frank said the new craft was called a Boston Whaler, but a closer inspection of her hull showed she was no whaler at all, but rather a sort of modified sea sled. Where the sea sleds we knew had a big concave Vee running down the centerline of the forward part of their hulls, this boat had two smaller concave Vees on either side of a convex Vee section. If a sea sled could be considered an underdeveloped catamaran, then this newfangled Boston Whaler thing could be considered an underdeveloped trimaran. The concept for this new sort of boat came from the mind of Dick Fisher. The design was drawn by Ray Hunt.

Somebody saw a Boston Whaler upside down and decided her hull looked sort of like a cathedral. There have been a lot of small powerboats built since with "cathedral hulls," but the day Frank Hall introduced us to the shape was over 20 years ago.

Not long after our family moved to Maine, we decided we needed a boat for exploring the Maine coast. There were also guarded references by the teenage sons to waterskiing. Somebody mentioned a Boston Whaler and ducked, waiting for my explosive reaction. But they were dealing with a new man. Hadn't I already gotten a nice plastic sailing dinghy without being struck dead by lightning?

We got a 13-foot Boston Whaler, the original design in the series, like Frank Hall's boat. It came with a 33-horsepower Evinrude. I sent up a fresh array of lightning rods.

The boat looked businesslike sitting on her trailer in our driveway. What a feeling of mobility! Think of all the places on the Maine coast to which she could be driven and launched. Think of the water distances she could cover with that great mill on her stern. If Pop was watching my boating activities from some post-earthly existence, I hoped they had given him a sabbatical.

The new boat was 13 feet 4 inches long, with a beam of 5 feet 5 inches, and a draft of 6 inches. Her hull weighed 340 pounds. Roger Jr. and I could just barely lift the motor onto the transom. Full of water, the boat was supposed to be able to float 950 pounds.

I cannot call the Boston Whaler pretty or even handsome, but neither do I think she is ugly. She has that rugged, utilitarian look. She's one of the few boats I've

A Boston Whaler can carry all sorts of cargo. (Boston Whaler)

known that really lives up to the axiom, "Handsome is as handsome does."

We soon found that the Boston Whaler had amazing initial stability and carrying capacity. As roomy as the boat was, she always seemed to be able to hold up all the people and gear you could squeeze on board.

She seemed to be very strongly built. Certainly there was no "oil-canning" anywhere, and there was always the reassuring memory of that ad where they sawed one in two and the two guys then went about their business, each in his own boat. The Boston Whaler people back up their sense of humor with a 10-year hull guarantee.

The huge Evinrude started every time for us. You had to pull the string thrice, but on that third tug she purred to life and kept running smoothly until you shut off her fuel — all but just the one time.

The first time we opened her up, she really scared me with her speed. She ran very level and was very stable both running straight and turning, but it took quite a while to get used to the water rushing by so fast so close under your nose.

Trying to recall my destroyer days and make allowance for the great difference in height of eye, I estimated her speed at an honest 25 knots. I've since seen a performance table for the boat, and it turns out she was a bit faster than I thought.

Children (and certain adults) like to lie up in the bow watching the waves disappear under her at a fantastic rate. Watching her rapidly receding wake certainly gives you a sense of making great strides over the water when 6 knots is your idea of exuberance.

A boat with this kind of speed shrinks bodies of water. A cove that's adventuresome for a sailing pram is a boring puddle to a 25-knot speedboat. But then we learned a secret that a few speedboat people seem to have overlooked. The boat actually will run with the throttle in some other position than fire-walled. We began slow, enjoyable explorations punctuated by exhilarating speed-runs to and from the places where we wanted to spend time. Gradually we sail-and-oar types were learning a few of the things that most motorboat people know instinctively.

We used the boat a lot on Lake Megunticook. It's a lovely, complicated medium-sized Maine lake just a few miles from our driveway. There are lots of coves, islands, and secluded wooded shores with low, flat ledges for picnicking and swimming — and room to waterski.

Waterskiing, of course, has to be done at flank speed, and the waterskier has to zigzag back and forth across the wake of the boat seeing how far he or she can get out to the side on each zig and zag. This means that if you're

Her great stability makes her a fine expedition vessel. (Boston Whaler)

running the boat you have under your guidance an object traveling at high speed that is nearly 200 feet wide. And if you circle toward rather than away from the skier, you will probably never be allowed to run the boat again. I wondered if a boating family held back by its patriarch to pre-steam-engine ways of doing things could survive such sudden catapulting into the Evinrude era. We suffered no fatalities.

We did use the boat quite a lot for exploring. I recall launching at Thomaston and "doing" the whole St. George River below the town. We liked Maple Juice Cove best. As we headed back up the river from its mouth, we saw what a tremendous, imposing landmark is the house made famous by Andrew Wyeth in his painting *Christina's World.* I remember returning with Dean from an overnight island-camping trip in Penobscot Bay when we stopped off at Compass Island and got into one of the great stone-skipping contests of all time.

We were interested to see how the boat would behave in rough water. Going into a head sea, she pounds when a deep-Vee boat wouldn't. I suppose the trade-off is the Whaler's great initial stability, carrying capacity, and ease of beaching. In a nasty head sea, she had to be slowed right down to nonplaning speed so she wouldn't shake you to pieces.

I suppose you could flip her over running fast in a big sea if you caught one just wrong. It seemed as if you could run as fast as you wanted to, though, across the seas in the trough if you didn't mind getting wet when the top of a wave crest leaped her low freeboard. I thought the most dangerous time was running off before it in a big sea when you were tempted to speed up. She'd overtake a sea, climb up its back, and go hurtling off above the deep hole on the lee side. Down she'd come with a jarring crash. You couldn't see them coming, and I guess if one of these holes in the ocean were deep enough and misshapen enough, she could land in a way that would get her into trouble. But she always gave a sense of great security in rough water, because you knew you could be sensible and slow her down and then she'd be perfectly safe, if not dry.

The Boston Whaler's great stability makes her a very comfortable boat for such a small one. You can move all around in her with the same degree of care you use in your kitchen. It's true that her seats are too low to her floor to be comfortable, but I'd rather have my knees up under my chin than have to use a high-sided boat. We had a low railing on each side for hanging on and a high railing forward to hang onto when standing in the bow.

She has a towing ring well below the rail in the bow that also takes the hauling line on the trailer winch. There's a towing ring on each side of the transom to take a bridle for waterskiing. There's a nice big belaying pin mounted athwartships in the bow for the painter or anchor rode, and two more aft, one on each quarter.

The bow seat forms a covered locker that stays reasonably dry. We kept the day's chart in there.

We also kept 200 feet of half-inch line in the bow locker to use for come-what-may, and specifically as a haul-off. We had a 15-pound Danforth anchor lashed to the bow railing with a short anchor rode of about 50 feet on it. If we were going ashore on an island (our tidal range is about 10 feet), we'd put a block on the end of the anchor line and run the long haul-off line through it. When we landed we'd take both ends of the haul-off ashore, tie them together on the boat, and then be able to haul the boat off to her anchor and be more or less oblivious to the rise and fall of the tide. This is one use where the Danforth shines. You take a strain on it from the shore, so you know the general direction of pull isn't going to change much and that the anchor will have plenty of scope, thus circumventing the Danforth's weaknesses for general use.

We carried three 6-gallon gas cans stowed on rubber mats on the floor of the boat just abaft the steering thwart. Eighteen gallons of gas gave us plenty of range for a good day's exploring.

Way in the stern of the boat is a separate compartment bulkheaded off. This stern compartment acts as a drainable sump tank for the whole boat. Very handy.

The Boston Whaler is fitted with oarlock sockets, the rowing position being on the bow seat. We put a pair of big bronze oarlocks into the bow locker and lashed a pair of heavy ash 7½-foot oars to the starboard hand rail just inside the gunwale. The boat's shape is all wrong for rowing, of course, and she is quite heavy, but you can maneuver her around under oars if need be, and she will pull along slowly. The heights work out so that you can row comfortably standing up and pushing.

We used our Boston Whaler quite a lot for a few years, but then the older boys left home, and she began to gather leaves and twigs sitting in the driveway. Stephen, our youngest, was still too young for speedboats and waterskiing. So we sold the little vessel. Probably a mistake.

In a couple of years, I got feeling sorry for Stephen and all he was missing (a feeling he shared), so, as the boat had stayed local, Stephen and I borrowed her for a day's outing.

Early in the morning we went roaring across a perfectly calm Penobscot Bay to the west side of Vinalhaven Island. We explored the intricacies of narrow passages between a myriad of islands, one of which claimed our attention for a picnic lunch. We cautiously eased our way in through the narrow, mill-race entrance to The Basin, that great wild inland sea whose shores are the epitome of secluded beauty. We had a great day of cruising.

Not long after we started back for Camden in the late afternoon, the engine stopped running. We were opposite a stone beacon called The Monument at the western entrance to the Fox Island Thoroughfare.

I tried to restart the engine. Stephen tried to restart the engine. We drifted. We scratched our heads. We tried again.

I got out the oars and started to row the boat toward Camden, 8 miles away. Stephen tipped the Evinrude up out of the water.

The tide was flooding up the bay, putting the current on our quarter. We had a light breeze from the same direction. With these helpmates, I figured we ought to be able to get in by the time the long summer evening got dark. Stephen figured we'd be out there all night.

I must say I was surprised that it took so much continual work to keep her moving along at something like a knot-and-a-half through the water. As much work as a much bigger sailboat.

We kept at it, with Stephen giving me a little spell every hour.

And that, patient reader, is how Stephen and I came to hold the record for rowing a Boston Whaler from The Monument to Camden: 3 hours, 47 minutes.

24/ The *Espoir*

Length on deck: 33 feet 6 inches
Length on waterline: 31 feet 6 inches
Beam: 9 feet 5 inches
Draft: 2 feet 6 inches
Designer: Peter Thornycroft

If you are lucky enough to need a fast sea boat to tend an island, explore the coast, commute to work at a seaport, or do any other watery work that can put 23 knots to good use — or if you would just like to daydream about such good fortune — you ought to take a look at the *Espoir* (or should it be *l'Espoir*?).

This purposeful-looking British motorboat was designed by Peter Thornycroft — a famous name in such matters — about 25 years ago. To me she epitomizes the best tradition in fast English power craft, giving the impression that not much would have to be done to her besides changing her ensign to white to make her ready to deal with the enemy. Her topsides, of course, would be dark blue and her superstructure white. The proportions and angles of her hull and superstructure give her a good-looking shape.

Nor are these proportions and angles important merely for good looks. There is a tremendous responsibility involved in designing a boat that is to attack 23 miles of rough water every hour. Hugh Casson, a Britisher, wrote of "the fact borne of experience that seamanship is fun but it is also serious, for a human life can often depend upon the curve of a hull or the angle of a cleat." Mr. Casson was writing of low-speed sailing craft, but I think his remark applies even more to high-speed boats.

To be sure, the *Espoir* would be a bit corky in rough water with a fairly quick roll, though her keel would dampen things down to a reasonable gyration.

Her hull is easily driven; there is little to her underwater. She is flat enough aft to plane fairly easily. Judging from a photograph of her, she runs quite level at speed.

She has a fine entrance, but with lots of flare and sheer at the deck; dropping off a sea, she'd neither pound nor bury. Her forefoot is deep enough and the "sail area" of her topsides and superstructure is small enough so that she wouldn't blow off sideways too much trying to land on the lee side of a dock in a strong beam wind.

I'd like to see some protection for the wheels and rudders. Maybe on each side, land the lower end of the rudderpost on a stout bar deep enough to clear the propeller and then run it forward beneath the shaft to the hull.

The *Espoir* is 33 feet 6 inches long on deck, 31 feet 6 inches long on the waterline, with a beam of 9 feet 5 inches, and a draft of 2 feet 6 inches.

Her twin engines develop 354 horsepower to give her those 23 knots. Because she seldom has to slow down for rough water, she has done quite well in the Cowes-

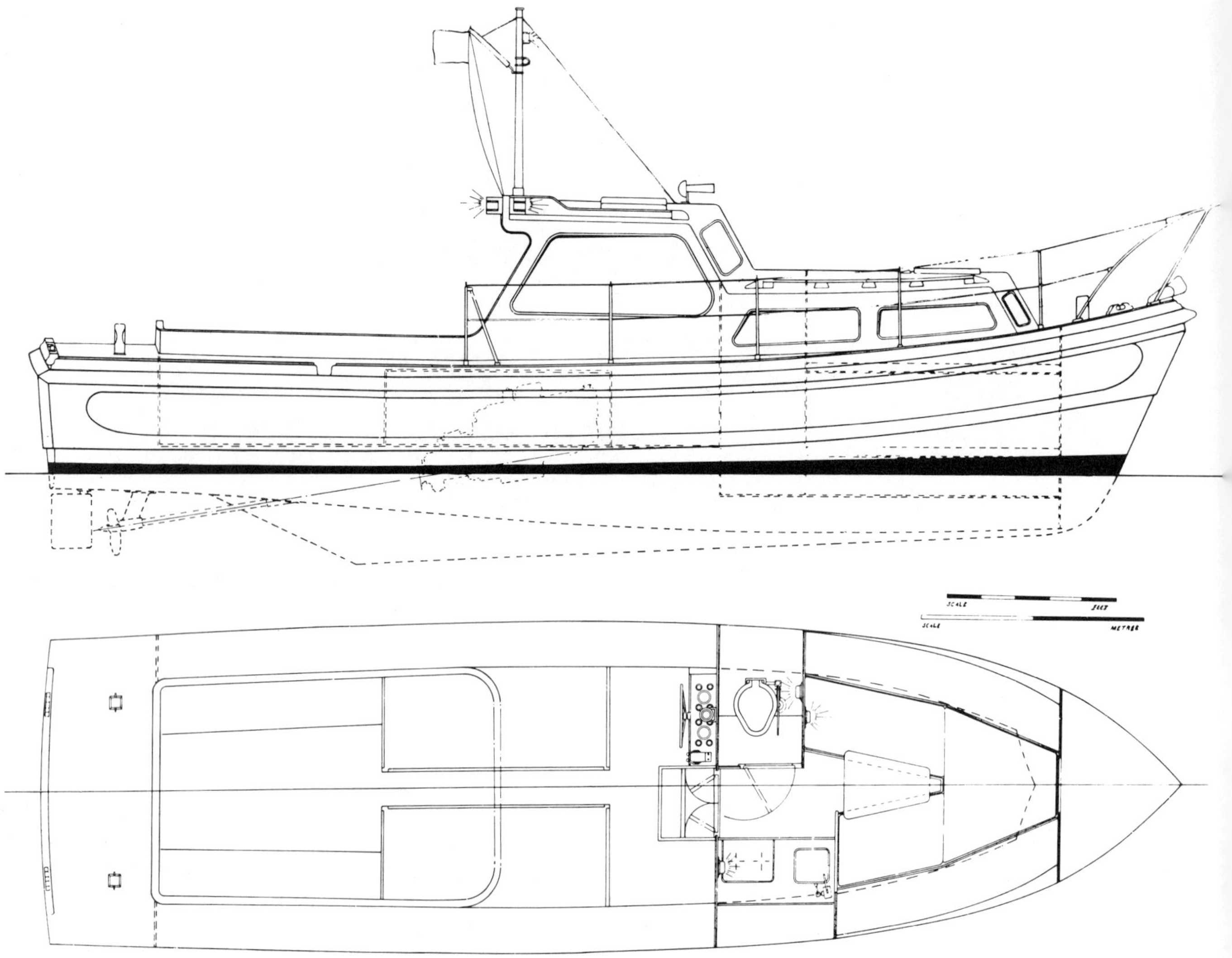

The Espoir*'s outboard profile and lines.* (Seamanlike Sense in Power Craft *by Uffa Fox)*

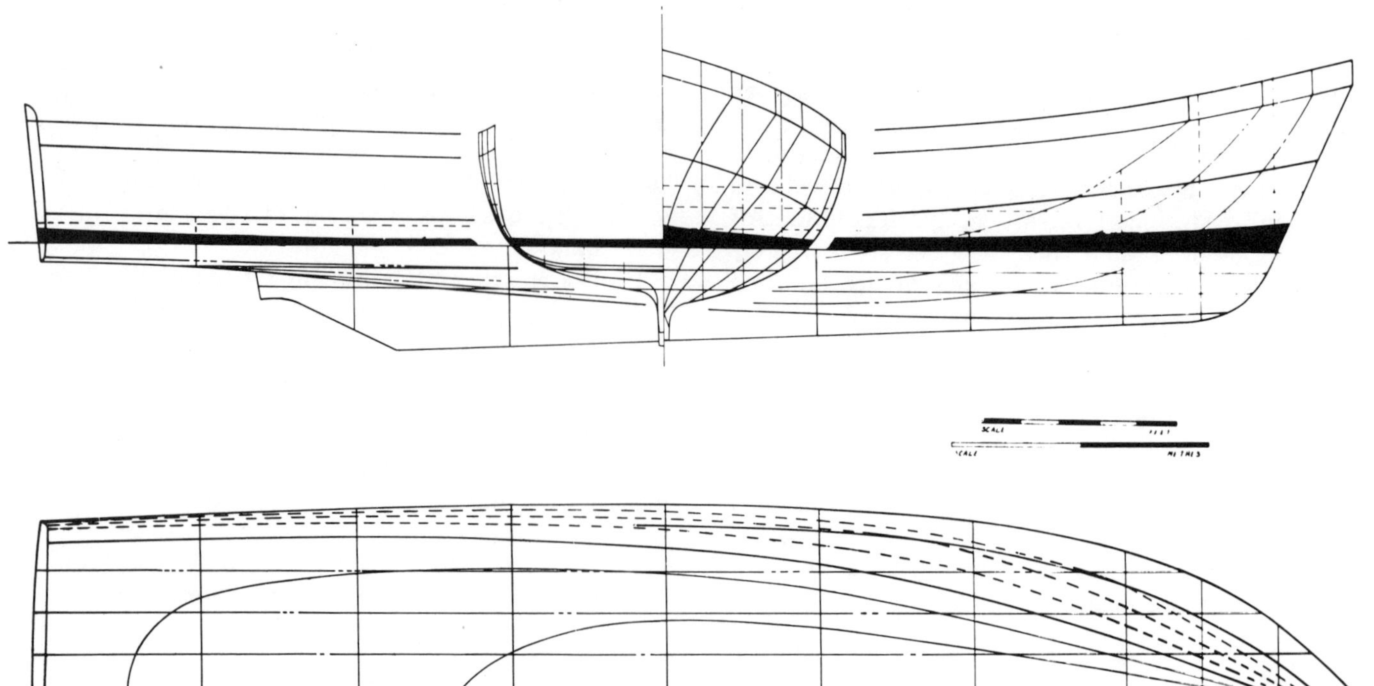

The Espoir *at speed.* (Seamanlike Sense in Power Craft *by Uffa Fox)*

to-Torquay offshore powerboat races, often beating plenty of faster boats on her high average speed and reliability.

I'll bet she'd make nearly 20 knots on one engine. I spent some time in one of my Uncle Sam's leaping greyhounds, and while it took four boilers and 60,000 horsepower to get her up to a shuddering 32 knots, on two boilers and 30,000 horsepower she'd do 28. And the *Espoir* has a hull shape that would let her ease along at slow speed when she wanted to without getting all inefficient and making a lot of waves.

Not being an engine mechanic, I just love the reliability of two engines in a powerboat. The *Espoir*'s engines are very accessible once the panels of their enclosures are removed.

She has wide enough decks so you can get forward easily inside the lifelines. And her pulpit forward gives you something to hang onto when you're working on her rather cramped foredeck.

The wheelhouse, of course, gives excellent protection to the steering station and allows an unobstructed but protected view to the navigator. She even has those wonderful, fast-spinning, circular sections in her windscreen, the kind that fling the spray off themselves with better results than most windshield wipers. Clever bloke who thought that up, eh?

Her low seats back in the open cockpit keep you down in the boat. The high engine boxes would make good seats or daybeds; traffic between them, to be sure, is single file.

Below, she has adequate cruising accommodations for two people. The starboard berth is 6 feet 3 inches long; the port one, a full 7 feet. She has a canopy that can cover the whole cockpit aft for rough or rainy weather. If the after seats folded over on themselves so that when unfolded their width would be doubled, she could sleep four extra people on deck under her canopy, or in fine weather, under the stars.

I'd want to put a 10-foot sailing and rowing boat across her stern on davits.

In *The Complete Book of Seafood Fishing,* Rob Avery made a wise comment: "Raise no eyebrows when you put to sea and you will be liable to come back into port again." The *Espoir* might attract admiring glances as she put to sea, but I doubt that she'd raise many eyebrows.

25/ A German Motorsailer

Length on deck: 26 feet 3 inches
Beam: 5 feet 11 inches
Draft: 2 feet
Sail area: 231 square feet
Designer: Arthur Tiller

My dream of a good powerboat that will sail recurred when I discovered a nice little V-bottomed *motorsegelkreuzer* in A. Techow's *Motorbootfahrers Handbuch* published in 1926 in Berlin. The boat was designed by Arthur Tiller.

With a little modifying here and there, this motorboat might just sail quite well. She probably wouldn't go fast enough to win sailboat races, but she ought to have a good turn of speed once her wind is freed a point or two. I'd give her leeboards and a Meadowlark-type fold-down rudder for increased lateral plane, but you'd still want to help her to windward with the engine at times or maybe just drop the sails and run her dead to windward until you could fetch comfortably to where you wanted to go. At the very least, her sails would save you a lot of fuel.

Her V-bottomed hull is reminiscent of the fine powerboats designed by William H. Hand.

This boat would drive along at, say, 7 knots with a small engine. Nor would a head sea slow her down much. I remember seeing a long, skinny Chesapeake Bay deadrise running fast and dry right into quite a big chop off Tolly Point just south of Annapolis, happily carrying a big gang of paying sightseers. She was some impressive.

The *motorsegelkreuzer* has quite good bearing in her quarters for sailing. Her chines would also help her under sail, for the lee one would dig in a bit and keep you from going sideways, while the weather one would lift out and protect you from spray. She's narrow enough and high-sided enough so that she wouldn't ship water over the lee rail when sailing.

She is 26 feet 3 inches long on deck, almost that long on the waterline, has a beam of 5 feet 11 inches, and a draft of 2 feet. She has 400 pounds of outside ballast on the keel. Her sail area is 231 square feet.

Her masts are in tabernacles and are short enough so that they could be dropped and raised fairly easily. With a little practice, you ought to be able to "shoot" a bridge in her under sail.

I'd be tempted to put the jib on a club and traveler to make it self-tending. I'd want a couple of reefs in the mainsail and one in the mizzen, even though it's true that she would balance under main alone or under jib and mizzen. She'd lie-to nicely under mizzen alone.

What about a big, standing-lug mainsail for light weather? It would have a long, light yard hoisting to the masthead and extending a few feet forward of the mast and a lot of feet abaft and above it. The tack and clew would be in the same positions as those of the leg-o'-mutton mainsail. The thing could be nearly twice as big as the working mainsail. It would be lightweight

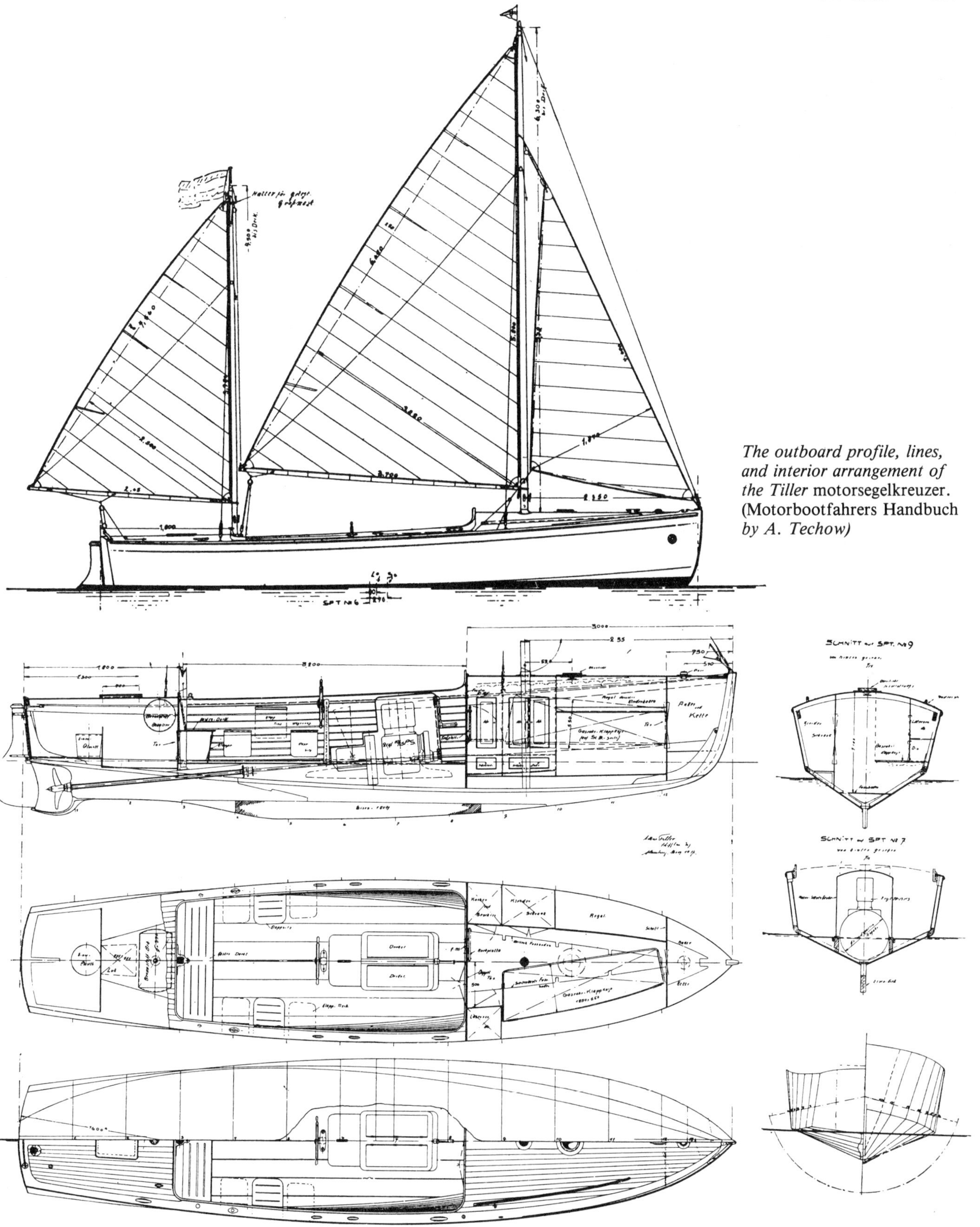

The outboard profile, lines, and interior arrangement of the Tiller motorsegelkreuzer. (Motorbootfahrers Handbuch *by A. Techow)*

and cut fairly full for maximum power, since you'd only use it reaching and running. Of course you'd want a preventer backstay to set up to keep the mast in her, and, naturally, you'd vang the lug yard to the mizzen masthead. Some fun.

The big stone-crusher of an engine is right in the middle of the boat. The machine could be a lot smaller and lighter today, but the big engine's function as inside ballast must not be ignored. Note the strut protecting her propeller and supporting the bottom of the rudder.

You could take quite a gang on a day trip in this boat's big cockpit. I'd want a just-the-right-height stool for steering under power. I'd extend the rudder head up above the rail and stick a tiller through it under the mizzen traveler so I could stand in the hatchway of her lazarette to steer under sail or when I got sick of the wheel.

It would be nice to chock yourself off in the after lee corner of the cockpit on that big thwartships seat and watch along her lee rail as she goes. The folding seats in the cockpit give you a lot of choices.

Let's give her a spray hood that unfolds like an accordion from the forward end of the cockpit and slides back to cover as much of it as you want covered, including the whole thing. We'll make it low enough so the main boom will clear it and so we can see over it comfortably when standing steering. (I used to dream of such contraptions when sailing my big old Herreshoff sloop, the *Aria,* on certain days, as I watched her gigantic cockpit collect gallons of rain.)

You'd want a step in each forward corner of the cockpit on the side of the boat; you'd use the leeward one to mount to the deck and go forward.

Under the foredeck is a cuddy with room for the usual cruising amenities and a bunk for one person. There's a big deadlight in the deck to keep the place from being dark and dreary. There's also room for a couple of people to sleep on the cockpit floor, one each side of the engine, under stars or spray hood as the weather dictates. In hot weather, you'd make sure not to run the engine near the time when somebody was going to sleep next to it; in cold weather, you'd make sure you did.

Is that a cedar bucket back in the lazarette, right where it belongs? I believe it is.

What a great little sailing motor launch for exploring interesting coastlines. You could have her built in Germany and start by tracing the route of Davies and Carruthers in *The Riddle of the Sands.*

26/ The *Magpie*

Length on deck: 46 feet
Length on waterline: 41 feet
Beam: 13 feet 1 inch
Draft: 5 feet
Sail area: 580 square feet
Designer: William Atkin

We hear a good deal these days about "sail-assisted power vessels." With the coming of the external- and then the internal-combustion engine, sailing vessels got an assist from power; as engines delivered more horsepower more reliably, sail was vanquished. Now, with the price of fuel so high, sail is coming back to curb the thirst of engines.

Of course, these developments are not sharply delineated. The motorsailer has been with us for some time, and who's to say whether a powerfully engined vessel with a short rig is a sailing vessel with auxiliary power or a power vessel with auxiliary sail?

Well, William Atkin considered the *Magpie,* one of the many cruising boats he "designed especially for MoToR BoatinG," definitely to be a powerboat. He gave her a schooner rig to help her on her way, steady her, and reduce her fuel bills, probably in that order of importance when he designed her nearly 50 years ago. Today, the last reason might well be first.

As usual, Mr. Atkin produced a handsome, purposeful-looking vessel. She has nicely balanced, short ends, with plenty of shape to her transom and outboard rudder, and a lively sheerline. Her buttock lines are very easy; she has a good run. She has a reasonable amount of lateral plane, and her beam has been kept moderate. The waterlines are fairly full forward.

The *Magpie* is 46 feet long on deck, with a waterline length of 41 feet, a beam of 13 feet 1 inch, and a draft of 5 feet. Her freeboard forward is 6 feet.

Her heavy hull would take some driving to keep her going. She'd be steady on her helm and would certainly heave-to steadily.

Billy Atkin gave no displacement figure for the *Magpie* in his write-up of her design, but judging from her scantlings, she ain't no lightweight. He specified: keel of white oak, 14 inches by 14 inches; oak frames, 2 inches by 2 inches on 12-inch centers, with every fourth frame doubled; 1½-inch white pine planking, sheer strake to be mahogany; clamp and shelf each 2-inch by 2-inch fir; floors at every other frame, 2-inch by 8-inch oak; ceiling, ¾-inch white pine or fir; deck beams, 2-inch by 2½-inch white oak; deck, 1½-inch white pine; pilothouse ¾-inch mahogany staving.

The only fancy specification was for diagonal brass straps, ¼-inch by 6 inches, on top of the house in way of the mainmast.

She was to have 5 tons of inside ballast consisting of cement laced with boiler punchings poured between the floors and leveled off even with their tops. Some builders would shudder, but Billy Atkin loved the stuff:

> In putting in cement ballast be sure the wood surfaces are absolutely free from oils and paints. The cement will then cling to the wood and there can be no danger of

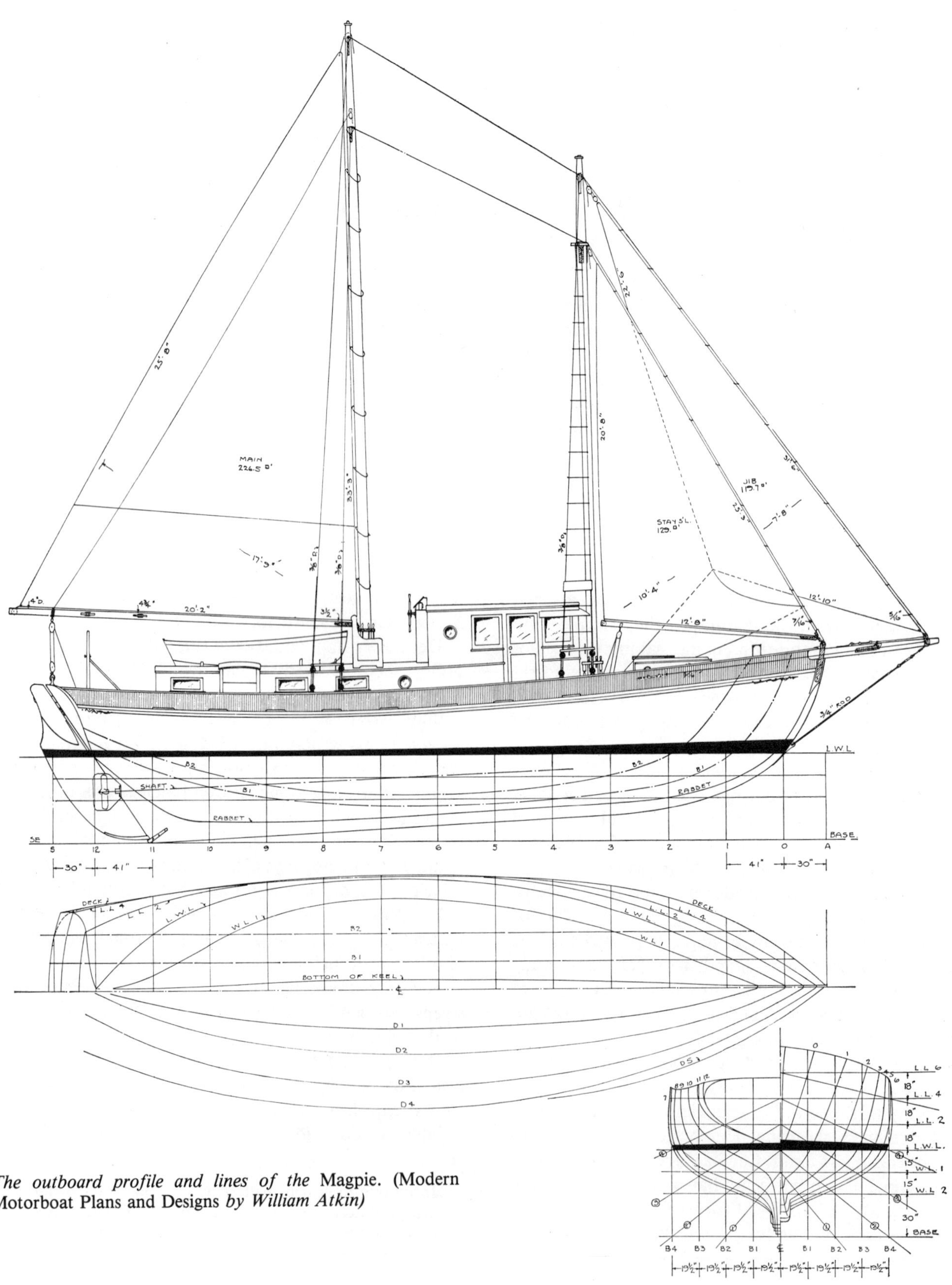

The outboard profile and lines of the Magpie. (Modern Motorboat Plans and Designs *by William Atkin)*

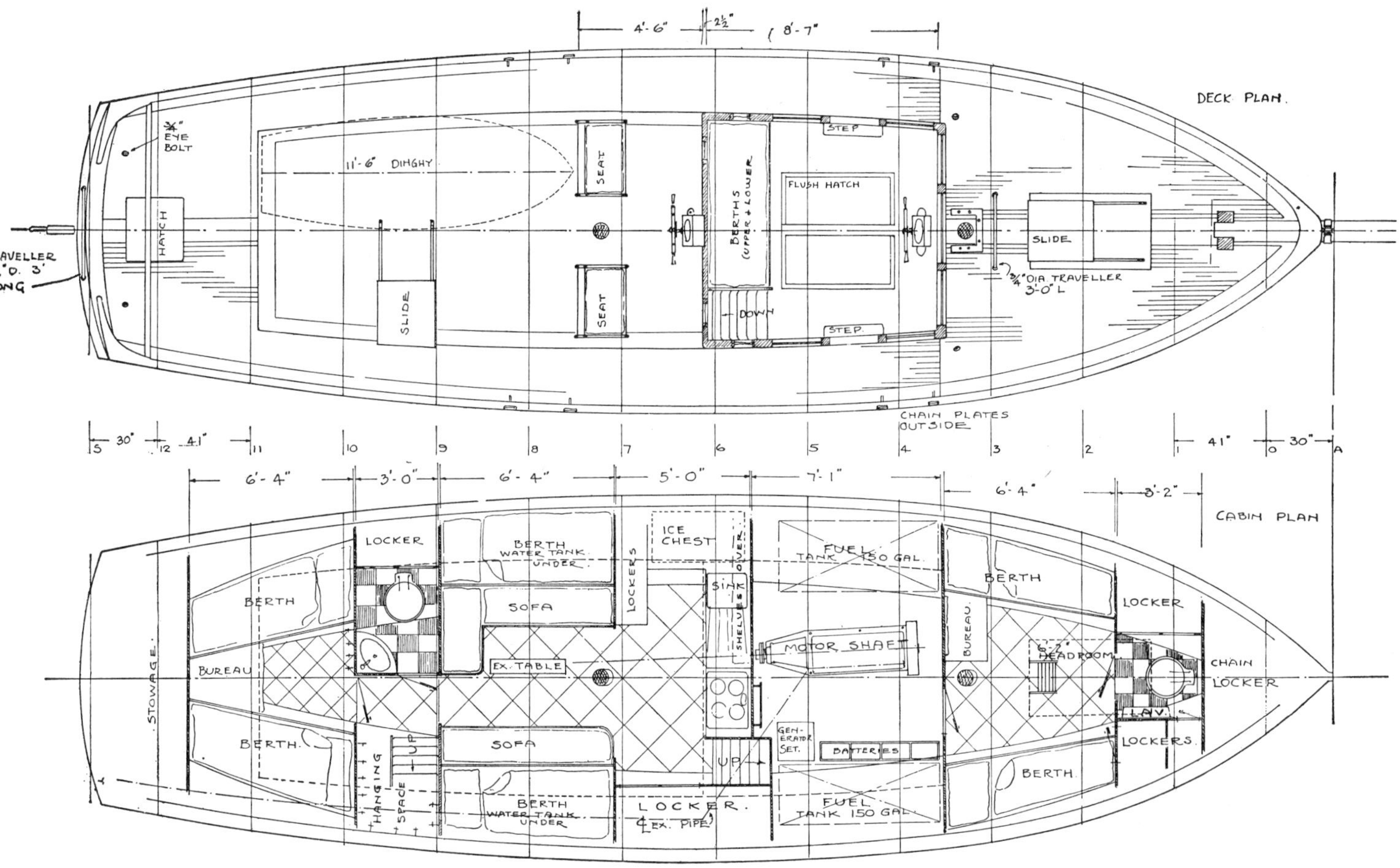

Her deck and accommodations plans. (Modern Motorboat Plans and Designs *by William Atkin)*

decay; in fact the cement will preserve the wood. I should put in the cement before the floor beams have been fitted and before the boat has been launched. Smooth off the top surface, and after the cement is perfectly dry, paint thoroughly with good deck paint. The bilge can be kept beautifully clean if it is cemented as described above. I do not know of a better way to treat the bilge of any boat that requires inside ballast.

Mr. Atkin estimated the *Magpie*'s cost at $9,000-$16,000 (pre-World-War-II dollars), depending on whether she were built plain or fancy.

The auxiliary rig spreads a mere 580 square feet of sail: 330 in the mainsail, 130 in the forestaysail, and 120 in the jib. She has no foresail, because her house and steering station are in the way.

Her rig has been kept simple. Her deadeyes and lanyards are cheap and reliable. Her leg-o'-mutton mainsail is held to the mast with mast hoops.

I'd have to rattle down the main shrouds and put a crow's nest up on the forward side of the mainmast, since there is no fore gaff to bang into it. And this is a boat on which I'd be tempted to rig a roller-furling jib, even though I'd want a plank on top of the bowsprit and a swordfishing pulpit on its end.

The thing to do with all that nice space between her masts is fill it with a fisherman staysail, with its head snugged up under the lower springstay and its foot coming down about even with the reef in the mainsail. With that beauty added to her sailplan on a reach in any kind of breeze, the fuel bill would be reduced to zero.

Another worthwhile sail in the *Magpie* would be a balloon forestaysail to pole out when running, because then, of course, the fisherman staysail would have to be handed.

On deck, she has a stout gallows frame to take the main boom; space for an 11½-foot dinghy on top of the house, as shown, ready to be hoisted out by the main halyard; a couple of nice seats beside the mainmast; and a high steering station amidships. I'd want to fence that steering station in, I think, and put a low wind deflector across the after end of the pilothouse roof to shoot the breeze up over your head.

The power schooner's inside steering station gives good visibility (unlike some you see these days). The wheelhouse windows drop into pockets. There are only two 6-inch portholes in the after bulkhead; I'd want windows back there too, so when I hear the whine of an outboard motor astern, I can tell right away whether or

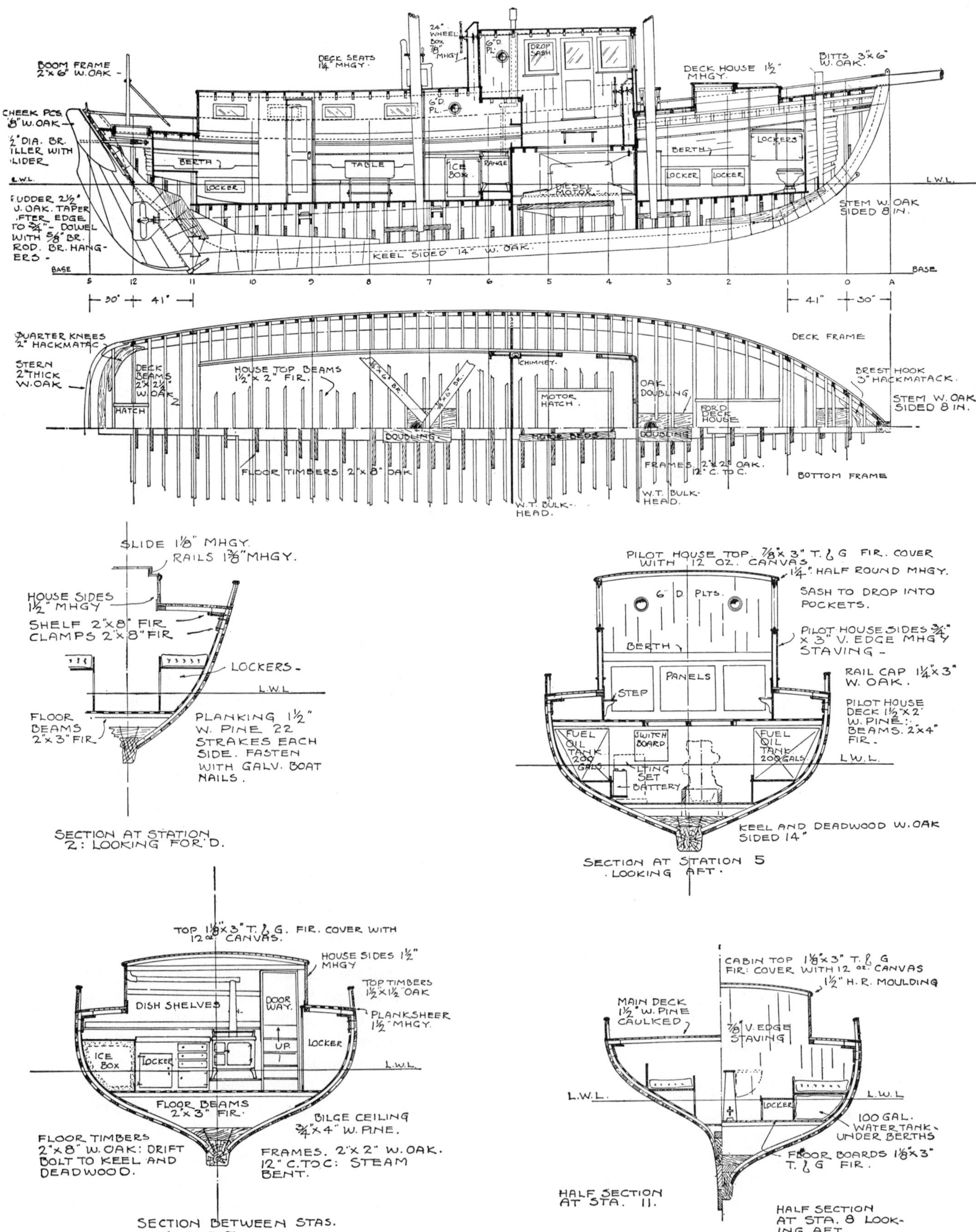

The Magpie*'s construction drawings.* (Modern Motorboat Plans and Designs *by William Atkin)*

not I need to run outside and screech at the guy to get his attention before he hits me. I'd want a chart table on each side of the wheel. Happiness is rolling along on a cool fall day steering behind glass in the sun with the lee wheelhouse door open.

The deck of the wheelhouse has a pair of big flush hatches so you can open the engine room right up; there's also a door into the place from the fo'c's'le. In any case, you have plenty of space around the big machine. (Mr. Atkin specified a six-cylinder diesel in the 65- to 100-horsepower range, such as a Redwing-Waukesha 80-90 Hesselman.) Her long shaft is nearly level. She has a separate generator set and plenty of batteries. I have always been intrigued, however, with the idea of starting a big engine like this with air and having a compressor that you start by hand. Then if you can keep the air system tight, you can start the engine. She'd go very easily at 8 knots.

There's a watertight bulkhead at each end of the engine room and a pair of 200-gallon fuel tanks in the wings. She has a 100-gallon water tank under each bunk in the saloon.

I don't know about those sideways companionways that used to be all the rage on powerboats. Great on the port tack, but what happens when wind and spray are coming over the starboard rail? I'd rather just put a hatch in the top of the house and climb up and over.

Her layout below is straightforward. The galley, saloon, and a couple of bunks are right amidships. She has a raised deck over the fo'c's'le, and there is over 6 feet of headroom under the fo'c's'le hatch.

She has no fewer than 8 bunks, including an upper and lower in the wheelhouse, so she could accommodate 8 souls.

Robert C. Leslie talked about this "soul" business in his wonderful book *A Waterbiography*.

> We were, to speak nautically, seven souls all told on board; though why sea-faring people should be thus spiritualized has always puzzled me. No one calls railway or omnibus passengers souls; they are always persons, bodily filling places or seats.
>
> It might, however, often be well if people, especially passengers, could leave their bodies ashore when taking a voyage — souls, we are taught, being so easily provided for in every way; while this would do away with that mortal dread of the sea so trying to some people. No one in a storm fidgets about his soul; it is his bothering body he always wants either to save himself, or someone else to save alive for him; and except in the case of a body too seasick to care, I have observed that the greater the real or fancied danger at sea, the less people trouble about their souls. This is, however, a digression . . . ."

Anyway, however many souls were on board the *Magpie,* I'll bet they'd have a fine time of it.

27/ A Fisheries Patrol Boat

Length on deck: 57 feet
Length on waterline: 53 feet 6 inches
Beam: 12 feet 9 inches
Draft: 5 feet 3 inches
Displacement: 57,340 pounds
Designer: William J. Deed

A designer of excellent powerboats sixty and more years ago was William J. Deed. He had a successful career with such companies as the International Shibuilding Corporation at Nyack, New York, and the Charles L. Seabury Company, Consolidated (later shortened to just Consolidated), in the Bronx, and working on his own, as outlined by Weston Farmer in *From My Old Boat Shop*.

When the U.S. Bureau of Fisheries wanted a service vessel for its station at Woods Hole right after World War I, it was natural that they should turn to Mr. Deed for the design. Billy Deed consulted with one W.H. Thomas, who worked at the station, about the requirements for the vessel. He produced a design that has a lot of appeal, to me at least, and one that could, with a slightly different arrangement, make a good power cruiser for today.

I think she has a handsome, businesslike profile. She has just enough overhang in her ends to look good; there's a lot of shape to her transom.

She should be an easy sea boat. She has enough keel to dampen rolling and she has just enough flare forward and just enough freeboard to keep herself reasonably dry in heavy going.

Her raised deck forward gives space below, the lifelines providing security on deck. The after deck has bulwarks to give protection, and the arrangement allows the vessel's nice sheerline to remain unbroken.

This fisheries vessel is 57 feet long on deck, with a waterline length of 53 feet 6 inches, a beam of only 12 feet 9 inches, and a draft of 5 feet 3 inches. Mr. Deed figured her displacement at 57,340 pounds.

She is narrow and fine enough to be easily driven. The designer thought she ought to do 12 knots readily. He didn't specify any particular engine, but he clearly had in mind a big, slow-turning machine.

Westy Farmer would applaud Deed's drawing of an actual propeller on the inboard profile plan, in contrast to what he derisively terms the "Z-shaped coat hanger" with which some designers equip their otherwise well-drawn vessels.

Besides her main engine, this boat has an auxiliary that can run pumps or a winch back at the mainmast and can even be hooked up to turn the main shaft and give the vessel bare steerageway. She has a 2 kw generating set. She would have considerable range; the big fuel tanks under the deck just abaft the mainmast hold 430 gallons each.

Her headsail and boomless gaff mainsail would save gallons of the expensive stuff, given a leading breeze.

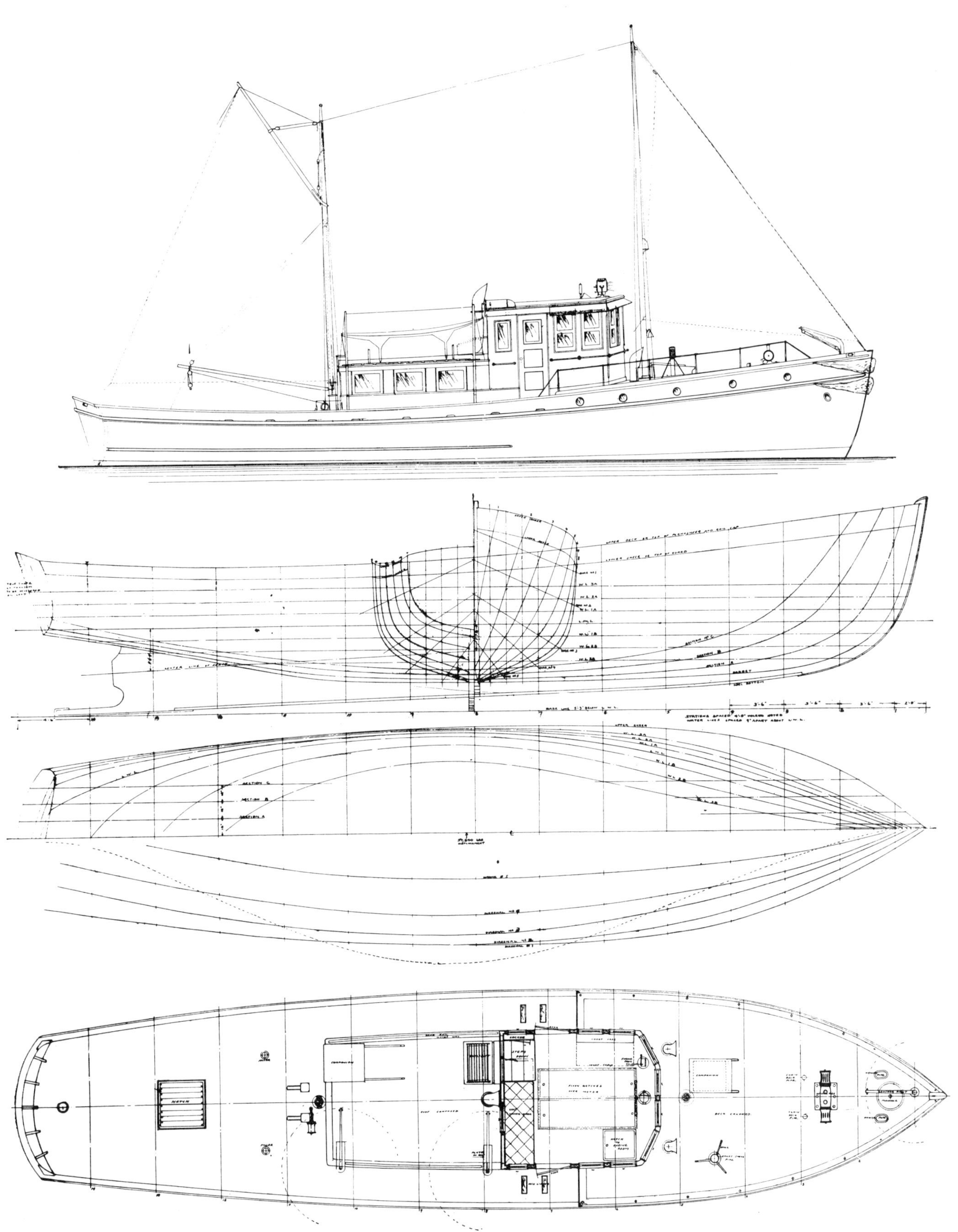

The outboard profile, lines, and deck plan of the Fisheries patrol boat. (The Rudder, *October 1919)*

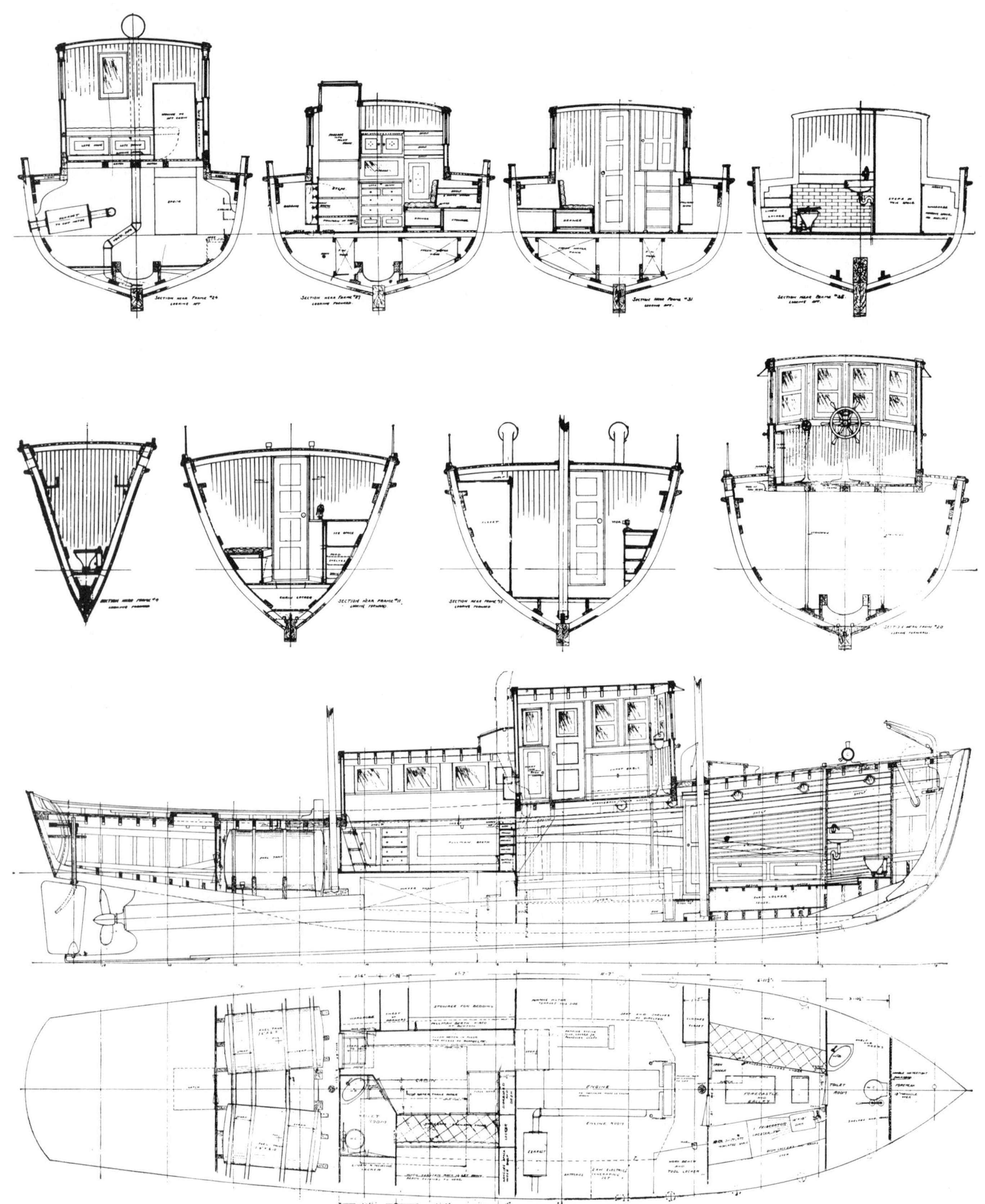

The sections and interior arrangement plans of the Fisheries patrol boat. (The Rudder, *October 1919*)

Her sails, of course, would also help her motion. She could lie-to nicely with just her mainsail set and sheeted flat.

The boat shown under its davits atop her house amidships has a length of about 10 feet. You could easily carry in addition a 14-footer on the stern, to be hoisted in and out with her cargo boom.

She has a spacious wheelhouse with a seat across two-thirds of its after end and a chart table in the forward port corner. You'd want a couple of stools in this fine place.

The hatch to the engine room is in the forward starboard corner of the wheelhouse. There are also big flush hatches running the length of the wheelhouse that can open wide to provide plenty of light and air to the machinery space should there be a lengthy maintenance or repair job.

The vessel's engine room has full headroom and walk-around access to the main engine. There is plenty of room for the auxiliary, the generating set, batteries, a workbench, seat, shelves, and a closet. Mr. Deed gave top priority in his layout to the engine room, which makes great good sense in a vessel of this type.

She has a tiny forepeak way up in the eyes of her, reached from the deck through an 18-inch manhole. This space is separated from the rest of the vessel by a heavy, watertight bulkhead. There's a big lazarette in the stern reached by a good-sized deck hatch.

The fisheries vessel is arranged with a fo'c's'le, galley, and head forward; and a cabin with two folding berths and a second head aft. If you wanted to modify this design for cruising, you could keep the same spaces, but change the fo'c's'le and galley forward into a double stateroom and make the after cabin into a galley on the port side and a saloon to starboard, with an L-shaped settee around the table.

So arranged, this old-timer would make an outstanding power cruiser for long coastwise explorations.

28/ The *Little Vigilant*

Length on deck: 70 feet 10 inches
Length on waterline: 63 feet 3 inches
Beam: 15 feet 6 inches
Draft: 5 feet 7 inches
Sail area: 643 square feet
Displacement: 47 tons
Designer: Eldredge-McInnis

Flag signals have been used at sea for a long time (over three centuries in the British navy alone), yet it is a rare small vessel whose master may emerge from his pilothouse, step briskly across an open bridge to a flag bag, clip a hoist onto a flag halyard, and two-block his signal smartly to a position on his rig where it may be seen by all who have telescopes clapped to their good eyes.

Maybe the flag is simply the black and yellow squares of Lima: "Stop. I want to talk to you." Or perhaps the captain is curious and hoists Romeo Victor: "Where are you bound?" Or helpful, making Echo Hotel: "Can I assist you?"

Say our little vessel is standing by another in trouble in a gale at sea. Now the signal can be that most hope-giving of all: Alpha over India — "I will not abandon you."

Drayton Cochran could make such signals from his wonderful motorsailer the *Little Vigilant,* for she has a nice pilothouse from which to emerge, an open bridge across which to stride with room on it for a flag bag right across its forward end, and a flag halyard to the springstay well clear of everything. The *Little Vigilant* is a real seagoing vessel, all the way through.

Mr. Cochran has had some fine vessels. (See the plans of the *Vigilant,* the 100-foot big sister of the *Little Vigilant,* in *More Good Boats;* and those of the big brigantine *Westward* in *Still More Good Boats.)*

The *Little Vigilant* is his favorite.

She was built from a design by Eldredge-McInnis of 1940 for a 1,000-bushel Maine sardine carrier. The design was very closely followed as to the hull; changes were made in rig, deck layout, and interior arrangement. The vessel was built of steel by Abeking and Rasmussen at Lemwerder, West Germany, and was launched in 1950. She was the first sizable yacht the firm built after World War II.

The *Little Vigilant* is 70 feet 10 inches long on deck, with a waterline length of 63 feet 3 inches, a beam of 15 feet 6 inches, and a draft of 5 feet 7 inches. She displaces about 47 tons. Her sail area is 643 square feet.

Mr. Cochran cruised in her in Europe over a 13-year period and never did get around to bringing her home to America. He wrote, "She sure was admired wherever I took her, which included Scandinavia, Africa, Greece, and Turkey, etc." Besides coastal passages, she cruised the inland waterways of Europe. "She was the most practical boat I ever owned," Mr. Cochran wrote, "and we could maintain her ourselves without outside help."

With the double-ended hull of the carrier boat, the *Little Vigilant* is as seakindly a vessel as there is. Her hull is very easily driven.

She has a fine entrance and a long run. Her sheer is bold for a 70-footer, especially forward. She has just enough overhang fore and aft for grace. She has fairly

Walter McInnis.

The Little Vigilant*'s outboard profile plan. (Drayton Cochran)*

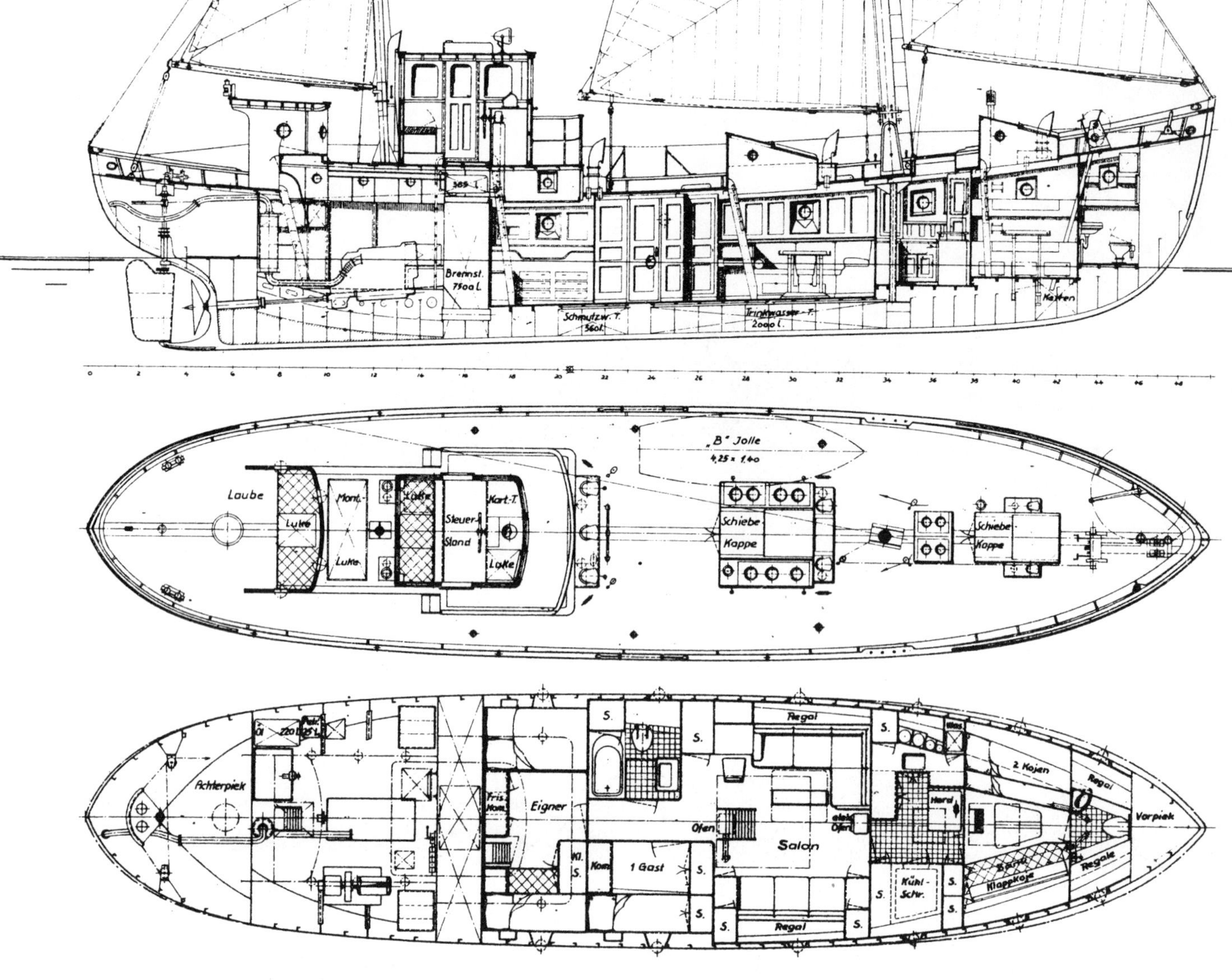

The Little Vigilant*'s deck and interior arrangement plans. (Drayton Cochran)*

hard bilges amidships, but very easy sections going toward her ends. Note how well-protected are her wheel and rudder.

The vessel certainly has a handsome profile with her short ketch rig, pilothouse, seamanlike deck layout, and able-looking hull. Her rig is well stayed, the standing rigging having good angles of pull without the need for preventers or spreaders.

The mainmast steps on deck in a tabernacle set at an angle so that when the mast is lowered it will just clear the port forward corner of the pilothouse. The mizzenmast is stepped atop the house, but it would be a bit tight lowering it because of the deck structures nearby. It's a relatively light spar, though, with a length of about 27 feet.

All the sails are self-tending; if you're using sails and engine to help each other get her to windward, you can tack by rolling the wheel over in the pilothouse without even stepping outside.

Her mainsail has an area of 311 square feet; the mizzen, 123; and the jib, 209. All the sails are loose-footed and mitre-cut. The mainsail can brail in to the mast to save hauling the gaff up every time.

I'd have to have a bowsprit on this boat, and of course it would have to have a swordfishing pulpit. Since the main rigging is all rattled down, why not give her a crow's nest on the forward side of the mainmast just above the gaff saddle? I think there is just room for it. A bowsprit pulpit and a crow's nest would give you two more fine spots from which to watch her go. And

Above: *The* Little Vigilant *under power alone.* **Left:** *Launching day.* **Below:** *She has plenty of room on deck.* **Bottom:** *Plating nearly completed. (All photos courtesy Drayton Cochran)*

Above: *Who wouldn't want to stand up to her wheel?* **Right top:** *She has a separate generating set.* **Right:** *In the galley.* **Bottom:** *A cozy corner in the pine-paneled saloon. (All photos courtesy Drayton Cochran)*

sometimes there is just no substitute for a lookout aloft.

I have written before about the sense of well-being that a vessel's pilothouse gives her crew. Could there be a better place than a wheelhouse in which to live out your old age?

The *Little Vigilant* would make you want to explore strange, and perhaps dangerous, coasts. You'd need plenty of big, first-class ground tackle in her, and that bowsprit would be mighty useful for its handling. You might find yourself anchored fairly often in conditions requiring an anchor watch for her protection, and that pilothouse would make such duty pleasant.

In fine weather you could put her on automatic pilot and go outside and pace back and forth across your open bridge, four paces to port and four to starboard, with or against the roll as whim might take you. Who wouldn't sell his farm . . . .

With her bulwarks and lifelines, the *Little Vigilant* has plenty of security on deck. The ventilators give her something of a big-ship look. There is room for a 14-foot rowing and sailing dinghy either to port or starboard of the midships hatchway.

You'd want deck chairs on the stern where that nice shelter would also let you huddle out of the wind. The deck shelter protects the main hatch going down into the big engine room; there's an emergency escape hatch from the engine room up through the port side of the pilothouse transom. She has a 6-71 GM diesel that shoves her easily along at 10 knots. There's a separate generating plant.

The original sardine boat design called for tanks to carry 500 gallons of fuel, but the *Little Vigilant* as a long-distance cruiser has much bigger tanks, stretching right across her full width beneath the pilothouse. They hold 1,950 gallons. There is a water tank in the bilge under the saloon that holds 520 gallons.

When the *Little Vigilant* was designed, the sardine carrier's two 500-bushel fish tanks amidships were replaced by a saloon, a single stateroom, a washroom, and a big double stateroom. Otherwise, her arrangement is very close to that of the carrier boat, with galley, fo'c's'le, and head forward; and engine room and lazarette aft. The motorsailer has three companionways: from deck to fo'c's'le, from deck to saloon, and from pilothouse to after stateroom.

She is bright below, thanks to her considerable headroom, big hatches, skylights, portholes in the topsides (which also let you see what's going on outside), and pine paneling and light-colored paint all around. The saloon has an L-shaped settee around the table and a big transom to starboard, and boasts both an open fireplace and a heating stove under the ladder to the deck. The washroom has plenty of room for a bathtub.

All in all, the *Little Vigilant* would be a fine vessel for, say, a family of five to cruise in. They could live on board for long periods of time, and the vessel would be comfortable whether puddle-jumping or passage-making to the ends of the earth. On a short cruise she could accommodate as many as nine folk.

Drayton Cochran wrote me not long ago: "I wish I had her now."

29/ The *Albatross,* Motorsailer

Length on deck: 83 feet
Length on waterline: 68 feet 2 inches
Beam: 15 feet
Draft: 7 feet
Sail area: 1,829 square feet
Displacement: 48½ tons
Designer: L. Francis Herreshoff

Imagine being so fortunate as to own a fine vessel whose plans were created by a designer of the caliber of L. Francis Herreshoff, and, when you wanted to consider a bigger boat, being able to turn again to Mr. Herreshoff for the design of your dreamship. Such a lucky man was Charles A. Welch.

He had had a 50-foot motorsailer, designed for him by Mr. Herreshoff in 1924, the *Walrus* (described in *Still More Good Boats).* In 1931 Mr. Welch asked the great Marblehead designer to draw up plans for a much-stretched-out, 83-foot version of the same general type of vessel, to be called the *Albatross.* As the plans of the later design show, the *Albatross* was to be a fine-lined beauty compared to the *Walrus;* both vessels are well named.

The *Albatross* is narrow, shoal, and light for her length. She has a well-balanced hull with low freeboard and a nice sheerline. I particularly like the shapes of her bow and handsome canoe stern. Elegant.

Her sections show well-hollowed garboards to keep her light and fine below the waterline. There's a bit of flare high on the bow, put there with a view toward dryness in a head sea.

Her bow and buttock lines are exceptionally easy; she has a long run. She also has a fine entry.

Her big rudder is well aft. All in all, she has enough lateral plane to work to windward under her moderate rig alone, though it is tempting to think of putting in a big centerboard to help her hang on better, or even tandem boards. Perish the thought.

The *Albatross* is 83 feet long on deck, with a waterline length of 68 feet 2 inches, a beam of 15 feet, and a draft of 7 feet. She displaces about 48½ tons, of which about 12½ tons is in outside ballast.

The vessel was to be built plank-on-frame, the plank to be Oregon pine finished to 1⅞ inches, and the frames white oak, 2¾ inches by 2¾ inches, 15 inches apart. To give a further idea of her moderate scantlings, her clamp was to be 2 inches by 8 inches, and her shelf, 3½ inches by 3½ inches, both of Oregon pine.

Her well-raked ketch rig breaks up her sail area of 1,829 square feet so that no sail is too huge. Her mainsail has 673 square feet; the mizzen, 515; the forestaysail, 290; and the jib, 351. Three people in a watch could handle her easily.

The permanent backstay on her mizzenmast tightens up the whole rig beautifully. The running backstays on the mainmast steady the spar and keep the forestay straight.

Note her vertical-cut, battenless mainsail and mizzen. Reaching and running, or working to windward with the lee engine ticking over, she could shorten down to

L. Francis Herreshoff. (Muriel Vaughn)

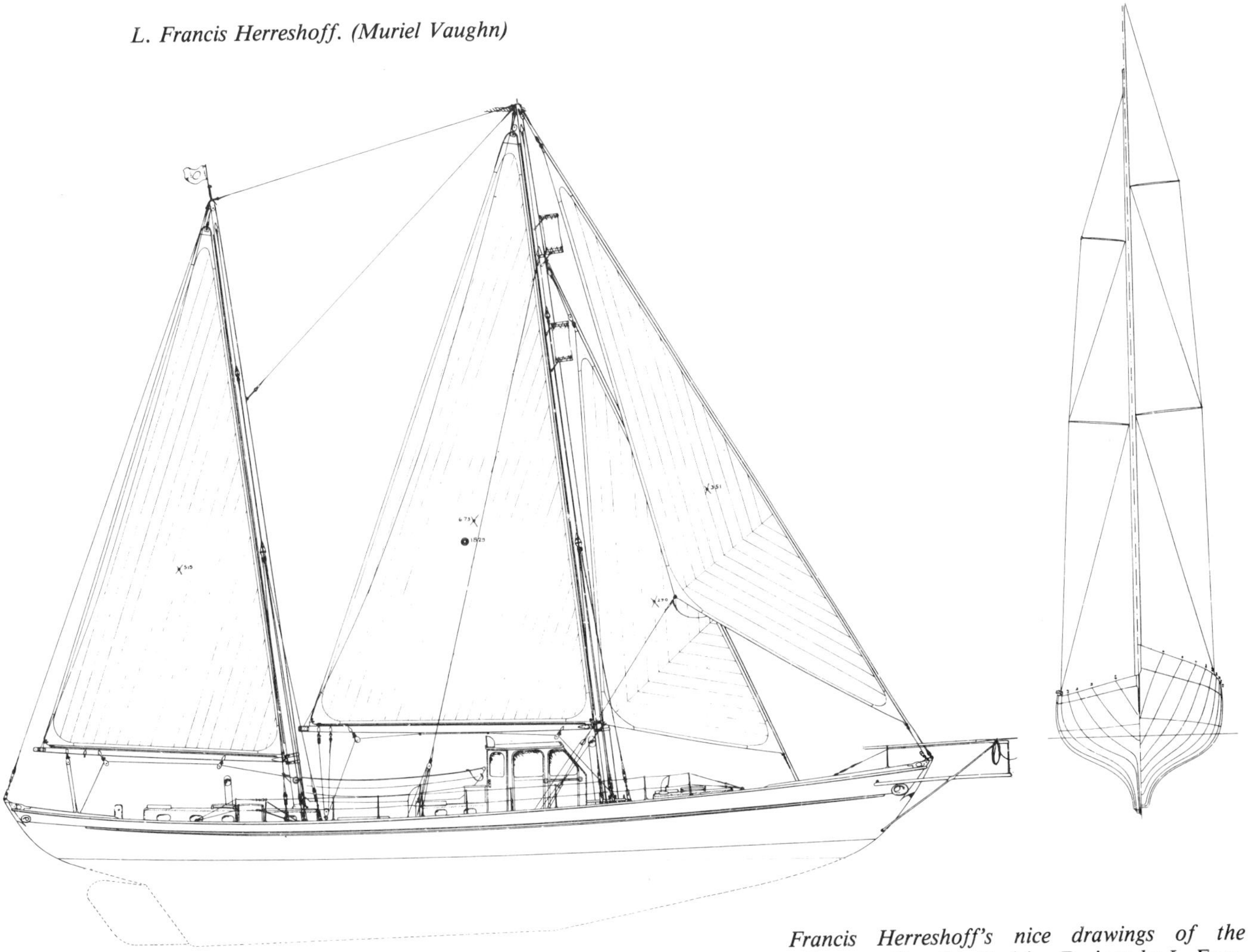

Francis Herreshoff's nice drawings of the Albatross. (Sensible Cruising Designs *by L. Francis Herreshoff, International Marine Publishing Company)*

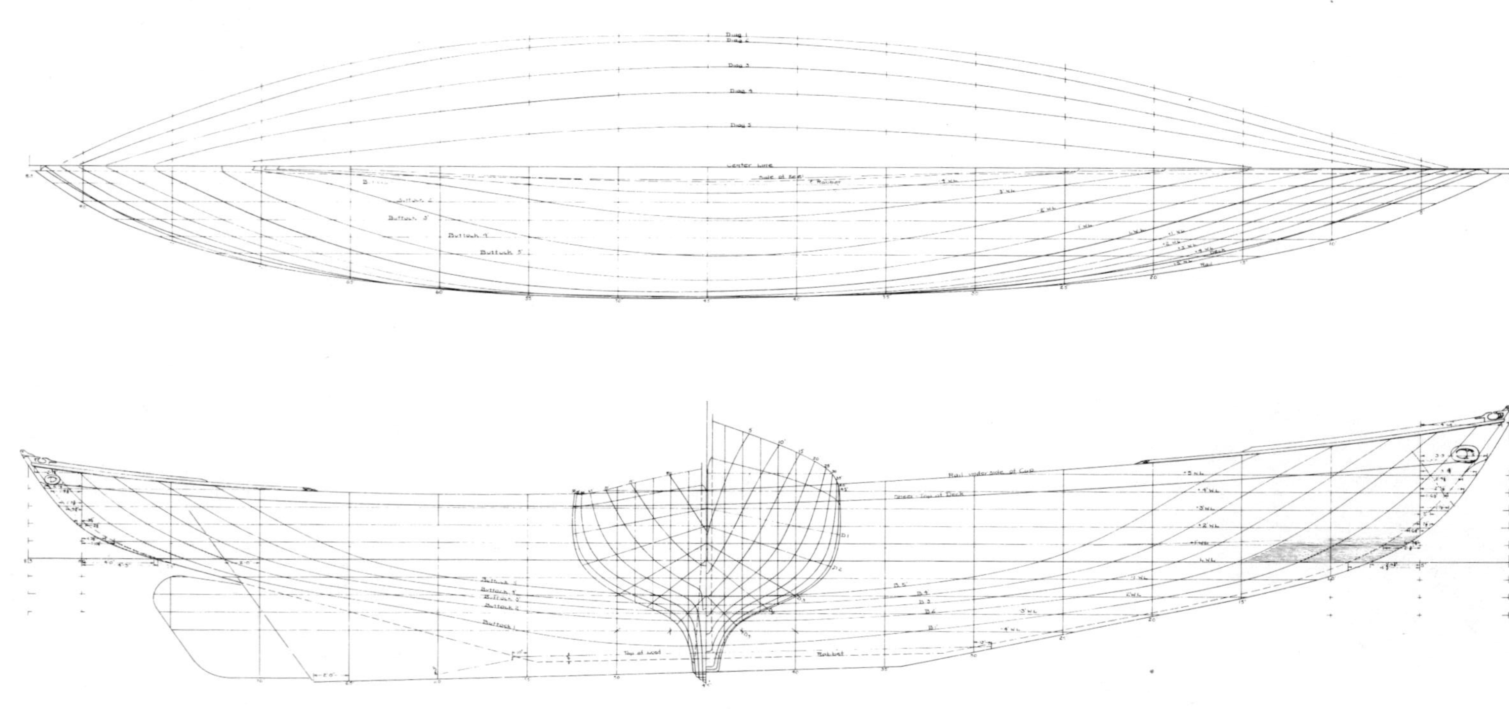

The lines of the Albatross. (Sensible Cruising Designs *by L. Francis Herreshoff, International Marine Publishing Company)*

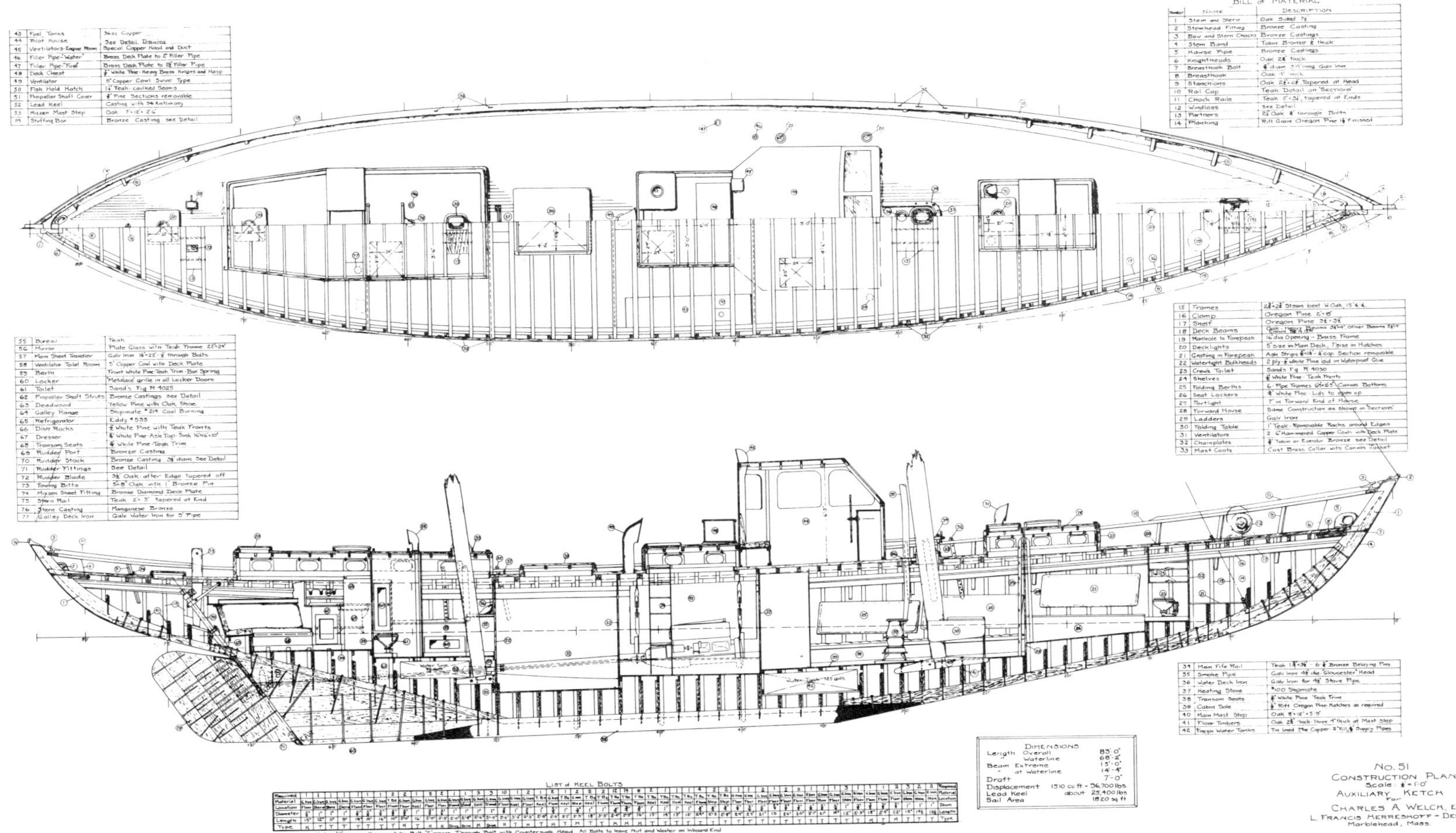

Her construction drawings. (Sensible Cruising Designs *by L. Francis Herreshoff, International Marine Publishing Company)*

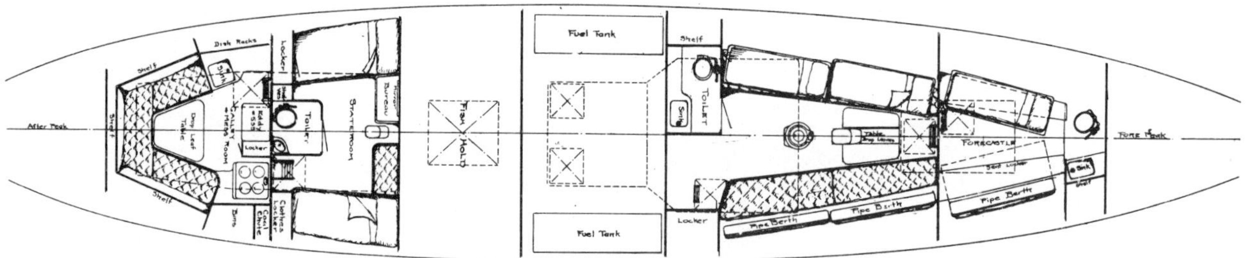

The accommodation plan of the Albatross. (Sensible Cruising Designs *by L. Francis Herreshoff, International Marine Publishing Company)*

mizzen and headsails, mainsail alone, or reefed mizzen and forestaysail. Handy rigs, all.

The two crow's nests aloft on the mainmast look enticing. Nothing like going aloft to get away from it all. Presumably, you'd have a good set of steps on the mast and a friend at the wheel to keep her from rolling or pitching too much while you climbed up and down. Her swordfishing pulpit, with its permanent railing and ingenious diagonal support, is also an otherworldly place to go. A perch on the mast or bowsprit can set you to dreaming when you should be looking for fish. Ishmael himself admitted it: "Let me make a clean breast of it here and frankly admit that I kept but sorry guard. With the problem of the universe revolving in me, how could I — being left completely to myself at such a thought-engendering altitude — how could I but lightly hold my obligations to observe all whaleships' standing orders, 'Keep your weather eye open and sing out every time.' "

You could use the main backstay tackle to hoist boats in and out. There is plenty of room for them amidships; the big dory shown goes well with her.

The *Albatross* would drive along easily at 10 knots under power. She has two engines for reliability. Mr. Herreshoff didn't specify any particular power plants, but I suppose they would each have about a hundred horses. Her fuel tanks are in the wings of the engine room. There is a 125-gallon water tank in the bilge under the after end of the saloon.

What a great place her wheelhouse would be! Solid comfort. Of course you'd want a wheel aft on the stern to provide variety and for steering on fine days.

The *Albatross* has the same layout as the *Walrus,* her extra length being used to add a fo'c's'le and a hold. She has many entries from her deck down into her accommodations, for she has no fewer than six watertight bulkheads without doors in them, so to go from any one of her seven watertight compartments to another, you must needs climb a ladder through a hatch to the deck, find the hatch to the compartment you wish to enter, and then descend through it on another ladder. These full bulkheads separate forepeak from fo'c's'le, fo'c's'le from saloon, saloon from engine room, engine room from hold, hold from stateroom, and stateroom from wardroom. The galley is in the forward end of the wardroom.

She has accommodations for eight people. There's a Shipmate "100" heating stove in the big saloon. A fine place to toast your toes after a snowy run.

The uses of her hold are limited only by her skipper's imagination. The *Albatross* could be some kind of purposeful vessel in the right hands.

Mr. Welch never got around to having a boat built to the design of the *Albatross.* Neither has anyone else, to my knowledge. This is a situation that ought to be rectified.

30/ The *Lelanta*

Length on deck: 65 feet 6 inches
Length on waterline: 46 feet 6 inches
Beam: 14 feet 7 inches
Draft: 8 feet 10 inches
Sail area: 1,790 square feet
Displacement: 40 tons
Designer: John G. Alden

I am glad I don't know how many hours I have spent dreaming over the plans of the full-rigged schooner *Lelanta* as redrawn so beautifully by Uffa Fox in his book *Sail and Power*. Suffice it to say that the vessel has appealed to me greatly ever since I made her acquaintance in the copy of the book my brother got for Christmas in 1937, the year it was published.

The schooner was designed by John G. Alden and built of steel by G. de Vries Lentsch, Jr., at Amsterdam in 1930. Her owner was Ralph St. L. Peverley, an American living at Ellesmere Port, up the Mersey River from Liverpool. He was a great Alden schooner fan.

I used to imagine sitting on that stern grating watching her slip along. Still do. When I was in the U.S. Naval Academy Sailing Squadron, I got to sail a big Alden yawl, the *Royono*. Her hull was shaped a lot like the *Lelanta*'s, but she was a bit finer and had a little less freeboard in proportion. She was a size bigger than the *Lelanta,* being six feet longer on the waterline. On these big boats (they seem big to me), you can be reaching off, seeming to be just lazing along, and you discover you're going something like 7 knots. The *Lelanta* is narrow and fine enough to be quite fast.

She has plenty of hull underwater, and this makes for a comfortable, able, seakindly cruising boat and one that can carry a lot. Her gentle sheerline is just barely enough: any less and you'd have to call her flat. I think she has very graceful overhangs fore and aft.

Note the straight bottom to her keel without much drag; she'd be an easy boat to haul.

The *Lelanta* is 65 feet 6 inches long on deck, with a waterline length of 46 feet 6 inches. Her beam is 14 feet 7 inches, and her draft, 8 feet 10 inches. Her displacement is 40 tons, and she has a working sail area in the four lowers of 1,790 square feet. (In 1938, Ralph St. L. Peverley had Abeking and Rasmussen of Lemwerder, West Germany, build him a 74-foot version, the *Lelanta II.)*

Her steel hull extends to the bottom of her keel, the lead ballast being poured inside the steel. Her teak deck is laid atop a steel structure of beams and straps so that the steel, not the wood, takes all the hull strain.

I think she has a beautifully proportioned schooner rig. Uffa Fox wrote: "To my mind a schooner rig is the strongest rig yet devised for small cruisers, and with the combination of sails that can be set from calm to gale is better than any other rig I know."

One reason she looks so nice is that her gaffs are well peaked-up. Her jib topsail and fore topsail look almost — but not quite — too small to bother with.

She has hollow wooden pole masts. Note the separate topmast backstays making up on the stern.

Left: *John G. Alden.* **Below:** *The* Lelanta*'s sailplan.* (Sail and Power *by Uffa Fox)*

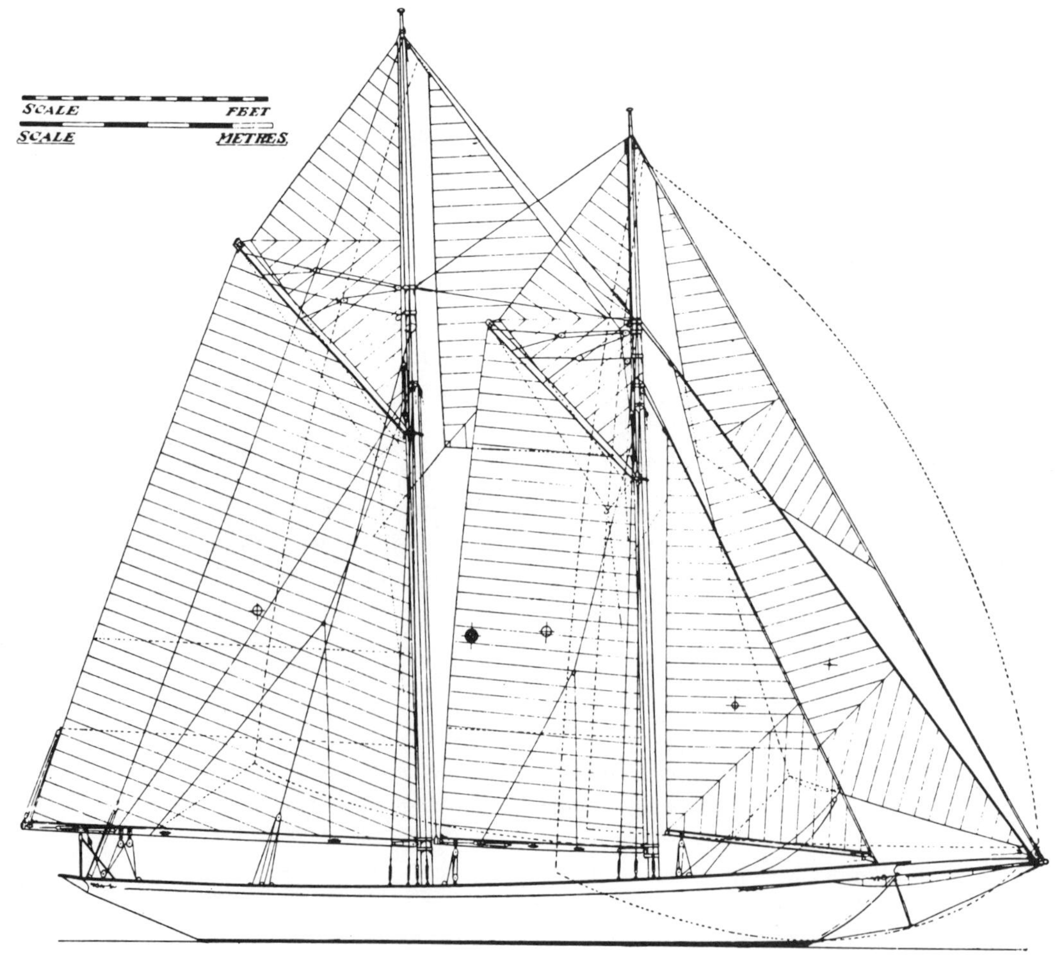

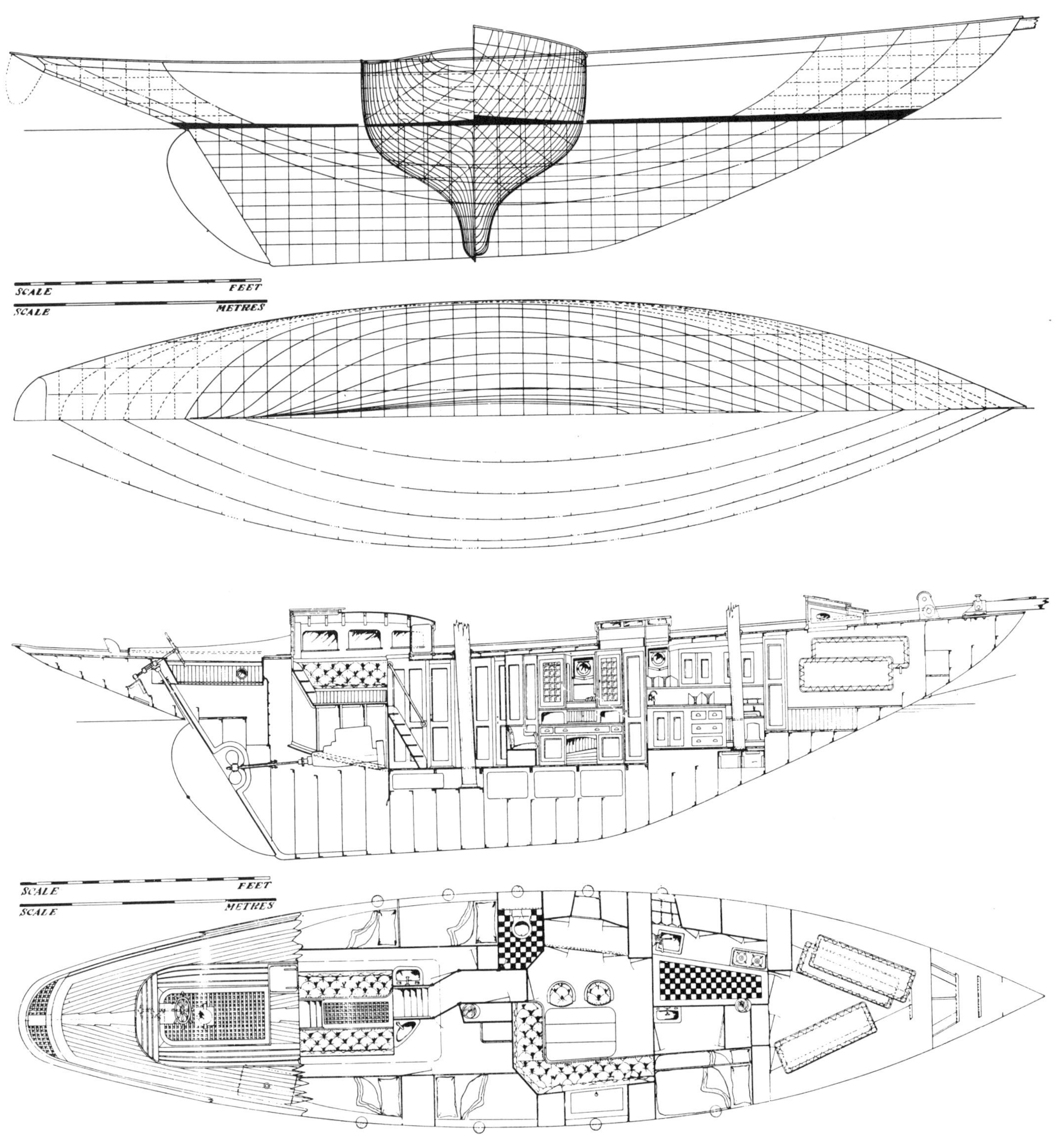

The lines and accommodations plans of the Lelanta. (Sail and Power *by Uffa Fox)*

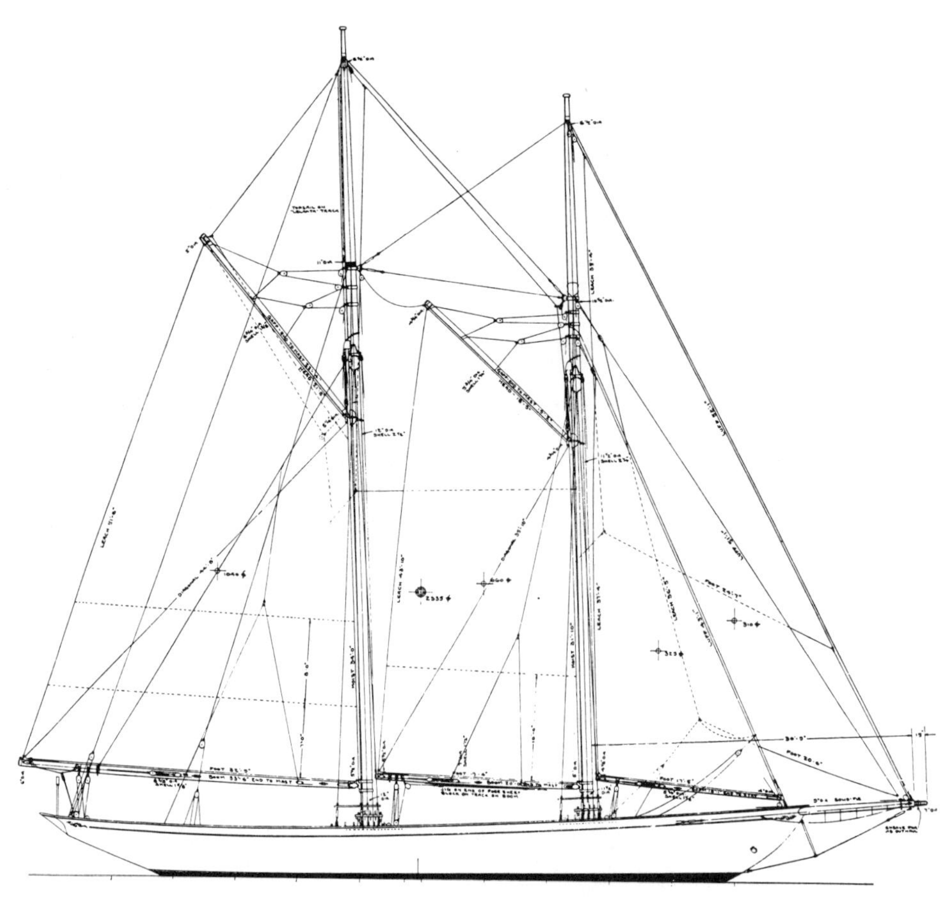

The sailplan and accommodations plans of the Lelanta II. (Yachting, *March 1938)*

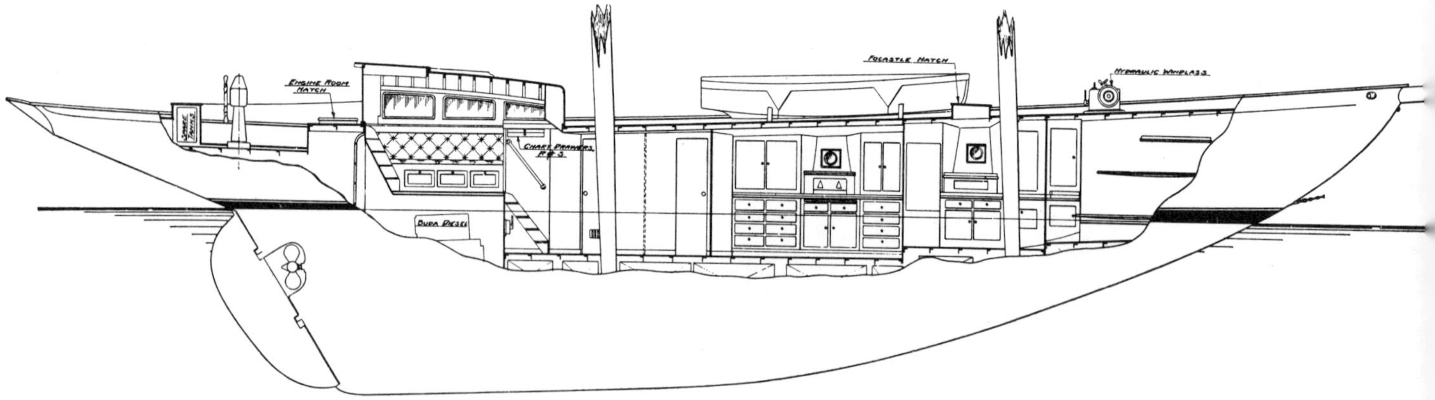

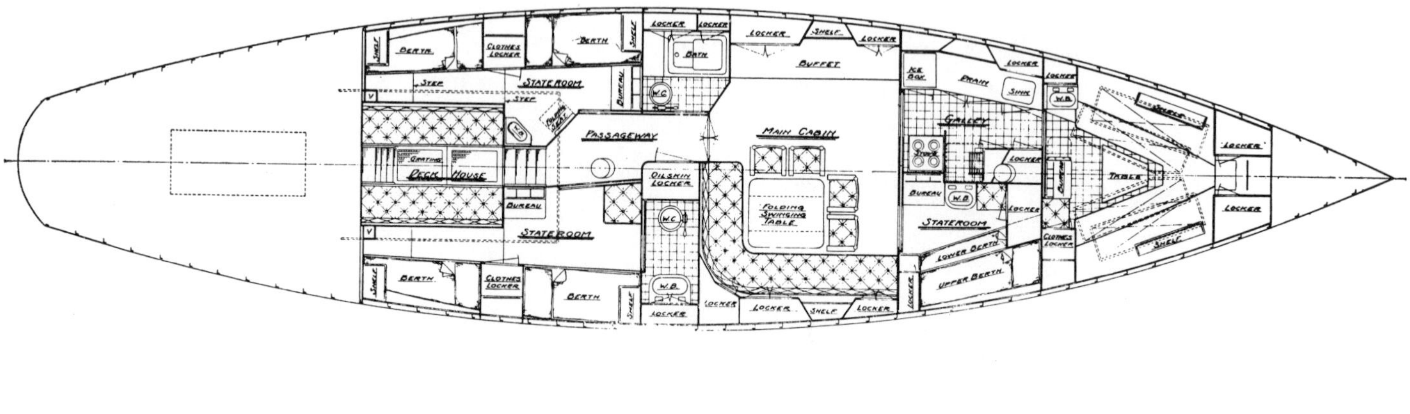

Her owner devised a fancy way of holding the luffs of her topsails to the masts still allowing the sails to be lowered to the deck when taken in. Slides on the luffs of the topsails ran up on jackstays as far as the hounds. At that point the jackstays entered slotted tubes fixed to the after sides of the masts. Where the slides entered the tubes, still on the jackstays, little four-spoked wheels held the jackstays lined up with the tubes as each slide passed into the tubes. Great stuff while it works.

When Uffa Fox spoke of combinations of sails that could be set from calm to gale, he was thinking of the *Lelanta*'s great spinnaker and balloon main topmast staysail (shown in dotted lines on the sailplan) for calm weather; and was visualizing the vessel hove-to under foresail alone, perhaps reefed, in a gale. Between these extremes are plenty of possibilities. At it breezed on, you'd shorten down to the four lowers; then put the first reef in the mainsail; then double-reef the mainsail and take in the jib; then take in the mainsail and set a main trysail; and finally either heave-to or run off with just the foresail set. There is plenty of sailhandling to do in a vessel like this, but it can all be done by a small crew if they work methodically and don't rush things, because nothing on her is too heavy for two people to handle.

She has a great amount of clear deck space from the mainmast forward for handling her sails, though you'd fill some of it, to be sure, with a sailing dinghy and a nice pulling boat, each with its own davits between the fore and main shrouds.

You go down into the engine room through a hatch in the bridge deck. She has a 30-horsepower Red Wing under the deckhouse floor.

That deckhouse would be a great joy. A fine place to be in bad weather when it's not your turn at the wheel. What good is a rainy day in port without a deckhouse?

I've always particularly liked Uffa Fox's drawing of the *Lelanta*'s accommodations: the buttoned upholstery, tile floors, turned-back bunks, nice deck planking, and that stern grating. One reason she seems to have so much room below is that she's not all full of huge heads. It's also true that her steel construction gives her some 15 percent more room inside the hull than would plank-on-frame construction.

Her saloon looks elegant; look at that big L-shaped settee, those chairs, and that great desk. The after staterooms would be most comfortable; you could do some real sleeping back in there off watch at sea. The galley is all right so far forward, for in such a big boat, even when going to windward, the motion would rarely make it untenable.

She has a row of portholes down each side, and because of the arrangement of her accommodations there are five on one side and four on the other. Do you think anyone would notice?

What a fine vessel the *Lelanta* would be for three couples to take on a world cruise, each couple standing four on and eight off during passages. There'd be little hardship to it. And who wouldn't want to sail her into a secluded cove, anchor, dive overboard for a swim, and climb back on board on her bobstay? With any luck at all, I'll probably spend a lot more hours dreaming over Uffa Fox's wonderful drawings of the grand Alden schooner *Lelanta.*

31/ The *Quicksilver II*

Length on deck: 64 feet 8 inches
Length on waterline: 47 feet 7 inches
Beam: 15 feet 4 inches
Draft: 9 feet 9 inches
Sail area: 2,484 square feet
Designer: Charles D. Mower

With this steady, moderate southerly blowing, we're just about to take an imaginary afternoon sail on Penobscot Bay in a 65-foot staysail schooner, the *Quicksilver II.* Designed just a half century ago by Charles D. Mower, this distinguished vessel raced with considerable success on the Great Lakes out of Chicago for a number of years. She was built at Hodgdon Brothers, East Boothbay, Maine, so it is good to visualize her back Down East. It is interesting to compare her design to those of three schooners of similar size: the *Lelanta* of the previous chapter; the *Brilliant,* designed by Olin Stephens; and the *Barlovento,* designed by Henry Gruber (both described in *Still More Good Boats).*

This will be one of those sails that takes place in the mind's eye. Do I detect a frown? You say you want something "real." Come, come. I "really" can imagine sailing this vessel today. You "really" can too. Let's go on board.

The *Quicksilver* is lying on a mooring in Camden's outer harbor, Sherman's Cove. Don't let the dinghy bump the accommodation ladder. That's it. Up you go. I'll just take the dinghy round her stern and hook her onto the falls of the davits on the port side. Heave her up now and put on the gripes. Nothing like having a nice varnished lapstrake dinghy swung out over the side to admire while you sail.

We've got room out here to get underway under sail. We'll haul the mooring down the port side, three or four of us to do that, and sheer her off on the port tack. Stand over to that plastic ketch, tack, and we should be able to lay out between Sherman's Point and the ledges. Start the mainsail up, will you, while I cast off the sheet and run these backstays forward. Now I call that mainsail some big beautiful sail.

Main and forestaysails up together. Now let's heave her ahead on that mooring pendant and pass it down the port side outside everything. Off she goes. With this nice breeze, I think she'll have plenty of way to tack. Round she goes nicely. Set up the weather backstays and give her the jib. She makes Sherman's Point easily — that big mainsail *is* a wonderful sail — and the gulls screech their welcome from the half-tide ledges just to weather as she threads the needle. Love that not-too-gentle rumble of the surge round the rocks and the way they break the waves up into foam.

The *Quicksilver* has very easy lines throughout. She has quite a deep, narrow hull, yet a long run starting from well forward. She has a somewhat airy look, with her rather long overhangs and the flare all around her waterline that makes her look as if she's sitting lightly in the water. And she has perhaps the best sheerline C.D. Mower ever drew.

The schooner is 64 feet 8 inches long on deck, with a

Charles D. Mower. (The Rudder, *March 1927)*

The sailplan and lines of the Quicksilver II. (Yachting, *October 1931)*

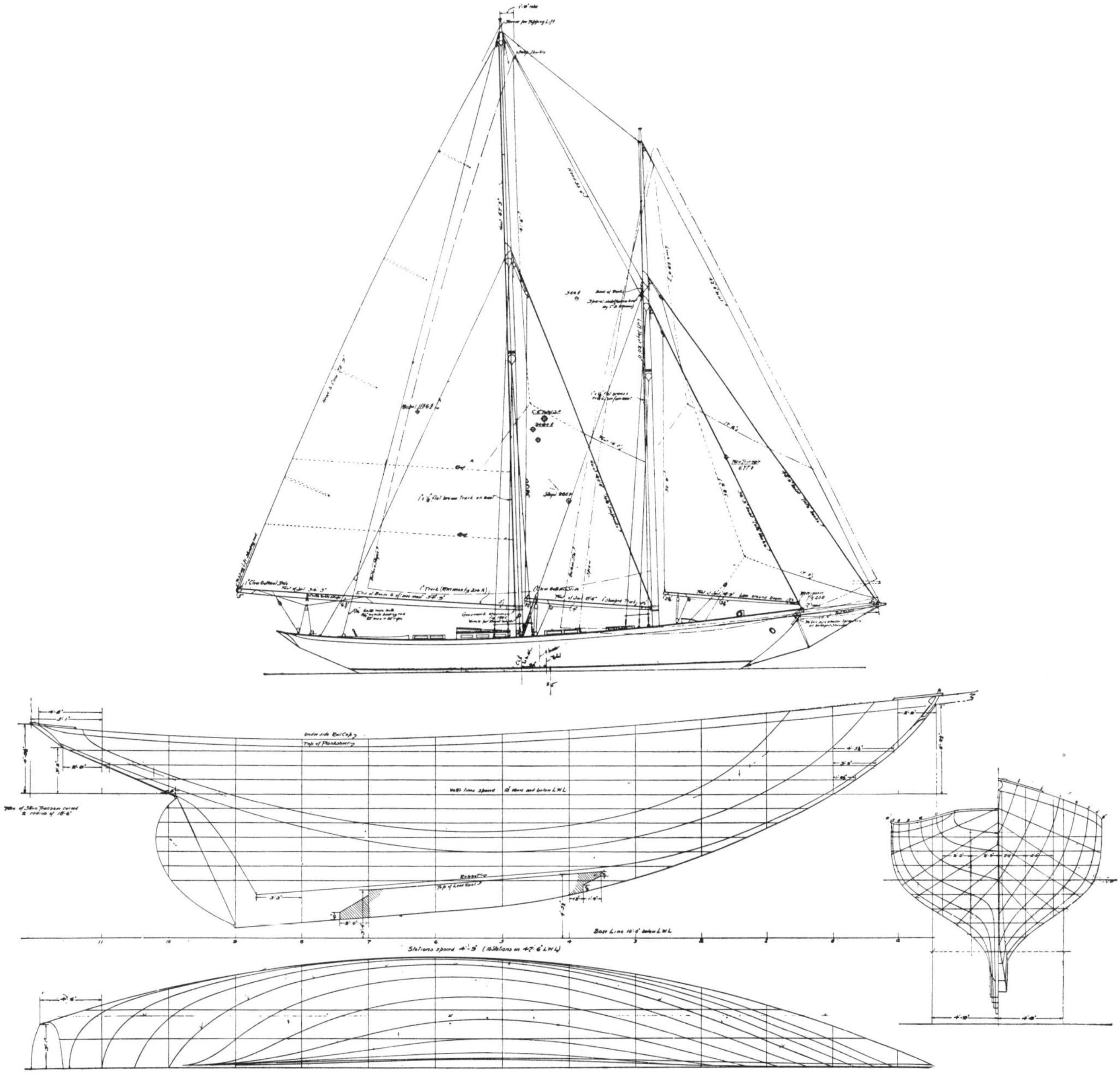

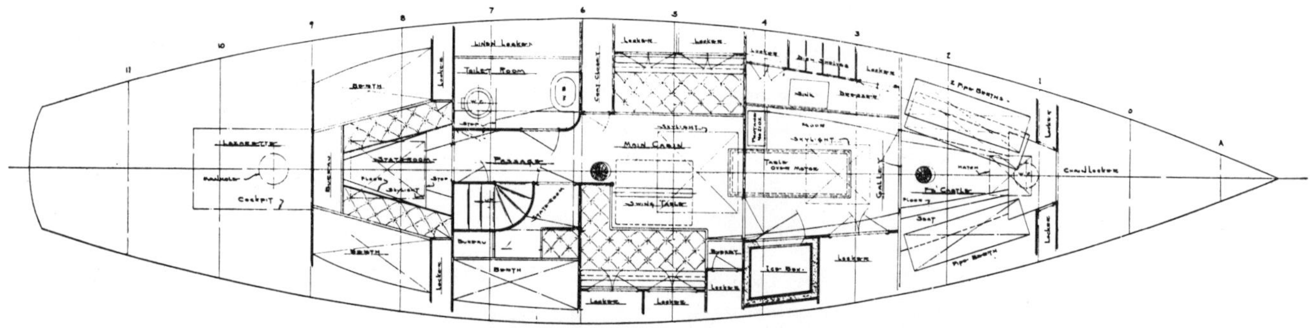

The accommodations plan of the Quicksilver II. (Yachting, *October 1931)*

waterline length of 47 feet 7 inches, a beam of 15 feet 4 inches, and a draft of 9 feet 9 inches. Her sail area is 2,484 square feet. She's double-planked, the outer layer being mahogany.

Let's harden her right up on the wind; get that mainsail in some more. Strap her down! She seems to want to go about for Mark Island. And let's clap on more sail and see what she'll "really" do.

Up with the jib topsail. Still only five sheets to play with, so let's give her what she really wants, that big, flat-cut main topmast staysail. Thunder it aloft. Two-block the throat and lay right into that tack line. Now stretch the peak all the way up. That quiets it a bit. Now trim her in and let's see what happens.

Puts her rail almost down. Now hear those bubbles hissing down the lee side and look at how she wants to go to windward. Oh my goodness, isn't this something? What do you suppose it's blowing, something under 20? Here, want to take her?

The complicated staysail schooner rig of the *Quicksilver II* is a fast and versatile cruising rig. You can think of her as a five-headsail cutter. There's a lot to it, of course. Many feet worth of masts. It's kind of tempting to think of leaving the foremast ashore and eliminating a couple of those headsails. After all, when we tack we're going to have to worry about three sets of sheets and two sets of backstays. You hadn't noticed we eased the lee runner on the foremast when we set the main topmast staysail? That's one we certainly can set up again before we tack.

The real problem with this rig is that you seldom see a staysail schooner with her upper staysail set. Most cruising people seem to say the hell with that four-sided monster, let's just let her go with the lower staysail. Lazy schooner people are better off with gaff foresails.

If we were going to take this boat to sea, we'd want to think about giving up the big mainsail for a big trysail, carry the main boom on deck until we get to the other side, and set up the topmast backstays right to the quarters permanently.

Cruising coastwise, we could snug her down with reefed mainsail and the two staysails in a hard breeze. If it gets worse, we can replace the reefed mainsail with a small trysail.

Her big mainsail is all very fine, but she does have a lot of her sail area in headsails that won't pull when running. She'd need a spinnaker or poled-out balloon jib. These sails would be good big ones for a schooner, thanks to her tall foremast. And think of the huge gollywobbler we can set.

No use standing in *too* close to Mark Island; there's a sunker off the north end just on the lee bow and it'll be just a couple of feet under at this tide. Let's get organized and put her about.

Set up the lee backstay on the foremast. One on the jibsheet, one on the jib topsail, and a couple of us on the main topmast staysail. I'll shift the main backstays. Any time. Here we go! She swings through the wind with majesty and power, to say nothing of considerable rattletybang and much flattening-in of various sails on the new tack.

Isn't she working down the bay in great shape? And against the tide, too. Is that an osprey screeching above Mark Island? That's a perfect crown-shaped Maine island. Just a thin line of dark brown at the water's edge, light, salty rocks above the tide line, and a dense forest o' them pointed firs. Oh, my!

How about giving us a little luff, so we can flatten in that upper staysail a bit and, yes, I ought to get a bit more on this weather backstay. Ah, she likes that. Why, she's going like a train of cars.

Below in this schooner there's plenty of room in every compartment. Look at the size of her head!

The engine, a six-cylinder Lathrop, is forward in the

galley. Her box makes a nice big kitchen table for laying out the makings of a meal and for leaning against in a seaway.

She has bunks for eight for coastwise cruising, and would make a fine long-range cruising vessel for five.

Why don't we ease her off and head back for the lighthouse on Curtis Island before we get so far to windward that it'll be a dead run? From here I think we can keep that big array of headsails full and have a nice reach.

Off she goes, straightening up and appearing to slow down, yet picking up speed as her six sheets are slacked away, to produce six perfect curves and six luffs not quite luffing.

Now stand by the weather fore rigging looking aft along her side and back at her quarter. She seems to just be flying away from the ocean's horizon out to the south'ard, especially when the ground swell heaves in under her.

It didn't take us long to get back to Curtis Island, did it? Down smartly with the main topmast staysail, plenty of hands to smother it. Let run jib topsail and jib halyards, hand over hand on those downhauls.

Now run her right off for that big white house up among the trees at the head of Sherman Cove. That ought to give us plenty of room to round up for the mooring. I wouldn't start her round yet; she has a lot of way, and she'll carry it. Now we might try it. I think she's just going to make it comfortably; look at how she's still moving the land past those boats abeam; she's still got a good deal of headway to work with.

Pendant all secure? Down with those staysails and let's flatten in the mainsail so she'll walk straight back.

Stow and furl up all those sails, set up on backstays, halyards, and — above all -- topping lifts, just so. Let's not be in a great rush to leave her. How about a toast to the vessel and her designer and builder? Kind of nice just to sit around for a bit and admire the sweep of her decks, the curve of her rail, and the majesty of those tall spars.

As we row ashore the wind has died, letting her lie across the ever-present Camden Harbor surge. What could be more graceful than the way those tall masts measure out the small arcs of her stately roll? Thanks for the sail, Mr. Mower and you builders at Hodgdon's. Glad *you* could make it, too. Really.

32/ The *Piccolo*

Length on deck: 52 feet 3 inches
Length on waterline: 35 feet
Beam: 10 feet 6 inches
Draft: 7 feet 1 inch
Sail area: 990 square feet
Displacement: 27,000 pounds
Designer: William Fife III

Lovely are the boats designed by the Fifes of Fairlie, Scotland. One of my favorites is the *Piccolo,* designed a half-century ago by William Fife III.

Her charms tend to hide the fact that she is a stiff, able boat, capable of being driven hard, thanks to considerable deep ballast. She has long, graceful ends; her counter, with its delicate, curved transom crowned-up nicely, gives her 10 feet of overhang aft. And she has, of course, the beautiful perfect sheerline of which Fife was master. Her bow and buttock lines are certainly easy. She has beautiful wineglass sections with lots of curve in the topsides. Her entry is fairly sharp. She'd certainly be a fast boat, sailing at a high percentage of her hull speed of about 8 knots a lot of the time.

The *Piccolo* is 52 feet 3 inches long on deck, with a waterline length of 35 feet, a beam of 10 feet 6 inches, and a draft of 7 feet 1 inch. She displaces 27,000 pounds. Her sail area is 990 square feet. Fife specified partial composite construction, with steel floors and knees connecting her frames and deck beams, and everything else wood.

Uffa Fox used the *Piccolo* as an example of the high state of the naval architect's and shipwright's art and craft when he wrote a book called *Sail and Power* in 1937. He said she was designed and built by "Fife of Fairlie." Fife of Fairlie! A wonderful phrase, conjuring up dozens upon dozens of the world's most beautiful boats, designed over a long period by three generations of artistic and practical designer-builders.

The first Will Fife, a wheelwright, went into the building of boats and small vessels around 1800 and established a yard at Fairlie, a small village near the mouth of the River Clyde. His son Will Fife Jr. began as an apprentice in the yard at age 13 in 1835, and ended up running it until 1881. That was the year Will Fife III took over. The third Will Fife designed and built yachts at Fairlie until World War II changed the nature of his production. After the war his nephew Robert Fife took over the operation of the yard. All of the Fifes were sailors, as well as designers and builders.

The Fifes could be considered the Herreshoffs of Scotland; and if their engineering practices were not quite as astute and innovative as the Herreshoffs', the artistry of their designs often surpassed that of the Herreshoff yachts.

In 1911, a young man named Archibald Macmillan came to work in the Fife yard. Mr. Macmillan thrived on the place and became superintendent under Will Fife III and Robert Fife. He eventually bought the yard from the family and, indeed, still goes to work there every day.

On a recent pilgrimage to Fairlie, I had the chance to

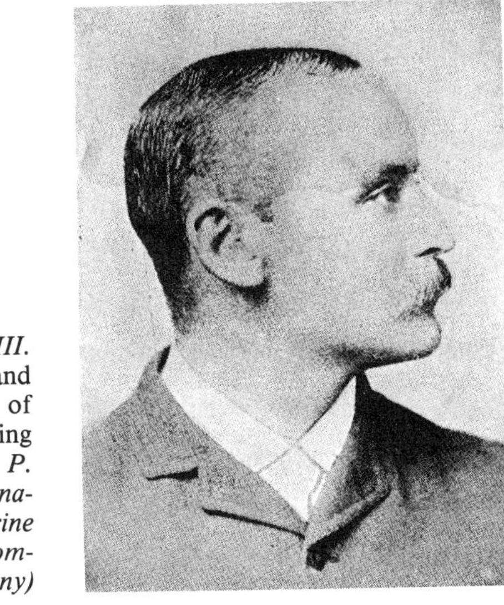

William Fife III. (Traditions and Memories of American Yachting *by William P. Stephens, International Marine Publishing Company)*

The sailplan of the Piccolo. (Sail and Power *by Uffa Fox)*

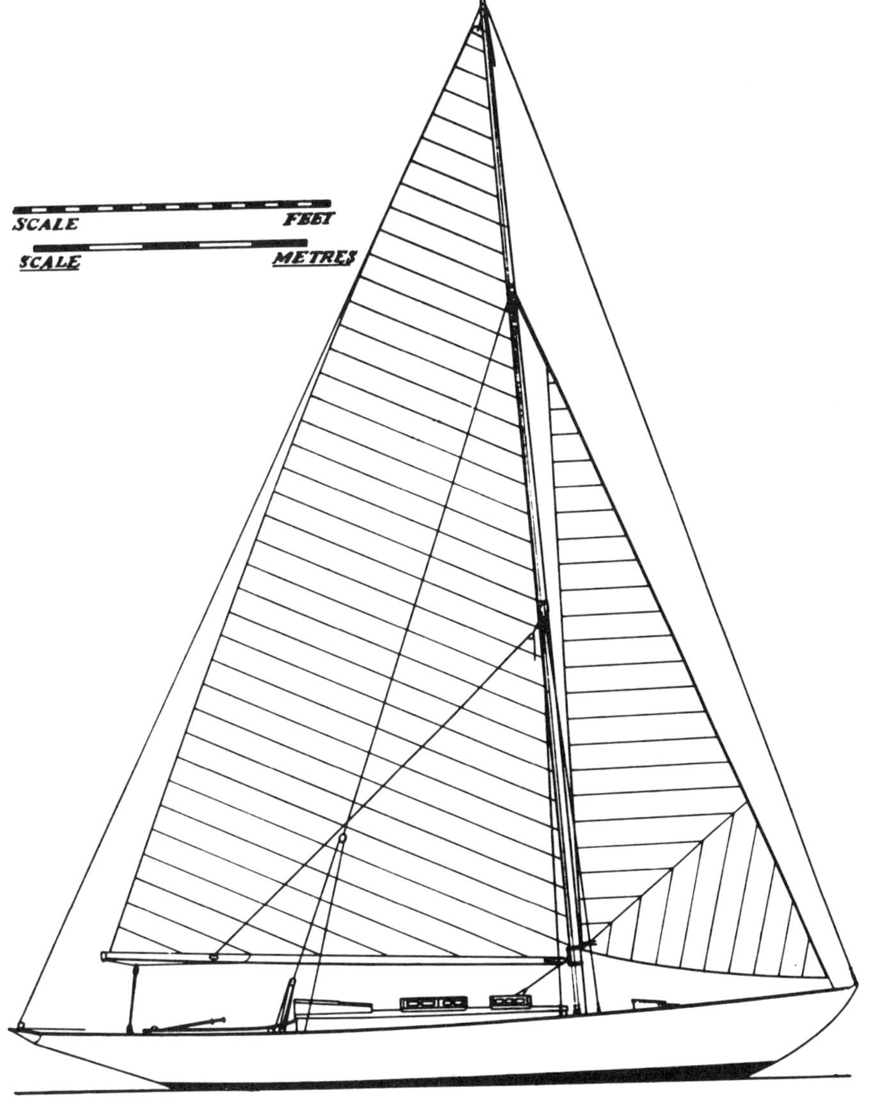

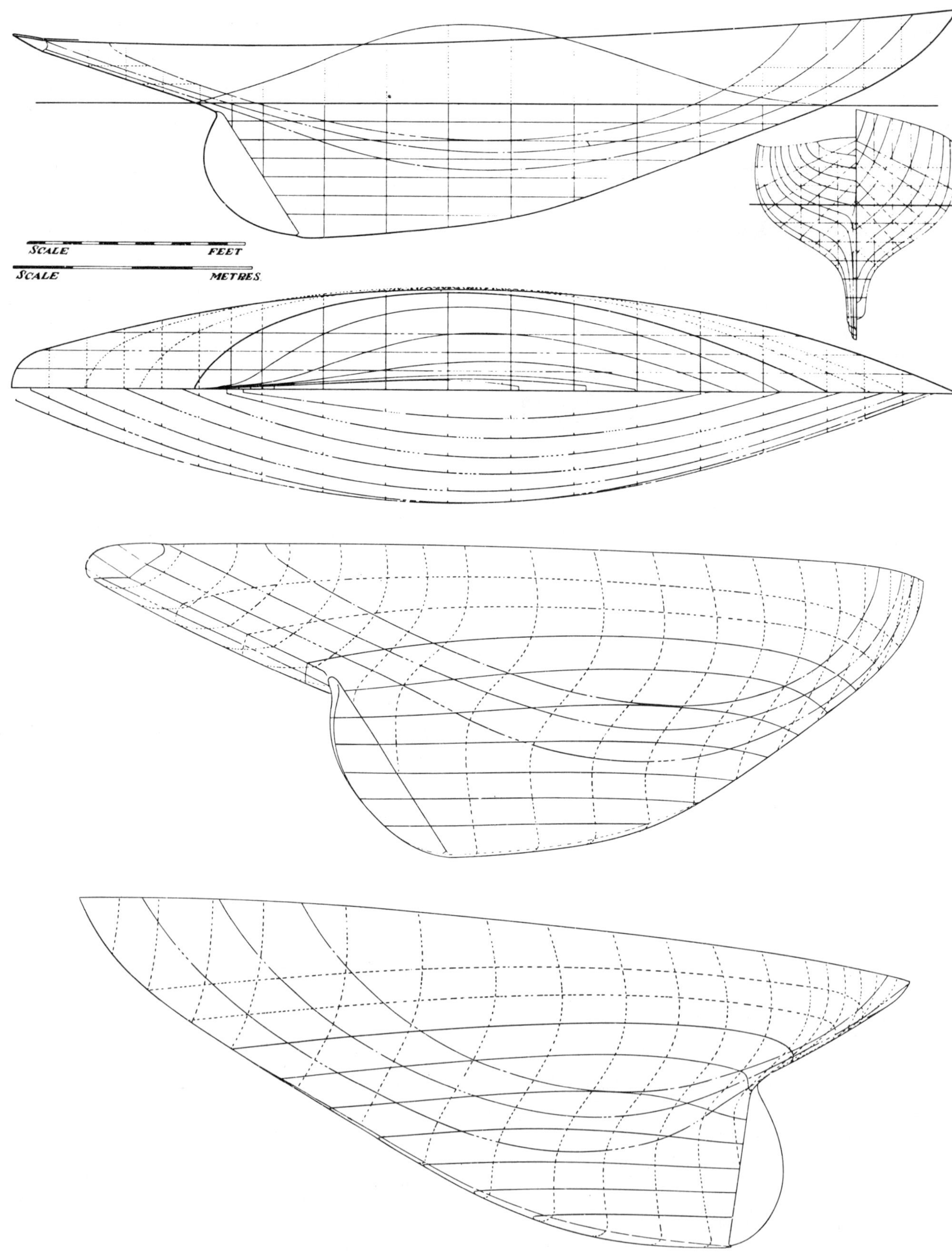

The Piccolo*'s lines.* (Sail and Power *by Uffa Fox)*

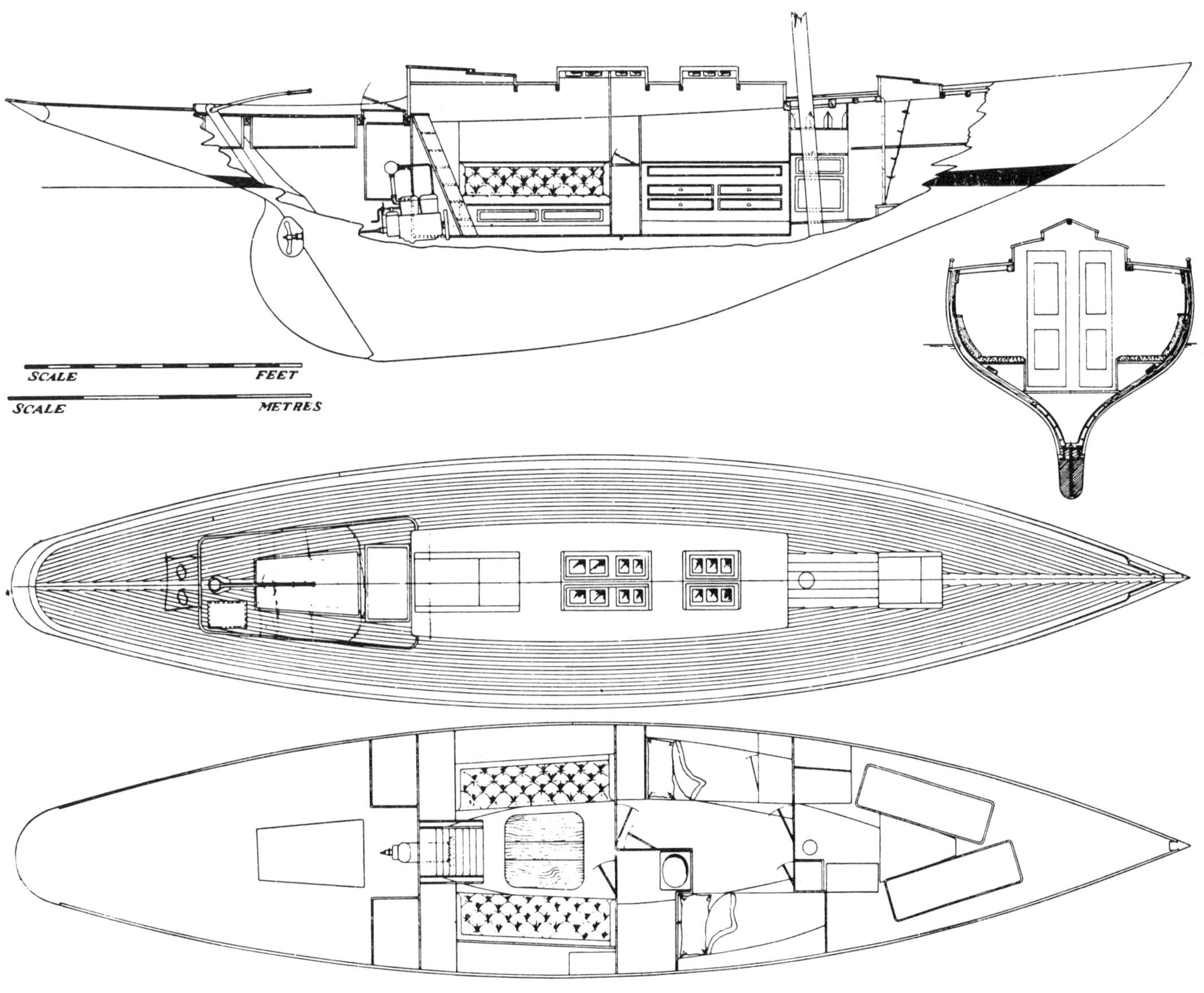

Her interior arrangement and deck plans. (Sail and Power *by Uffa Fox)*

meet Archibald Macmillan and reminisce with him a bit about the old days. He's a lively Scotsman, never livelier than when telling you how he won a race in a Fife boat.

We stood talking under his 35-foot double-ended Fife sloop, the *Navarra,* hauled up in one of his sheds. Through the shed's open end we looked out on Largs Channel between Fairlie and Great Cumbrae Island, tumbling with the white horses of a Force 8 gale — and then whipped frothy by a half-hour of Force 10. And rain. "You'd think it had never rained before," said Mr. Macmillan. It was a perfect day to stand in the big Fife shed watching the water off Fairlie and imagining how a Fife boat like the *Piccolo* would face the gale. She'd show no more than a tiny trysail and spitfire jib, and her drenched crew would have to do some hanging on, but she'd work to windward as long as the gear held up to the fury.

Archibald Macmillan spoke of Will Fife III as being a perfectionist and an artist. "Everything had to be right, and everything had to be eye-sweet."

As Uffa Fox knew, the *Piccolo* measures up.

Her raked mast looks good and carries a big mainsail (736 square feet) to give her drive. Note the running backstays with a four-part tackle set up on the hauling part of a two-part tackle, giving eightfold advantage. You'd want to unhook the lower tackle and leave it behind when running the stay forward off the wind. Note also that the boom will just clear the permanent backstay no matter how high it might lift in a wild jibe.

Of course you'd want to be able to reef the mainsail. Roller reefing would make sense on this boat — backed by two sets of reefing cringles and eyelets to take lacelines for the day it won't work — and you'd move sheet and topping lifts to the end of the boom.

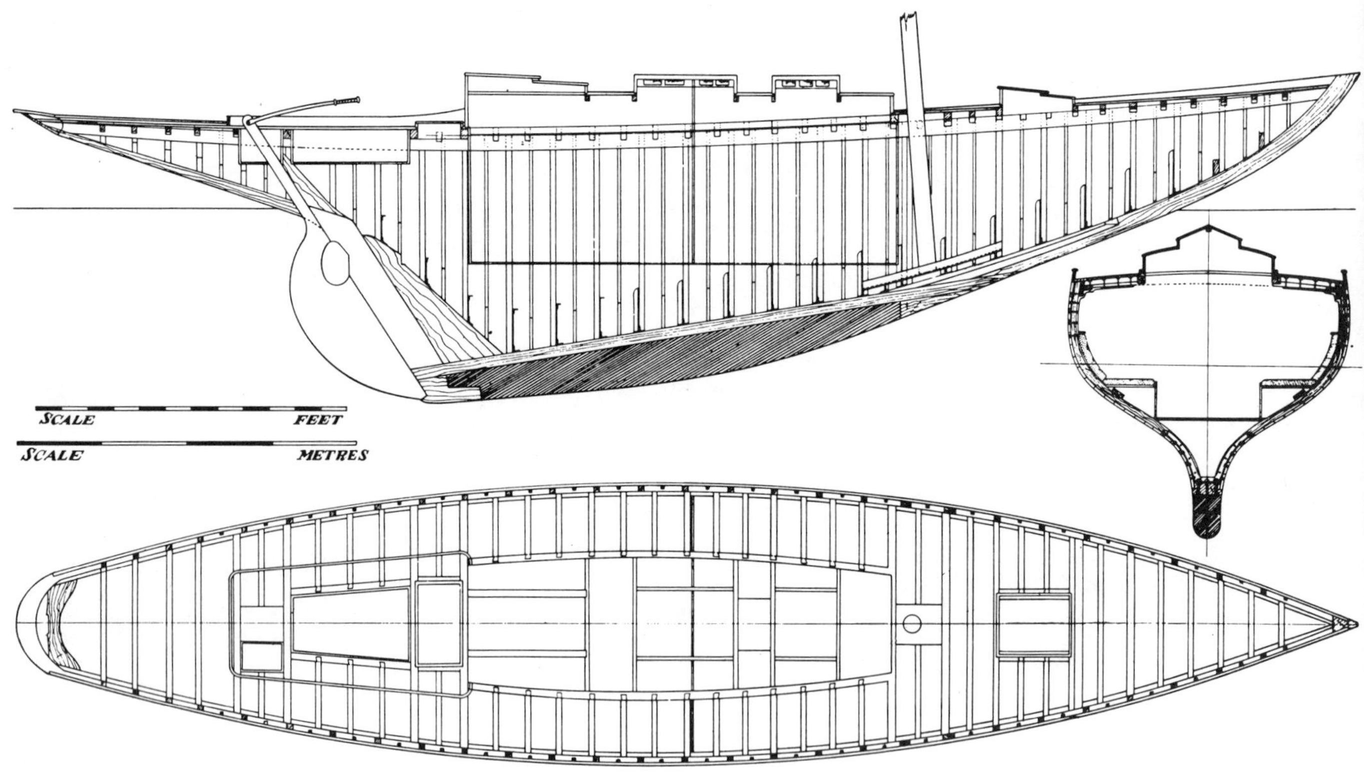

The Piccolo*'s construction drawings.* (Sail and Power *by Uffa Fox)*

For light weather you'd have a genoa jib, cut fairly high on the foot for visibility, to set on the forestay and a huge masthead ballooner to set on the headstay, to say nothing of a couple of sizes and weights of spinnakers.

Mr. Macmillan calls the yard the Fairlie Yacht Slip Ltd., but local residents still call it simply "The Shipyard." Vessels were built there in the open until 1880. Now the place consists of a conglomeration of buildings: three big building sheds of black corrugated iron, and a handful of small brick shops and storerooms jammed onto a waterfront strip of land of maybe an acre and a half. It's hard to believe that this unimposing spot is where so many beautiful and famous yachts took shape. Only the biggest Fife designs were built in other yards. In one of the building sheds there's a small graving dock. In the corner of another stands a boiler for melting down lead for outside ballast. Outside the door of the third a sheerpole is rigged with a tackle for hoisting out spars. There's still a cradle and a set of ways, but somebody's going to have to shovel sand off the rails before the next boat is hauled or launched.

The yard is a bit down-at-the-heels, but is still intact, and contains numerous relics. I saw molds, considerable board-feet of teak, a binnacle, a propeller, plenty of tools, and a "store" filled with all sorts of fascinating boat junk.

It appears that a half-dozen men are still on the payroll. In the yard's heyday, 100 men went at it all day; during World War II, 250 worked building minesweepers.

Back in one of the brick buildings is the office. Stepping into it in 1982, I was meeting Archibald Macmillan, but it could just as well have been an appointment with Will Fife III in 1882. The darkly paneled, smallish room was illuminated only by what light in the rainy sky a single window allowed to enter. Yet the dimness could not hide great treasures. The Fifes' drawing table with drawers of plans. Half models. Photographs of Fife boats sailing and in dry-dock. It's the kind of place you'd like to be accidentally locked up in for a week or two. It's the place where the *Piccolo* was designed.

Doesn't she have a lot of deck space? There's room for a 12-foot dinghy atop the house. To be sure, her cockpit is a bit cramped.

Below is a decent engine room. She also has a very nice saloon, a comfortable stateroom, and a sizable WC with entry from either. It's the galley that suffers in this arrangement, for it is tucked away forward where there is scant headroom and plenty of motion in a head sea.

The famous Fife boats are legion. There was the 56-foot clipper-bowed cutter *Minerva,* commissioned by Boston lawyer Charles H. Tweed. She was sailed from

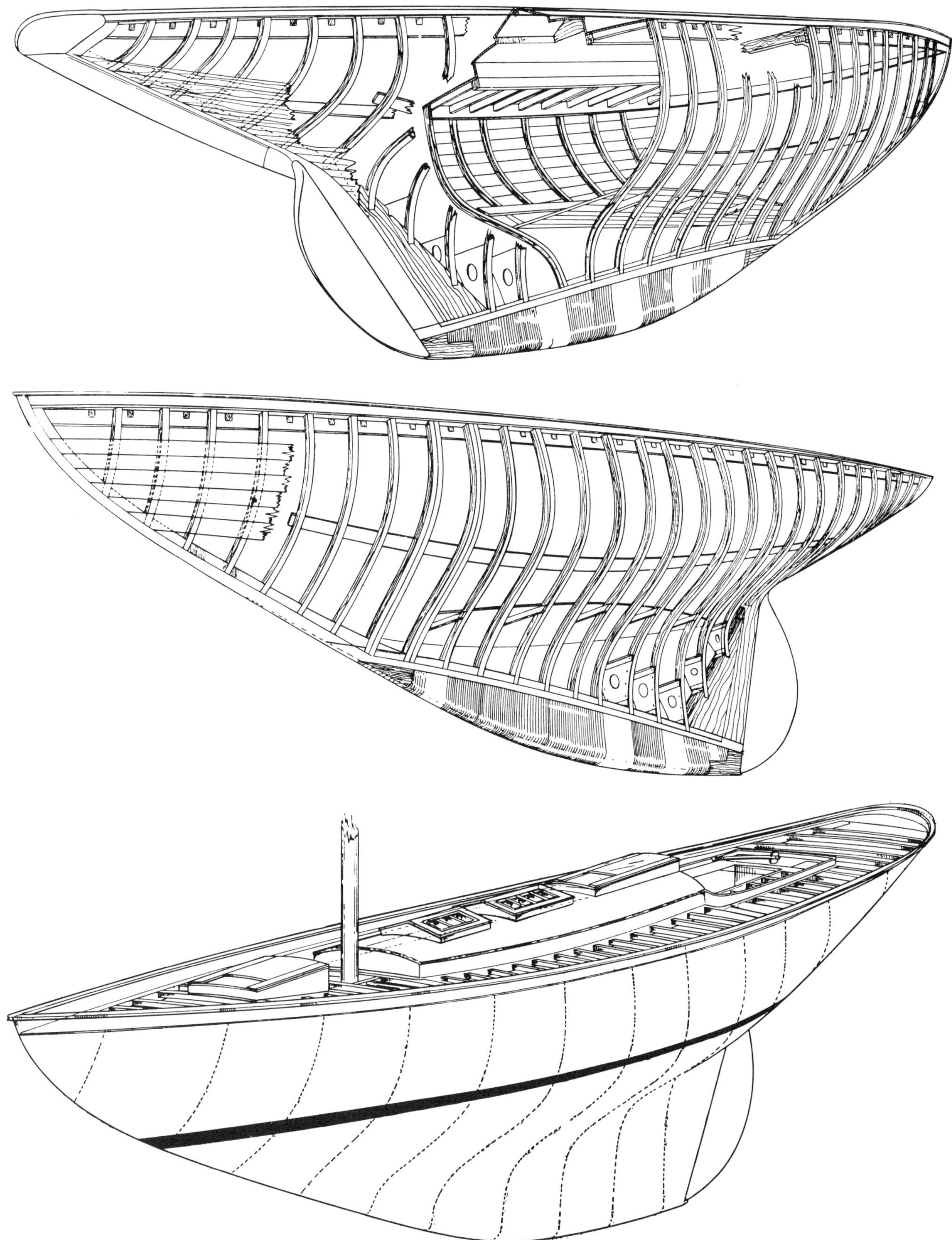

Uffa Fox's wonderful drawings showing the Piccolo*'s construction details in perspective.* (Sail and Power *by Uffa Fox)*

Fairlie to Marblehead in 28 days by Charlie Barr and a crew of three. She became the boat to beat in the 40-foot (waterline) class in 1889 and 1890. There was the 126-foot yawl *Ailsa,* a competitor in the 1905 Transatlantic Race. There was the racing schooner *Cicely,* a 133-footer; and another, the "little" *Susanne,* a mere 110-footer. There were the America's Cup contenders *Shamrock I* and *Shamrock III.* There were long series of successful six meters and twelve meters starting in the early 1920s. There was the big marconi cutter *Hallowe'en* in 1926, still going strong in American waters as the yawl *Cotton Blossom IV.* And there was Claud Worth's canoe-sterned ketch *Maud,* described in *Good Boats.*

If the *Piccolo* is Uffa Fox's choice to illustrate the near-perfection of a boat by Fife of Fairlie, it was the *Latifa* that was chosen by Fairlie itself. On the hill just behind "The Shipyard" stands a stone church, and atop the church's tower is a weather vane. It's the *Latifa* with just her mizzen set, to keep her head-to-wind at her mooring.

33/ The *Latifa* and the *Evenlode*

LATIFA
Length on deck: 70 feet
Length on waterline: 52 feet
Beam: 15 feet 3 inches
Draft: 10 feet 2 inches
Sail area: 2,200 square feet
Displacement: 41 tons
Designer: William Fife III

EVENLODE
Length on deck: 50 feet 6 inches
Length on waterline: 35 feet
Beam: 11 feet
Draft: 7 feet 6 inches
Sail area: 1,053 square feet
Displacement: 13.6 tons
Designer: William Fife III

The most exciting music I have ever heard is the bagpipes of the *Latifa.* The great yawl — she's the greatest yawl in the world as far as I am concerned — had sailed over from Britain for a Bermuda Race soon after World War II. Pop and I, in a much smaller yawl, were lucky enough to be anchored in Newport to watch the fleet assemble.

The *Latifa,* with her fabulous sheerline accentuated by a gently sheered boottop, was in a class by herself in terms of grace and beauty. And early every morning a bagpiper would walk her foredeck and send his mysterious disharmonies across the water to us. The weird sound seemed to tell history.

The *Latifa* is another creation of William Fife III. She has, in all respects, as beautiful a set of lines as there is. Her overhanging curves in bow and canoe stern give her grace, and her stern is broad enough to give her some bearing aft. Her wineglass sections are lovely. She's deep enough to hang on going to windward and to heave-to well.

The *Latifa* is 70 feet long on deck, with a waterline length of 52 feet, a beam of 15 feet 3 inches, and a draft of 10 feet 2 inches. She displaces 41 tons and sets 2,200 square feet of sail.

Her mainsail is well shaped, its reasonably tall aspect ratio giving good drive both on the wind and off. Her mainmast stands 88 feet above her deck. She'd maneuver well in harbor under mainsail alone.

In heavy weather the big yawl could jill along under staysail and mizzen, but she'd need a reefed mainsail or a trysail to go to windward in a gale.

She can set a huge range of headsails. The baby jib topsail shown hardly seems worthwhile, but bigger ones would be. A really big Yankee jib topsail would be a wonderful sail on her. She'd have a balloon forestaysail and could have a huge balloon jib.

You'd need a crew of some size in a big boat like this. Hoisting, reefing, and furling the mainsail would be some work, as would handling big headsails, to say nothing of dealing with her ground tackle.

She'd be handy and maneuverable for such a big boat, and with all her sail area would, of course, need no engine.

The *Latifa* is big enough to have a flush deck and deckhouse. The arrangement gives lots of deck space. Naturally, you'd want a good dinghy or two on board. Her skylights are objects to be admired, as is her deckhouse, whose chart table would be a joy.

Below, her fo'c's'le, designed for a paid crew, could today be a fine dormitory for youngsters. The galley is

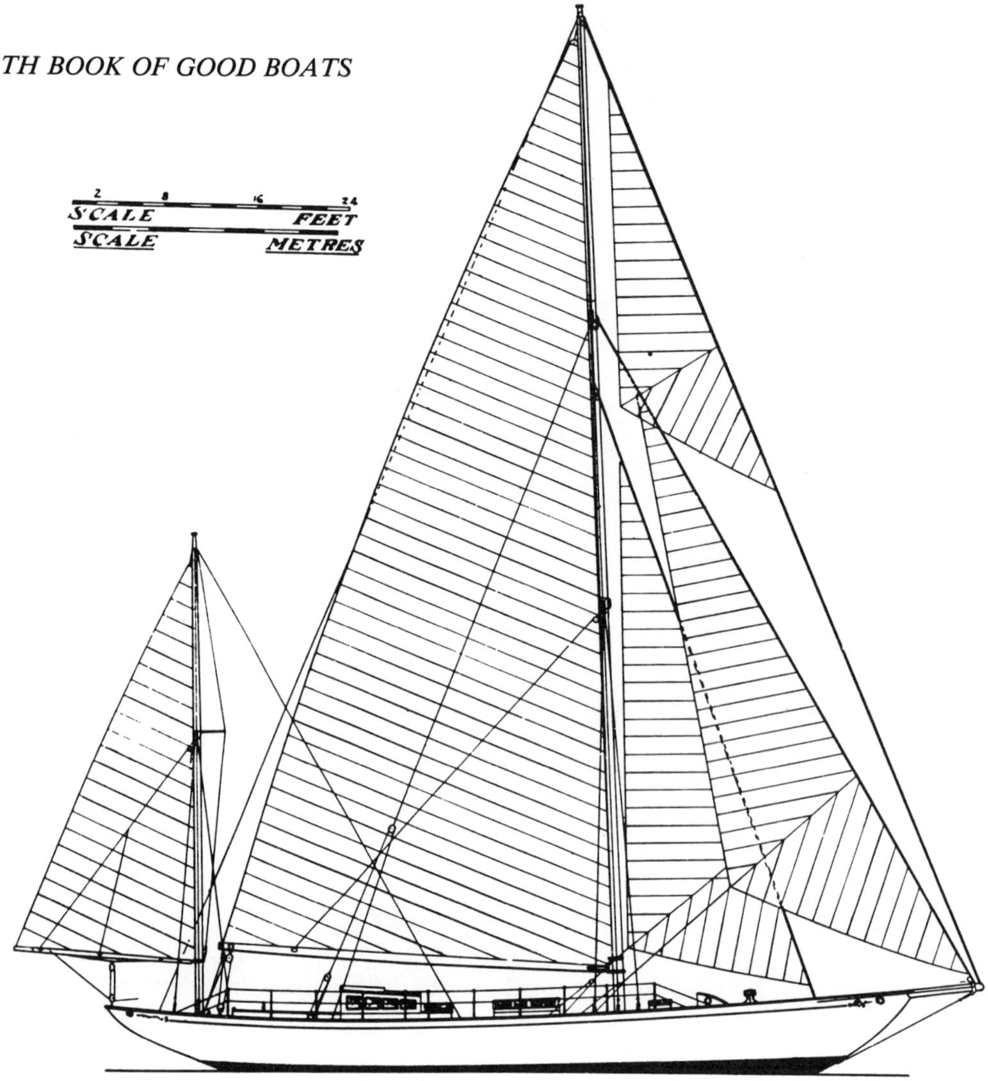

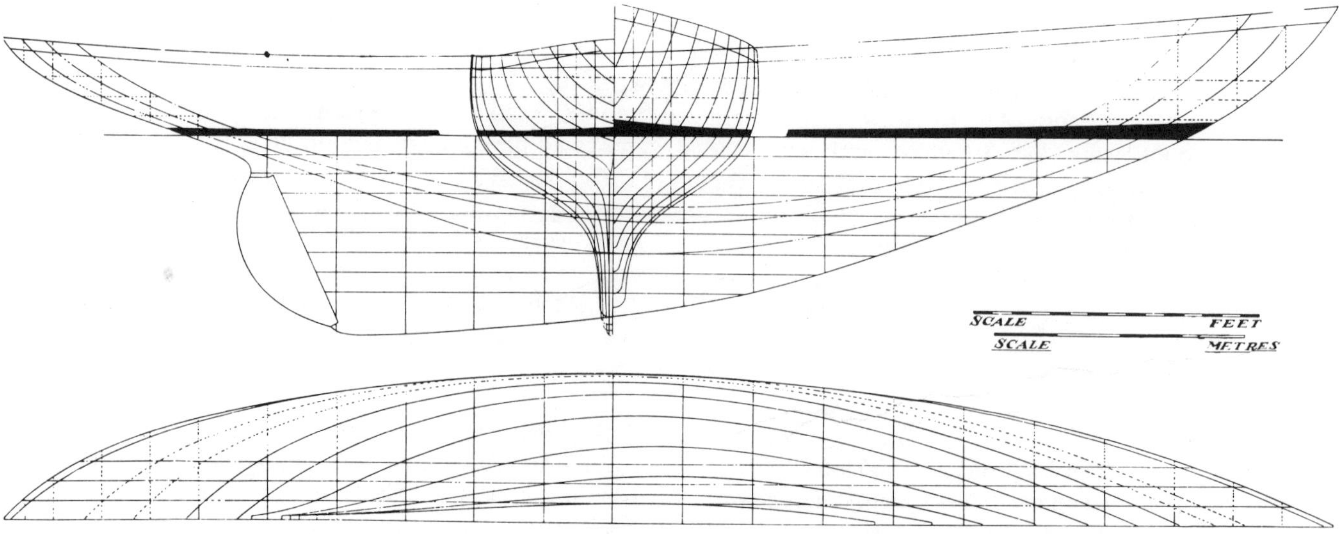

The Latifa*'s sailplan and lines.* (Racing, Cruising and Design *by Uffa Fox)*

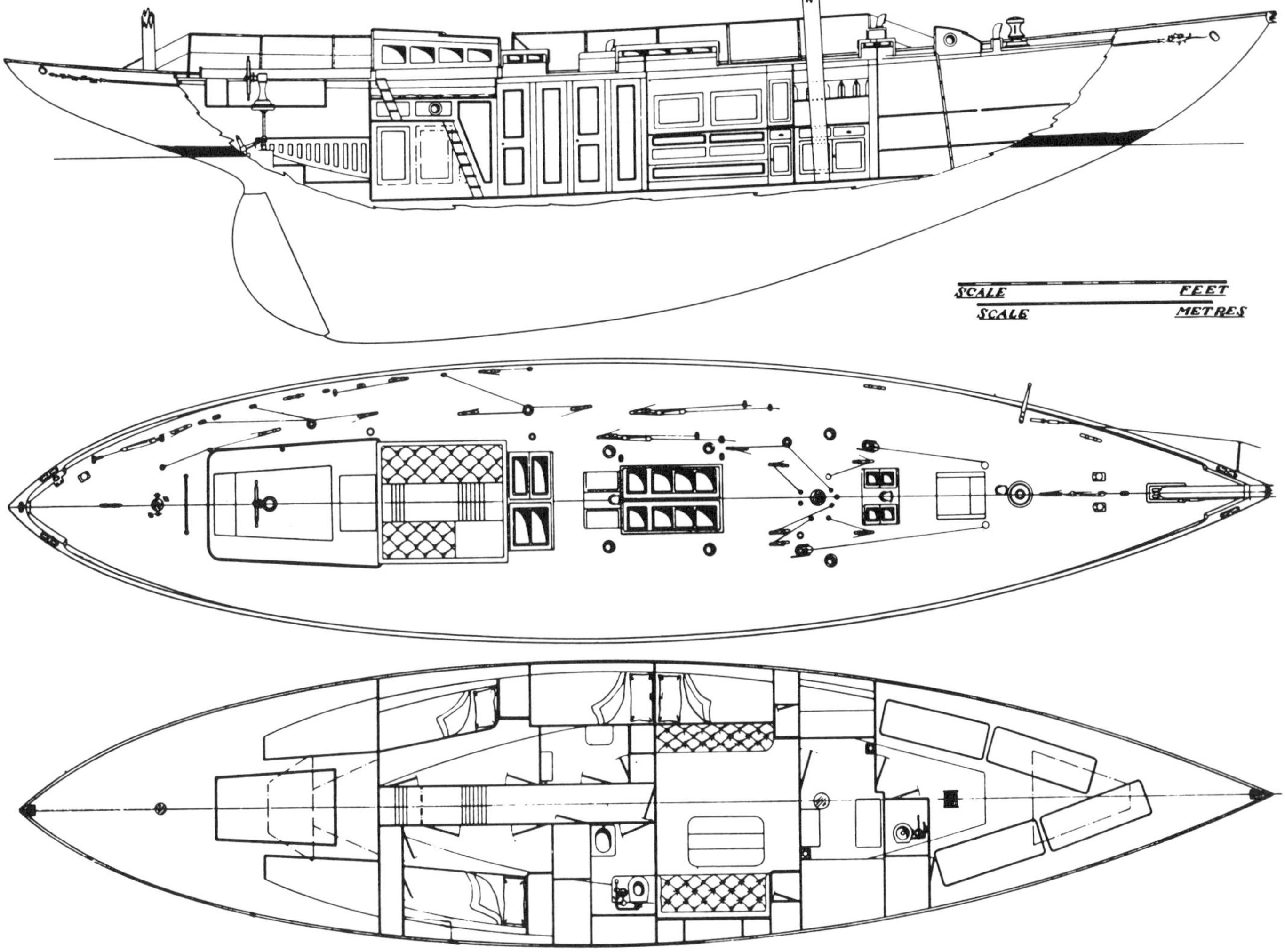

SCALE FEET

SCALE METRES

The Latifa*'s interior arrangement and deck plans.* (Racing, Cruising and Design *by Uffa Fox)*

The Latifa *running with just enough breeze to fill her spinnaker.* (Yachting)

The Latifa *sailing fast full and by.* (Yachting)

forward by the mast. There's a big comfortable saloon in the middle of the vessel, with three single staterooms aft.

The *Latifa* would have a good turn of speed on any point of sailing. In one particular race she sailed 11¼ miles in one hour. Standing up to her wheel and guiding her through a big seaway would be some kind of fun. Watching her pointed stern leave the seas astern would be endlessly wondrous.

If William Fife's 70-foot *Latifa* is on too grand a scale for serious boat dreaming, try your imagination on his *Evenlode,* a 50-foot version of the same type. She is as lovely a vessel as the *Latifa,* though subtly different.

The *Evenlode* is slightly more cut away forward and has a somewhat finer stern than does her big sister. She has fuller waterlines and less deadrise forward but finer waterlines and more deadrise aft than does the big yawl. She's a little deeper in proportion and so can give up some stability in her stern; Mr. Fife made it the most graceful canoe stern there is.

The *Evenlode* is 50 feet 6 inches long on deck, with a waterline length of 35 feet, a beam of 11 feet, and a draft of 7 feet 6 inches. She displaces 13.6 tons and has a sail area of 1,053 square feet.

She has a simple jib-and-mainsail rig. She could and should set a variety of larger and smaller jibs and would

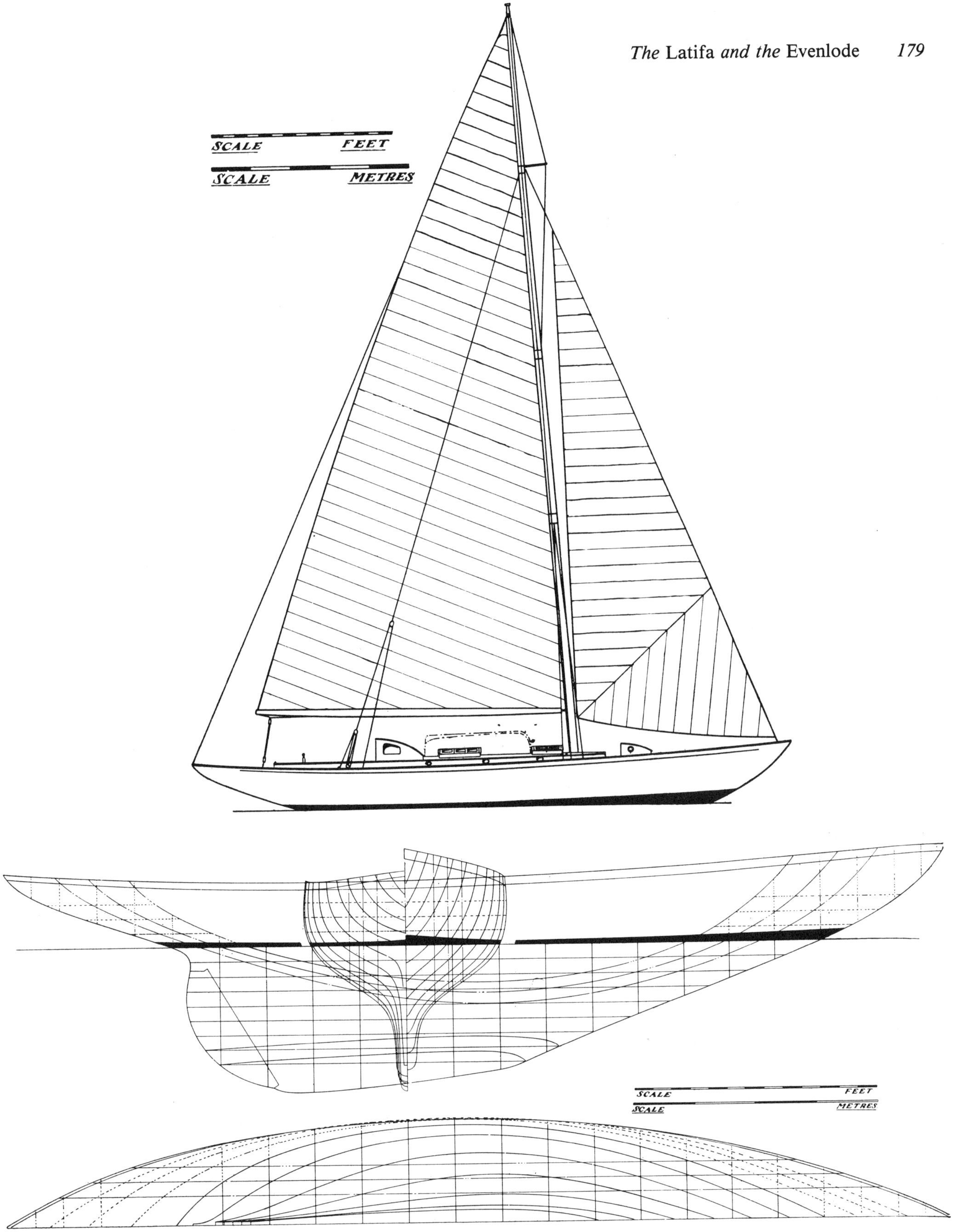

The sailplan and lines of the Evenlode. (Racing, Cruising and Design *by Uffa Fox)*

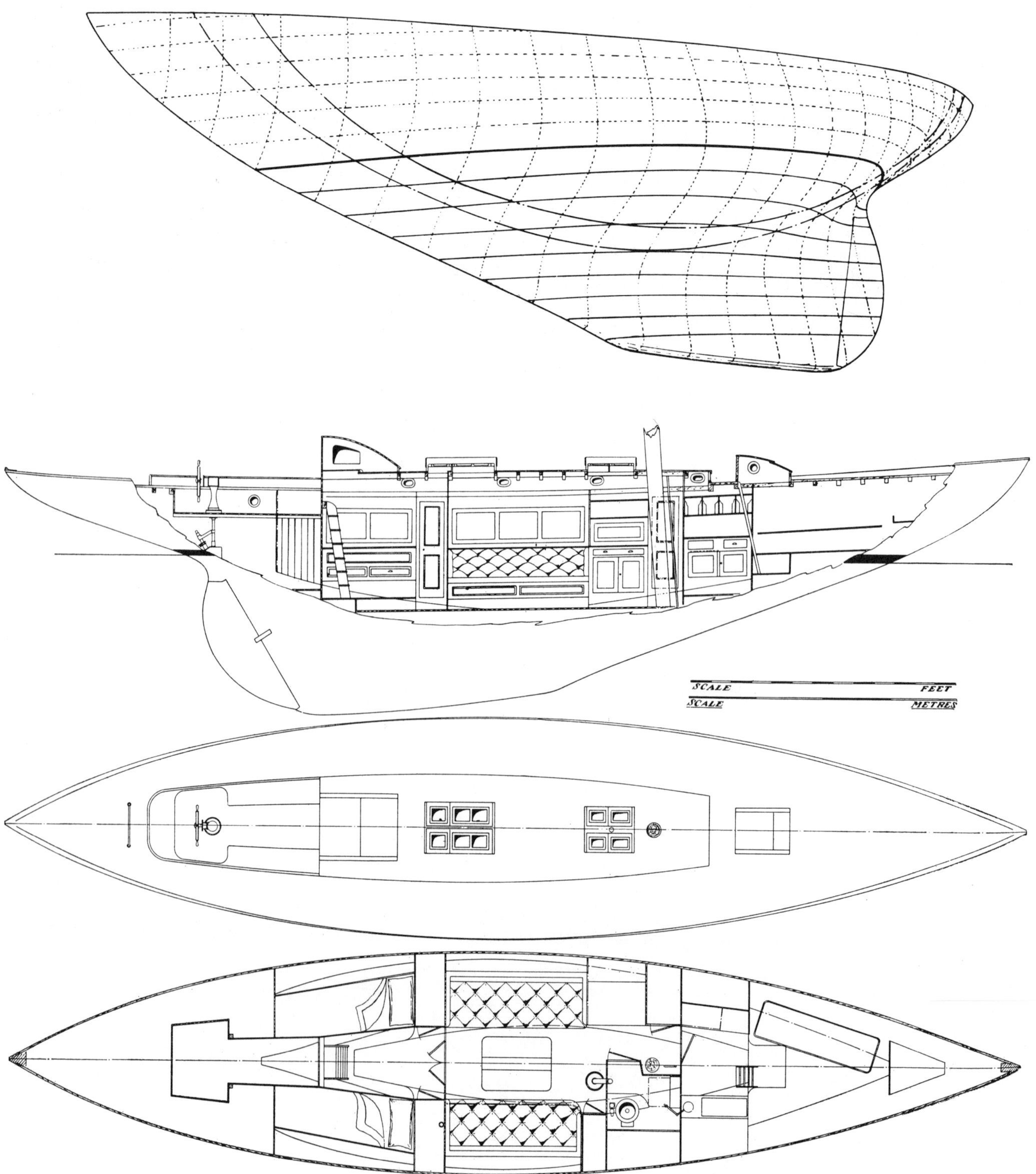

The Evenlode*'s lines in perspective and her interior arrangement and deck plans.* (Racing, Cruising and Design *by Uffa Fox)*

reef her mainsail and set a trysail at times. Her raked mast looks good and her mainsail, like the *Latifa*'s, is shaped to drive her well whether working to windward or running off.

Her companionway doghouse and booby hatch to the fo'c's'le with their nice curves add to, rather than detract from, her appearance. That high hatchway over the companion and the absence of a bridge deck give easy and protected access below. A watchmate can stand in the hatchway out of the cold and wet and still see out. Her narrow house leaves plenty of deck space for working the vessel.

Her galley is forward of the mast, and many folks would be tempted to move it aft and shift the quarter berths forward. If the cook complains of a head sea you can heave-to or run off briefly until the soup is served, but the only way to satisfy would-be sleepers complaining of a head sea would be to stop the vessel for a whole watch.

In either the 70-foot or 50-foot size, these Fife double-enders are not likely to be surpassed for sheer beauty. They represent a high point in the artistry of yacht design.

34/ The *Widgeon*

Length on deck: 38 feet
Length on waterline: 25 feet
Beam: 8 feet 7 inches
Draft: 6 feet 3 inches
Sail area: 850 square feet
Designer: William Fife Jr.

Occasionally a man and a boat come together with a stretch of coast to produce what seems to be perfect cruising. And if the man should happen to write a book about the boat and the coast and how he used the one to explore the other, then — in your mind's eye, of course — you can experience some perfect cruising.

Such a combination, a half-century ago, was Captain J.R. Harvey, a retired Royal Navy hydrographic surveyor; a lovely 38-foot Fife cutter, the *Widgeon;* and the west coast of Scotland. The book that lets us join the *Widgeon* for four summers of perfect cruising is called *Sailing Orders.* It was published in London in 1935 by Alexander Maclehose & Company.

Captain Harvey bought the *Widgeon* for £200 and sailed her north to Scotland from Bangor in northern Wales. He cruised in her between Arran and Skye; these were his home waters, for he had grown up spending summers on Islay. Being a professional chartmaker as well as a highly competent small-boat sailor, he took a great interest in the navigational details surrounding safe entry of many a tricky Scottish cove. The geography of that coastline is complicated, but after tracing the *Widgeon*'s meanderings forward and backward through sound and firth on Captain Harvey's nice fold-out track charts, you gradually become familiar with places like Crinan, Oban, Tobermory, and even Captain Harvey's boyhood stomping ground, Bruichladdich.

The *Widgeon* was built to the lines of a late 19th-century racing class, the Dublin Bay Sailing Club 25-foot (waterline) A class. Designed by William Fife Jr. late in his career, she had been built in 1897 by Hilditch at Carrickfergus, Northern Ireland, just down Belfast Lough from the city. She was over 30 years old when acquired by Captain Harvey.

The *Widgeon* has the lovely, sweeping sheer and long, graceful counter that William Fife Jr. gave many of his later designs. She has the gentle sections of a fine-lined, deep-draft, heavily ballasted boat. She gets her power from her deep and heavy ballast and so can have a slim and lovely hull form. Nor is her beauty marred by superstructure. Either watching her go by or watching her go from on board would be pure pleasure.

The *Widgeon* is 38 feet long on deck, with a waterline length of 25 feet, a beam of 8 feet 7 inches, and a draft of 6 feet 3 inches. The Dublin Bay 25-footers have 3¼ tons of outside lead ballast, and the only major difference between them and the *Widgeon* is that the latter has an iron keel of 3 tons.

Her construction is stout. The only element that might be criticized is the installation of mere metal straps where we would expect to find floor timbers. At

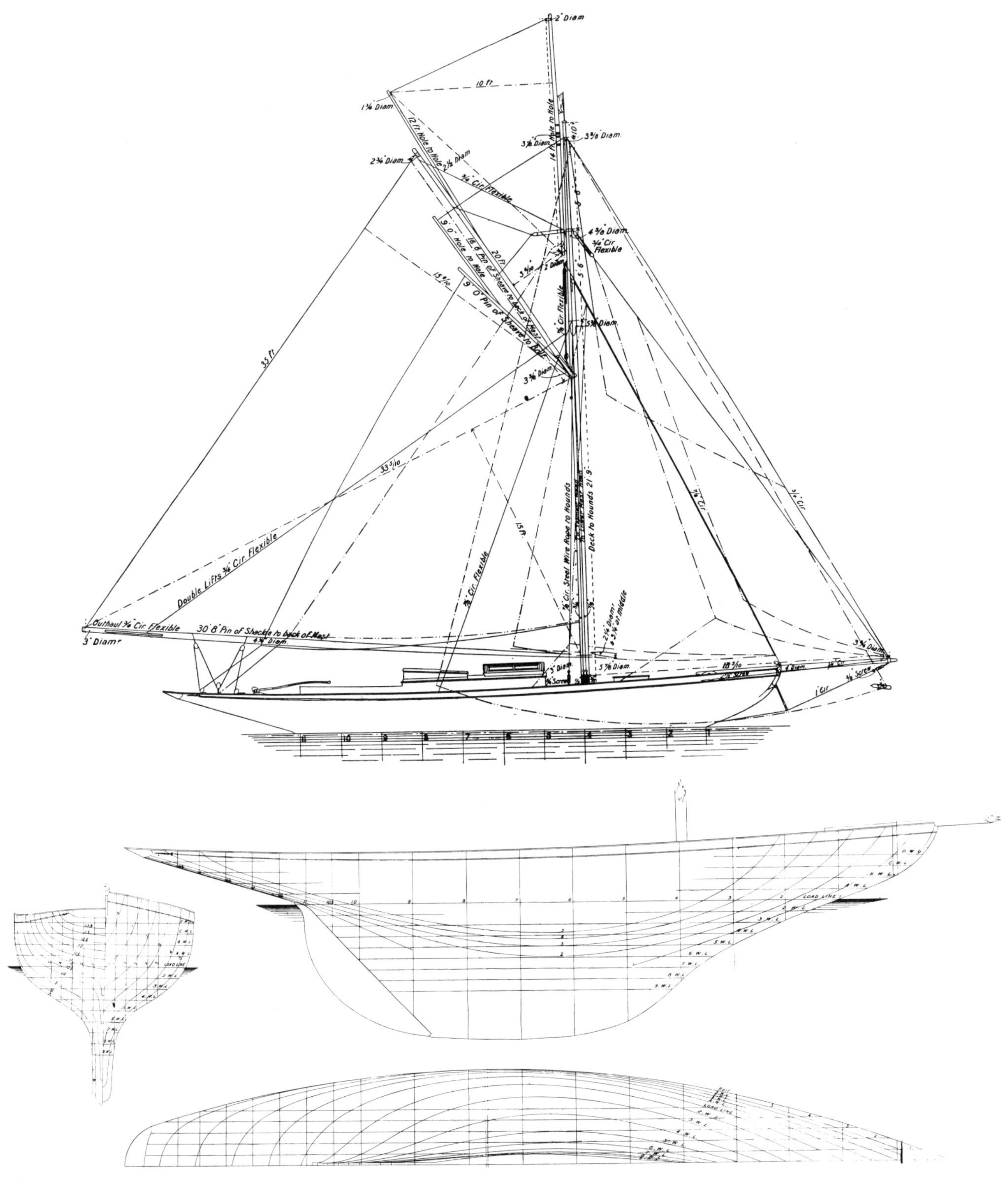

The sailplan and lines of the Dublin Bay 25-footer. (Dixon Kemp's Manual of Yacht and Boat Sailing and Yacht Architecture)

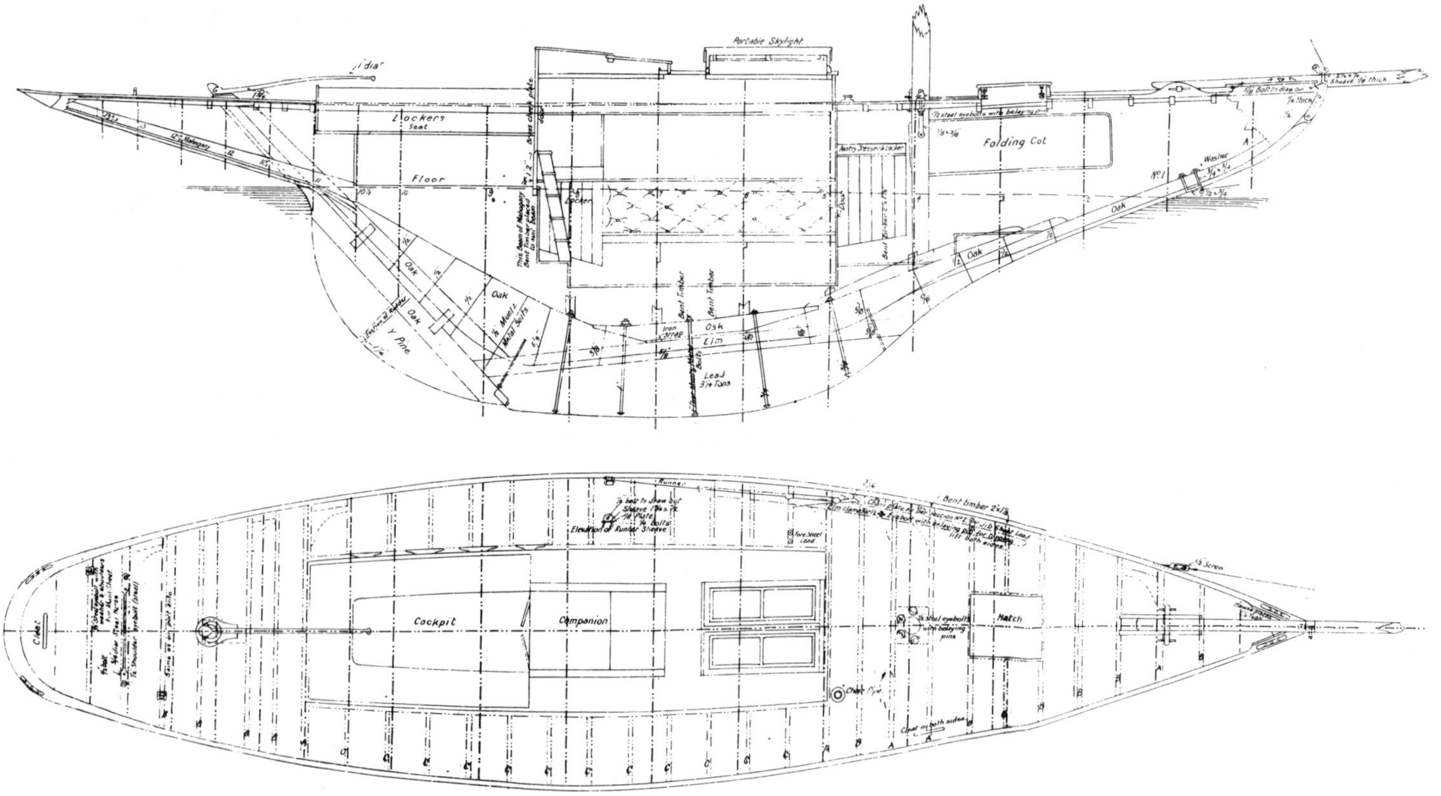

The construction plans of the Dublin Bay 25-footer. (Dixon Kemp's Manual of Yacht and Boat Sailing and Yacht Architecture)

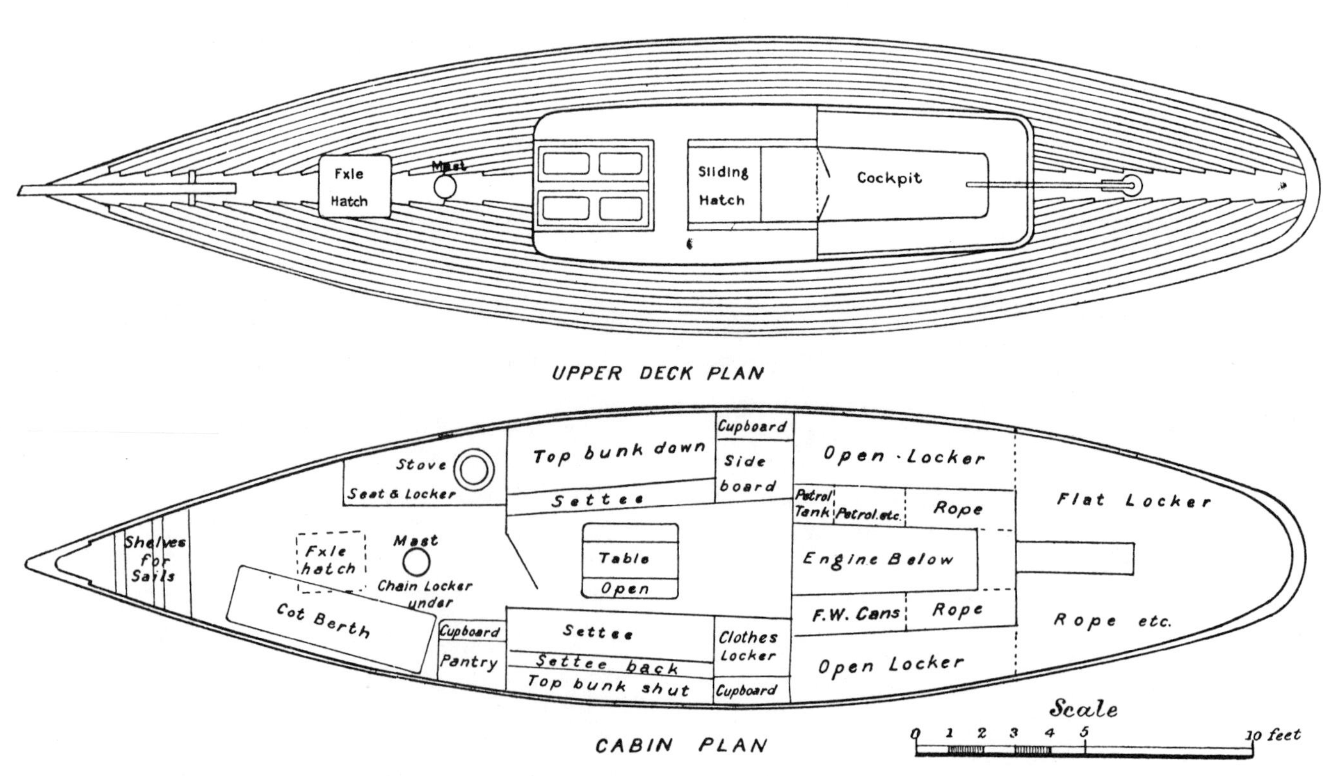

The deck and cabin plans of the Widgeon. (Sailing Orders *by Captain J.R. Harvey)*

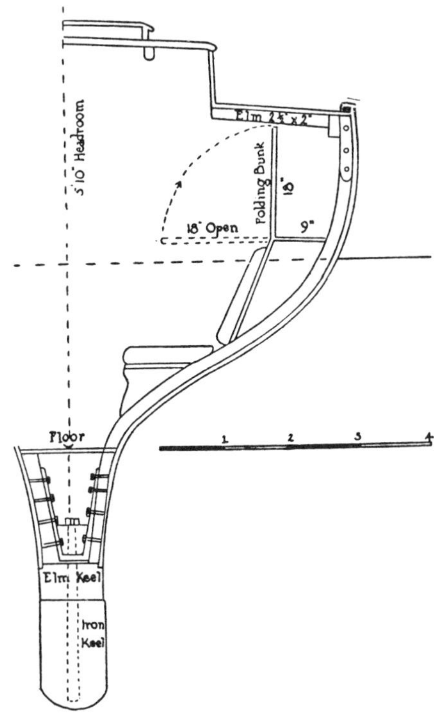

The Widgeon*'s section, showing the folding bunk arrangement.* (Sailing Orders *by Captain J.R. Harvey)*

the heels of each pair of frames, she has a strip of ⅜-inch by 3½-inch galvanized iron running down the inside of one frame, under the keelson, and up the other frame. These are bolted through frame and planking, and they form the meat of a sandwich between wood keelson and wood keel, this being all clamped tight by the ballast keel bolts themselves. All fine, had the straps been made rigid athwartships with a metal web work.

The *Widgeon*'s frames are of oak, sided 1¾ inches and molded 2⅝ inches at the keel and 1½ inches at the deck. The frames throughout the middle part of the vessel are doubled below the waterline and are spaced 30 inches apart. The frames in the ends of the vessel are spaced 15 inches apart. The shelf is pitch pine, 4½ inches by 1⅜ inches; the clamp is elm, 3½ inches by 1½ inches. She has two longitudinal bilge stringers on each side, of pitch pine, 2¼ inches by 1½ inches. The planking is 1-inch stuff, pitch pine below the waterline and yellow pine above. The sheer strake and covering board are of teak. Her deck beams are elm, 2½ inches by 2 inches. The deck is 1-inch yellow pine, but it was leaking so badly all over when Captain Harvey got the boat that he had a new deck laid of 1¼-inch teak.

The original cutter rig of the Dublin Bay 25-footers (shown in the sailplan) had 850 square feet of sail. In the *Widgeon,* this rig was cut down to 700 square feet in 1926, bringing the end of the boom even with the counter. In either case the rig is quite low for its area, and Captain Harvey found that the *Widgeon* would stand up to her sail very well in a breeze. With her mast well aft, she has a rather shortish bowsprit, yet the martingale gives her bow the look of a big yacht.

The big sailplan shown has plenty of light stuff to get home with when the wind is dying, for the Dublin Bay 25-footers had no engines. She has a huge balloon jib (to say nothing of a balloon forestaysail) and a big jackyard topsail. This last sail, with its 14-foot jackyard and 12-foot club, might get shouted at when being set or taken in but would certainly be much admired when up there shoving her along. She also has a gaff trysail for a gale.

Captain Harvey also had plenty of sails to go with his smaller rig in the *Widgeon.* He had a trysail, both a jackyard and a jib-headed topsail, a big balloon jib that could be poled out as a spinnaker, a baby jib topsail and a small working jib in addition to his three lower working sails. He kept the working jib set flying; he fitted his forestaysail with a club.

The *Widgeon*'s mainsail had roller-reefing gear, and Captain Harvey wisely had cringles in the sail for a third reef in case the gear should fail. He reported that the roller-reefing gear worked fine as long as you were very stingy about easing the peak halyard when you reefed.

The *Widgeon* either carried a 9-foot dinghy on top of her house, or else she towed it. Decisions, decisions.

Her cockpit is 6 feet long, with its floor just a tiny bit above the waterline. Captain Harvey had horizontal weather boards of 1-inch teak fitted at the top of the coaming to cover the forward 3½ feet of the cockpit, and had a canvas cover for the rest of the opening. In rough going, these weather boards could be put in place and you could protect yourself with the canvas cover when steering. Not a bad idea for keeping the water out.

The *Widgeon* had a two-cylinder engine under her cockpit floor driving a feathering propeller under the starboard quarter. The thing ran intermittently, and almost never in the Crinan Canal.

Down below, she has two high folding wooden bunks above the transoms, so four people can sleep in the cabin. The cook must operate as best he can in the after end of the fo'c's'le; I'd want to give over one of the after corners of the cabin to the galley. The headroom under the beams in the house is 5 feet 8 inches, a bit more under skylight and companionway slide.

Captain Harvey had a wonderful time cruising in the *Widgeon* in the lovely and often stormy waters of west Scotland with his children and with friends. He does not record his wife's ever setting foot in the boat.

He took a great interest in how she sailed under various sail combinations and in her maneuvering

The Widgeon *beating up one of her lochs.* (Sailing Orders *by Captain J.R. Harvey)*

characteristics. "To anyone accustomed to a shallow draft boat the distance a deep-keeled heavy displacement boat will carry her way is always astonishing. *Widgeon* in a strong breeze will travel 70 to 100 yards to windward easily."

Captain Harvey continues:

> I was busy trying *Widgeon* under different weather conditions. With full sail, i.e. mainsail, staysail and big jib, she would sail herself going to windward with the helm lashed amidships. With the mainsail rolled down until the claw for the main sheet on the boom was just on the rolled part of the sail, she balanced very well with the staysail and small jib or with the big jib and no staysail, or with another three rolls in the main, a reef in the staysail and the small jib. Until the claw is on the rolled part of the sail it is troublesome and wants watching. If you think it is going to blow hard and that you may have to reef in the open, it is best to roll the sail until the claw is in this position before you start. To close reef the sail after this will then be quite easy. With the mainsail rolled down until the gaff jaws were about four feet from the boom she was best with no staysail and the small jib. I was under this sail with a reefed staysail in the Sound of Jura in bad tide rips and a wind of nearly gale force, and after taking the staysail in *Widgeon* was very easy and comparatively comfortable. I find the staysail a very useful sail as it alters the balance very little, is a powerful driving sail, is easily hoisted or taken in, and, being set on hanks on the forestay, is easily controlled.
>
> *Widgeon* handles quite well under jib only, and will come about and also go to windward a little if necessary.

And in rough weather with the wind on the quarter:

> *Widgeon* took the seas very well indeed, and although she occasionally buried her bowsprit and the water came up level with the deck by the cockpit, she never shipped any heavy water. She certainly wants watching, and as I had over five hours at the helm, I had plenty of exercise.

Or again:

> After rounding the light *Widgeon* would not lie up for Peel under the jib only. So we set the mainsail with about seven rolls down, equal to about two reefs. By this time it was 8:45 a.m.; the wind had been increasing since 6 a.m. and was now coming off the land in hard squalls from the east. Once the mainsail was hoisted we had a grand sail to Peel and did 14 miles in under two hours. Before we got to Peel the squalls were coming black from the shore and must have reached gale force at times. I could have wished for an easier passage for the sake of my crew but for myself satisfaction at the behavior of *Widgeon* outweighed all discomforts.
>
> I was very joyous about her: first because of the way she had picked her step through the tide rips off Calf Sound, under the jib only — we had jumped about a bit, but never taken a drop of heavy water; secondly, because of the way she had stood up to her canvas with the mainsail hoisted. She was always perfectly easy to handle under the jib, or jib and double reefed mainsail. I felt that I had got the very boat I wanted for the west coast of Scotland, with its fierce squalls and narrow lochs, where your boat must sail well to windward.

And finally:

> It is the grandest feeling I know, sailing to windward in a big sea with a fresh breeze, in a boat which has been really built to sail.

Amen, Captain Harvey.

35/ Mr. Simpson's Cutter

Length on deck: 33 feet 3 inches
Length on waterline: 24 feet
Beam: 8 feet
Draft: 4 feet 6 inches
Sail area: 493 square feet
Displacement: 4¾ tons
Designer: H. Hardey Simpson

I met Mr. H. Hardey Simpson and his graceful little English cutter in Watmough Bay, Lopez Island. This lovely place is one of the San Juan Islands, in the northwest corner of the United States. Actually, I met them on the pages of the October 1908 issue of *The Yachting and Boating Monthly,* the grand old English magazine. When I read that Mr. Simpson had often sailed among the islands inside Vancouver Island, for some reason, I began imagining myself joining Mr. Simpson and his cutter for a 30-mile sail round Lopez Island. We started and ended the circumnavigation, of course, at the island's prettiest anchorage, Watmough Bay.

It's true that this little niche in behind Watmough Head at the southeast corner of Lopez is exposed to a northeast breeze, but this early morning the wind is southwest, gentle. Probably breeze up to fresh before the day's over.

When I dropped on board the irresistible cutter, Mr. Simpson professed to be glad to see me. He said he didn't really like singlehanded sailing and would welcome some help with his headsail sheets and so forth. He interrupted watching an eagle up on Chadwick Hill through his binoculars long enough to tell me this. Then he went back to it before muttering that he hoped the fog wouldn't blow in too early from the Strait of Juan de Fuca.

The cutter was designed by Mr. Simpson for his own use. He was not a naval architect, but he had knocked around in a lot of different boats whose many faults he tried to avoid with this design. I think he created a fine, well-thought-out little vessel; certainly he drew her plans beautifully.

"Just run those backstays forward, will you?" Mr. Simpson said as he snapped shut his binoculars case. "I'll let go the mainsheet."

I did as I was bid, commenting that his running backstays, sliding on a wire span along the deck, reminded me of a similar backstay arrangement that I knew with a track instead of the wire. I mentioned to Mr. Simpson that this backstay arrangement included a line from the backstay through a forward block leading aft, so you could haul the backstay forward right from the cockpit. "Might not be a bad idea," he allowed. (I didn't let on that this was a "modern" rig used on the Concordia yawls.)

We hoisted the big gaff mainsail, Mr. Simpson on the peak and I on the throat. Somehow the thrill never palls of seeing the gaff rising, horizontal and majestic, the sail coming to life and rattling its rows of reef points. The halyards are single parts of wire with rope tails. There is a snatch block where the tail meets the wire, and another snatch block on deck. So when you've done

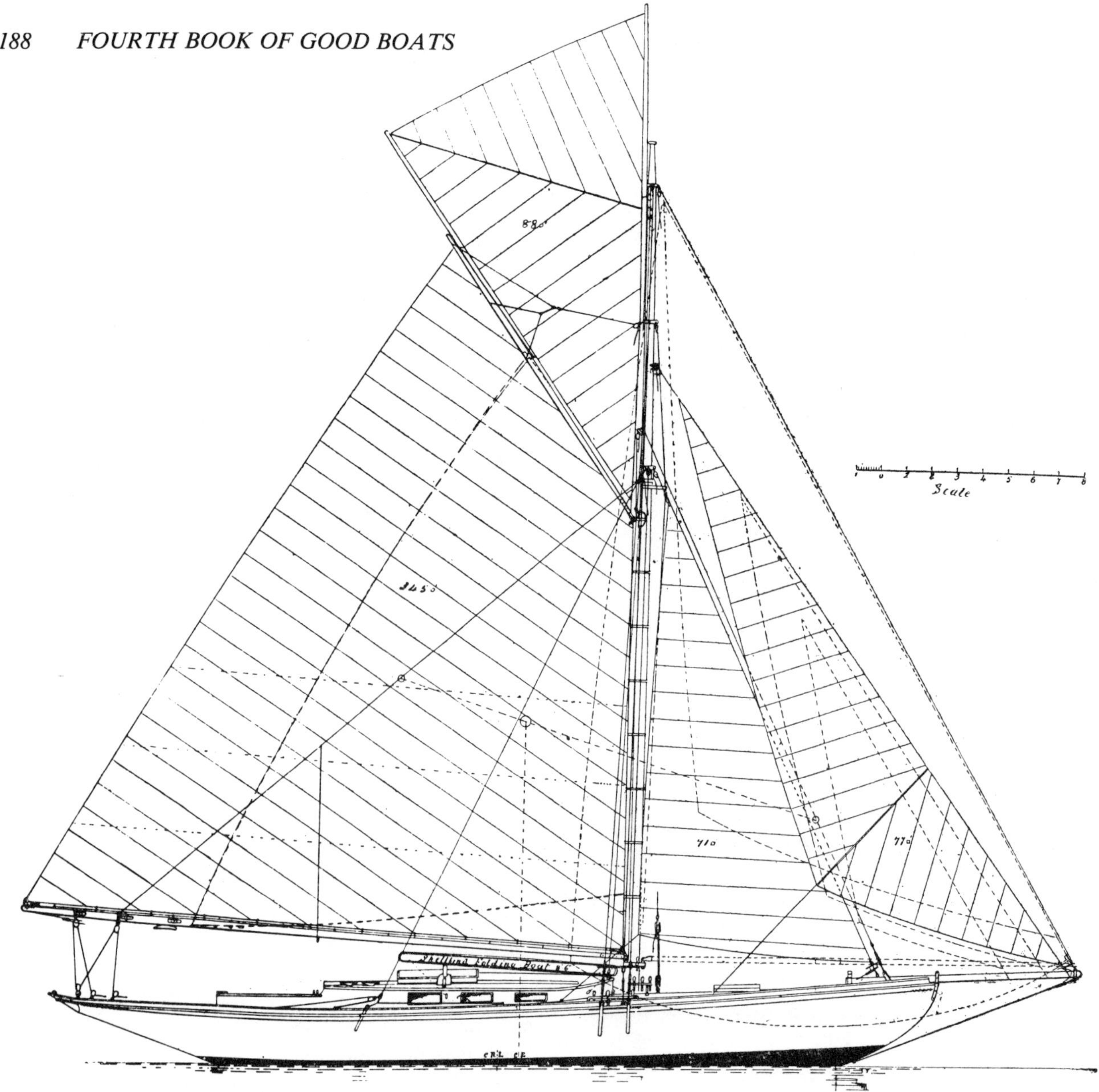

The sailplan of Mr. Simpson's cutter. (The Yachting and Boating Monthly, *October 1908)*

all you can with the single part, you use the rope tail to rig yourself a jig tackle on the snatch blocks, and then set the sail right up hard with little effort. Pretty work.

When the sail was set to his satisfaction, Mr. Simpson moved aft to the tiller, giving the back of his hand to the whole bow of his cutter with a wide gesture. This I took to mean, "Let's get underway." At any rate, there was no objection from back aft when I hauled the anchor right up and brought it aboard. It was the big port bower, but I had little difficulty slipping it into its place just inside the port rigging, one fluke outboard. The inboard fluke, I noted with satisfaction, fitted nicely into a wood pad with a piece of brass shaped to cover it so sheets couldn't get foul. As I was doing this, I heard a rumpus up forward over my shoulder and turned around to find that Mr. Simpson had unrolled both his jib and staysail, with their Wykeham Martin gear, and sheeted them home to pay her head off. He spun her round and we were off, running out of the anchorage.

Mr. Simpson's cutter is 33 feet 3 inches long on deck, with a waterline length of 24 feet, a beam of 8 feet, and a draft of 4 feet 6 inches. She displaces 4¾ tons, nearly half of which is in her lead keel.

Her lines show a graceful hull. I like the combination of her soft spoon bow and long, overhanging counter. These long ends increase her sailing length and thus her

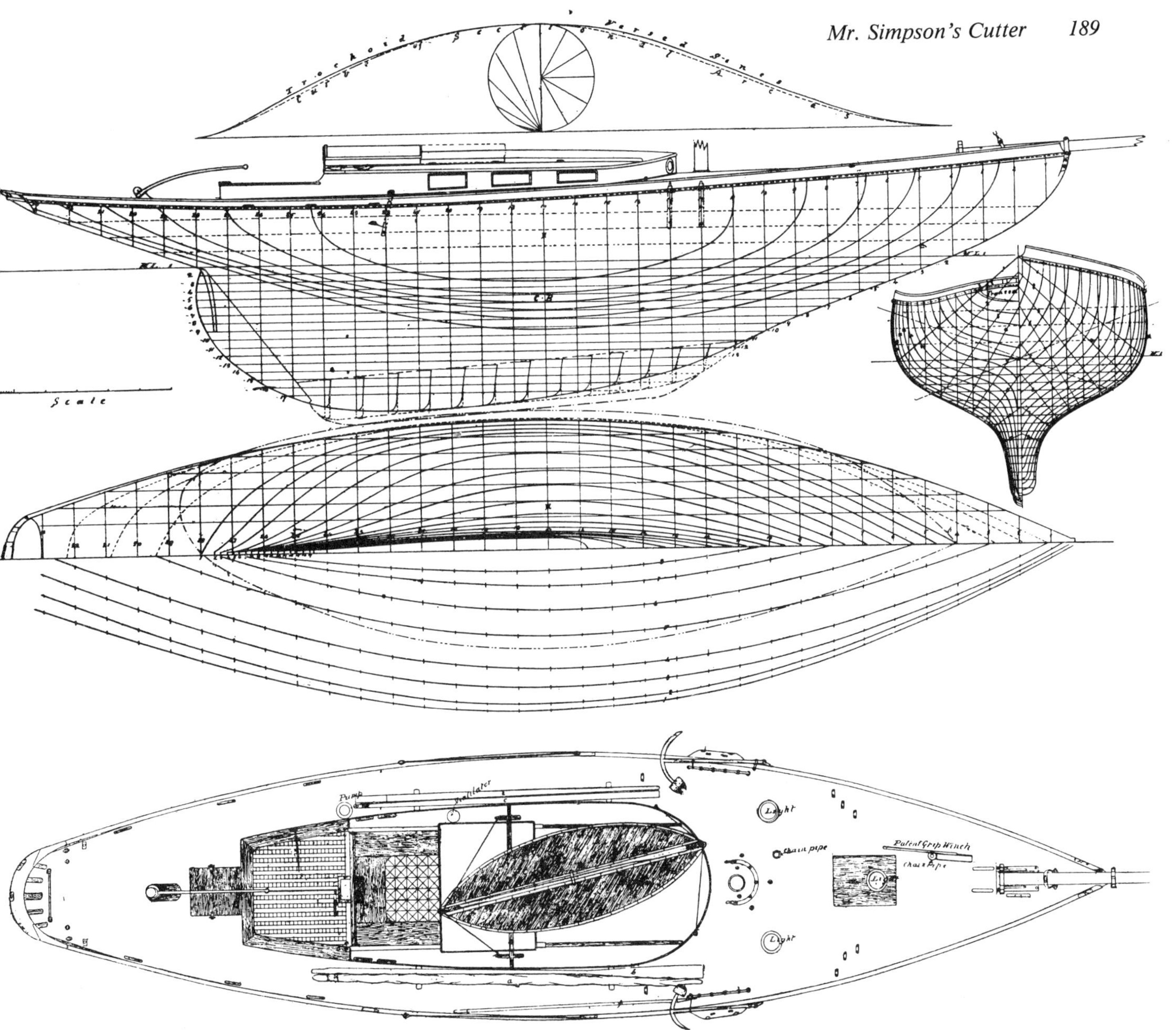

The lines and deck plan of Mr. Simpson's cutter. (The Yachting and Boating Monthly, *October 1908)*

speed, and give her deck space — as well as beauty. Yes, they can pound on occasion, and carrying around their weight would make a modern racing sailor wince.

She has very easy bow and buttock lines. The rocker on the primary keel shape shown is for maneuverability when taking or leaving the ground. (That's English East Coast stuff; we hoped not to have to make use of this feature during our circumnavigation of Lopez.) The lowest keel shape shown is to get the same weight of ballast if, for economy, iron were substituted for lead. The intermediate keel shape shown is Mr. Simpson's idea of making her steadier on the helm if she were built for an owner who didn't have to worry about her taking the ground at her mooring.

She has nice wineglass sections, with a moderate turn of bilge, and just enough tumblehome to make her look interesting. The waterlines are convex throughout, with the sharpness of the narrow boat.

Mr. Simpson said we might as well go round the island clockwise and head out into Juan de Fuca right off the bat to see how bad the fog was going to be. So we bore up round Boulder Island, flattened in the sheets, and put her hard on the wind on the starboard tack. Once clear of Watmough Head we found a moder-

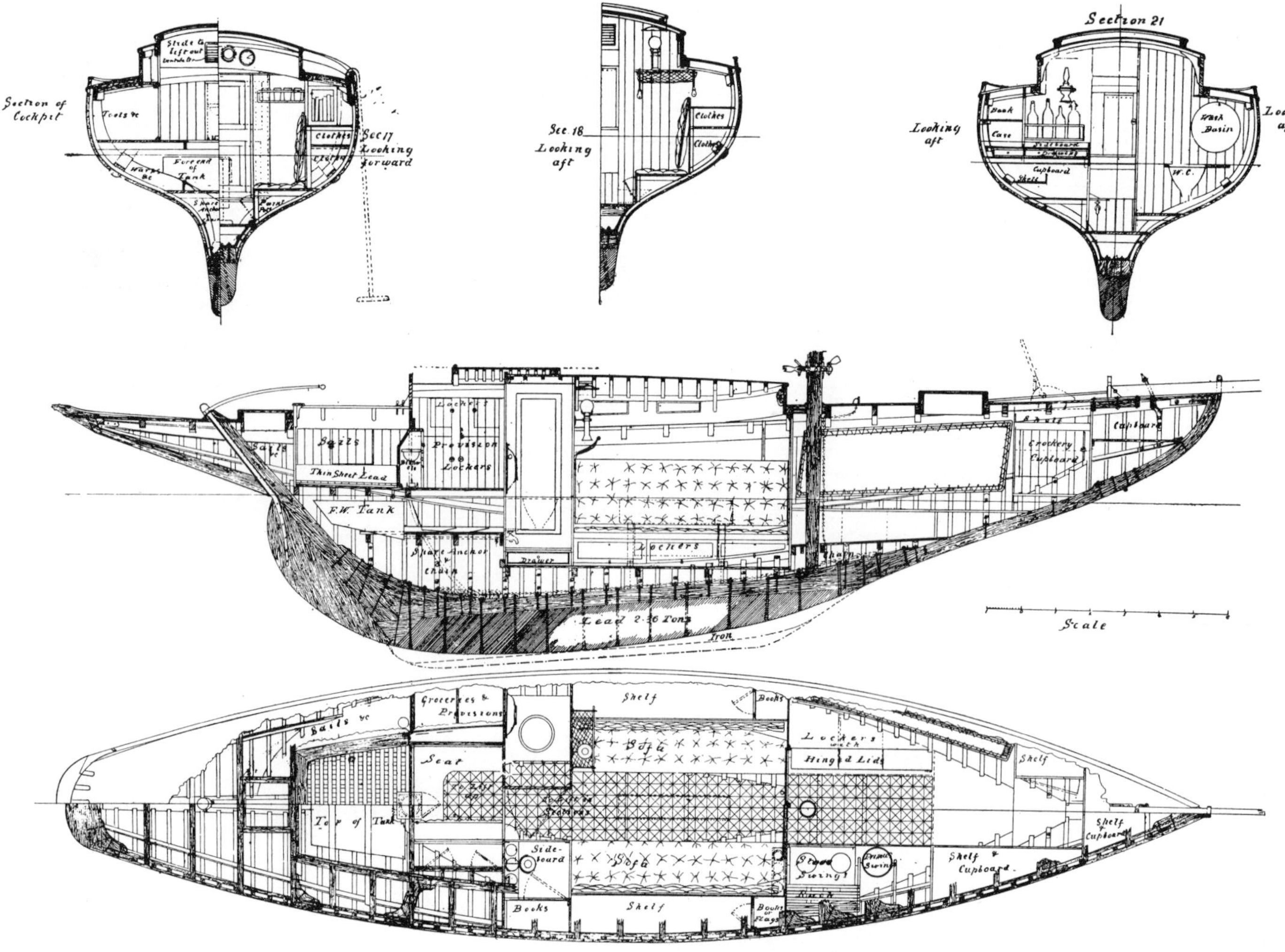

The interior arrangement and construction plans of Mr. Simpson's cutter. (The Yachting and Boating Monthly, *October 1908)*

ate breeze, a strong fair tide setting us nicely to weather, and a fairly long sea steepened by the shoaling bottom and the outgoing tide and topped by plenty of white horses. The vessel obviously loved these conditions; she pranced to windward like a frisky pup. And we nearly had our breath taken away, as always happens when the white peaks of the Olympics first come into view.

Mr. Simpson got out his binoculars. He scanned the horizon to windward, looking way down the strait in disbelief. He couldn't believe that he couldn't see any fog yet. "That's funny," was all he dared utter. When we thought we could weather Iceberg Point we put her about, and she went even better on the port tack than she had on the starboard, since the sea was a little more abeam.

Mr. Simpson specified rather light scantlings for his cutter, but he spaced his timbers close together. Her frames are molded 1⅛ inches and sided 1½ inches. She has iron floors. Bilge stringers run right forward to the stem and meet at a breasthook. Her deck is ¾-inch tongue-and-groove stuff; the cabintop, only ⅝-inch tongue-and-groove; but the beams and carlins are closely spaced, and there are hanging knees in the house. Deck and cabintop are both canvas covered.

With a sail area of 493 square feet she has a fairly generous rig, though she is certainly not over-rigged. The mainsail has 345 square feet; the staysail, 71; and the jib, 77. Her club topsail adds another 88 square feet, up where it does some good. The topsail's jackyard and club are both bamboo; they are slightly bigger in diameter than would be solid spars, but weigh only a bit more than half as much as would solid sticks.

The starboard deck was a bit cluttered by the topsail, rolled up on its spars and encased in a waterproof bag, together with a 12-foot oar. The obstacle to be avoided on the port deck was a jointed spinnaker pole, folded in half and lashed down. Much of the cabintop was taken up with an 8½-foot folding dinghy of the Shellbend type.

I wondered how much of this paraphernalia we'd use on our circumnavigation. I wouldn't have minded getting out the topsail or the spinnaker pole, and would have found unfolding the dinghy intriguing, but I wasn't so sure about that 12-foot oar. I like to row, but I didn't relish the idea of shoving the 5-tonner through some narrow pass between the islands against the tide. Mr. Simpson wrote in 1908, "In these days, when motorboats and auxiliaries bid fair to oust all pleasure craft propelled by wind alone, a design for a small cruiser unprovided with mechanical power may seem rather out of date; nevertheless, being so devoted to sailing, for its own sake, as to remain unaffected for the prevalent yearning for petrol, I have made no provision for it in this design for a 24-foot waterline boat."

As it turned out, none of this gear was put to use this day. We nicely weathered Iceberg Point, with its lighthouse, and were able to crack off just a bit and head for the lighthouse on Cattle Point on the south end of San Juan Island. She made good progress up the Middle Channel, despite the foul tide pouring out. We bore off more yet and fought through between San Juan and Lopez islands into San Juan Channel for a broad reach up the west side of Lopez. I took the tiller while Mr. Simpson swept his binoculars along the shore looking for the great blue heron. The cutter was wonderful to steer, just the right combination of steadiness and responsiveness. We had a quiet sail up the island.

The cutter has plenty of other sails besides her mainsail, working forestaysail, working jib, and jackyard topsail. The dotted lines on her sailplan will show you a small, loose-footed, gaff mainsail for hard weather; a small, hard-weather jib and a tiny spitfire; and a big masthead jib topsail, as well as the spinnaker. If she were mine, I'd be tempted to go to the sailmaker for a small storm trysail and a balloon forestaysail. Might as well have the whole works. But I didn't let on to Mr. Simpson that I thought he had any gaps in his wardrobe.

The strut and jackstay on the forward side of the mainmast keep the peak halyard from bending the masthead aft. A good rig. Mr. Simpson said that maybe he should have put shrouds on his bowsprit. I agreed.

Running her off dead before it, we discovered why Upright Channel was so named. We bucked the tide between Flat Point on the starboard hand and Canoe Island to port. Then the foul tide eased off a bit as we ran on down to Upright Head at the north end of the island. As a matter of fact, by the time we jibed round Upright and put her up close to the wind on the starboard tack, the tide seemed about ready to turn. So we stood past Humphrey Head and over to Blakely Island in slack water. It breezed on to fresh, and the cutter began dipping her rail into the foam hissing down her side. Some fun!

Mr. Simpson had ducked below right after we'd come on the wind, and I was just going to call down that we ought to be thinking about tacking when up he popped with sandwiches and cold beer just in time for me to turn over the tiller and get ready to shift the headsails over. But Blakely Island is high, steep, and bold, so we let her go right in under Bald Bluff while we rolled up the staysail so we wouldn't have to bother with its sheet on the many fairly short tacks that were ahead of us. Mr. Simpson brought her round at the last minute. Then we could enjoy the rugged, high beauty of Bald Bluff over the stern — and lunch — at our leisure. Mr. Simpson thought he saw an eagle wheeling way up among the high crags.

The cutter has an unusual and very sensible cockpit arrangement. It's divided into a proper cockpit forward with a full-width hatch over it and a self-draining steering well aft. There's a solid, watertight bulkhead between cockpit and steering well. This bulkhead is low enough to be stepped over, the sole of the well being at the same level as the seats in the cockpit. A heavy board slides into place atop the bulkhead if you want to seal up the cockpit completely with its hatch shut.

You perch on the wide coaming top of the well to steer. I found this perfectly comfortable. I suppose in a calm you'd want to get out a folding canvas chair.

I wondered about rigging up lines to the tiller and leading them forward to some kind of contraption so you could steer from up in the cockpit if you wanted to. Such a rig might be particularly useful for a singlehander in rough open water. The cockpit is wonderfully well protected and is a great place to stand and watch her go.

Both cockpit and steering well have plenty of lockers around their outboard sides. There is room for a spare anchor and chain under the cockpit sole and for a 15-gallon water tank under the steering well.

We tacked again under the lee of Frost Island and beat on up Lopez Sound between Lopez and Decatur islands. She romped to windward in the fresh breeze and flat sea over just the tiniest beginning of a foul tide. It didn't take long to get all the way up to the Ram Island beacon, where we laid her off nearly before it to run out through Lopez Pass. Now the tide strengthened against us. And astern, driven between the island hills by the sou'wester, came the fog. No matter. We could beat up under the Lopez shore to Cape St. Mary and then make short tacks on along the bold shore back to Watmough Bay. Let it get as thick as it wanted to.

Down below, the cutter has a cozy cabin. The transoms are the right width for sitting, and their backs fold down to become berths the right width for sleeping. Since these bunks can be tilted, they make good sea berths. Again Mr. Simpson came up with a clever device later to be used, as it happened, in the Concordia yawls. (Of course Mr. Simpson and Waldo Howland, the sailor responsible for a number of the good ideas worked out in the Concordia yawls, never knew each other, being a couple of generations apart. I was going to tell Mr. Simpson about the Concordias but held my tongue in the belief that the time warp might confuse him unnecessarily in the middle of a fine sail.) Nor did I interrupt his enjoyment of sailing his fine little vessel to windward by remarking that I thought he ought to have swapped galley and head in his cabin arrangement, putting the head up under the forward hatch where there is only 3 feet 9 inches headroom, and moving the galley aft where there is 5 feet 3 inches under the beams.

Beat up the Lopez Island shore, we did, with the fog swirling down off the hills and rolling ever thicker up Rosario Strait. We never saw the Kellett Ledge can, though we certainly passed within 500 yards of it.

By the time we tacked up into Watmough Bay, rolled up the jib, and let go, you couldn't see anything but the steep cliff of Chadwick Hill. We were glad to be in.

After joining Mr. Simpson in a toast to his fine little cutter, I took my departure. Man and boat quickly vanished in the swirling mists.

36/ A Fast Ketch

Length on deck: 55 feet
Length on waterline: 44 feet
Beam: 10 feet 6 inches
Draft: 7 feet 6 inches
Sail area: 1,000 square feet
Displacement: 15 tons
Designer: L. Francis Herreshoff

Vessels have surely been raced from the beginning. What sea captain worth his salt, whether he be in command of an elegant clipper ship or a crude dugout, wouldn't want to test his craft against the competition?

Yachts designed strictly for cruising get raced too, of course, on both a formal and an informal basis. Some of the greatest feats of race-winning occur when the master of the losing yacht in a match race never realized a race was on. Later, the winning skipper tells his friends, "Why, you should have seen the good old *Vindicator* sail right past the *Sally Ann* this afternoon! It was if the *Sally* was hove-to." He fails to mention that the *Sally Ann* was under reduced sail in a moderate breeze, her gang concentrating on a couple of mackerel jigs astern.

Races are organized for cruising boats with limits on light sails and crew carried, specifications on minimum accommodations, or various combinations thereof. Such restrictions generally produce good cruising boat racing for a few seasons before some sea lawyer figures a good way round it all and cleans up. Then you have to start all over again.

Cruising boats should be raced on occasion. It's good for boat, skipper, and crew to have to drive the boat occasionally at her maximum speed over a prescribed course, including windward work. It's particularly beneficial for a cruising boat to race in hard weather, for it is under such conditions that you learn things about your boat that you wouldn't learn if you were cruising under the same conditions. It's a good thing to know just how much driving she really will stand. Better to find the weak points in hull and rig racing round the buoys in a breeze than up against a lee shore in a hard chance.

L. Francis Herreshoff devised a rating rule for the racing of cruising boats in 1931 for the Corinthian Yacht Club at Marblehead, Massachusetts. The rule was based on a given sail area for each class, such as 500 or 1,000 square feet. He designed a lovely 55-foot double-ended ketch as an example of what his rule might produce for the 1,000-square-foot class.

Mr. Herreshoff's rule provided for the standard rig and propeller allowances of the day, and he included penalties for excessive overhangs, low freeboard, narrow beam, lack of bulwarks, and small cabinhouses.

Francis Herreshoff's restricted sail area cruiser is 55 feet long on deck, with a waterline length of 44 feet, a beam of 10 feet 6 inches, and a draft of 7 feet 6 inches. She displaces 15 tons.

The sail area of 1,000 square feet is computed using 100 percent of the fore triangle, 281 square feet. The jib shown in the sailplan has an area of 300 square feet;

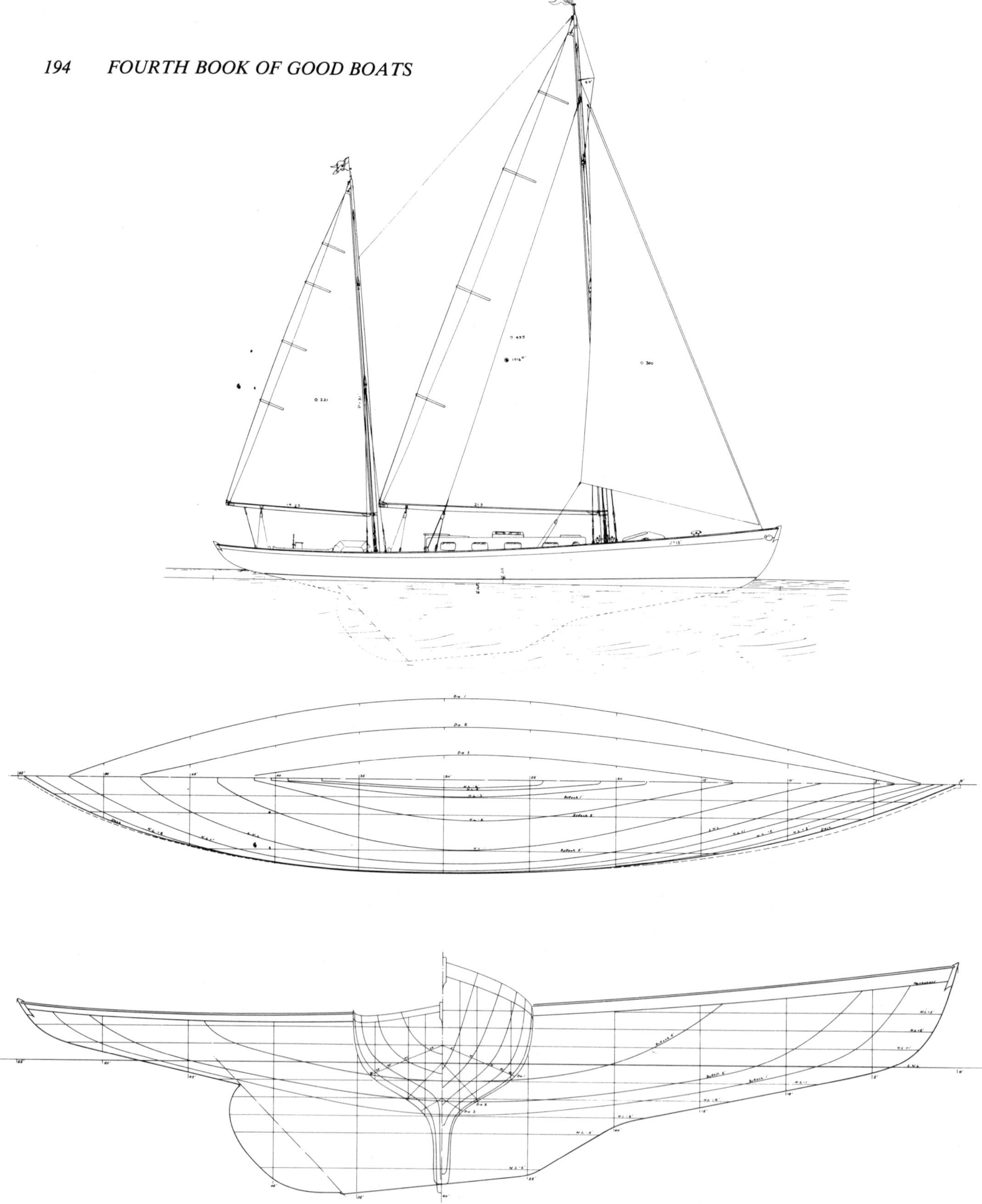

The sailplan and lines of the 1,000-square-foot restricted sail area cruiser. (Sensible Cruising Designs *by L. Francis Herreshoff, International Marine Publishing Company)*

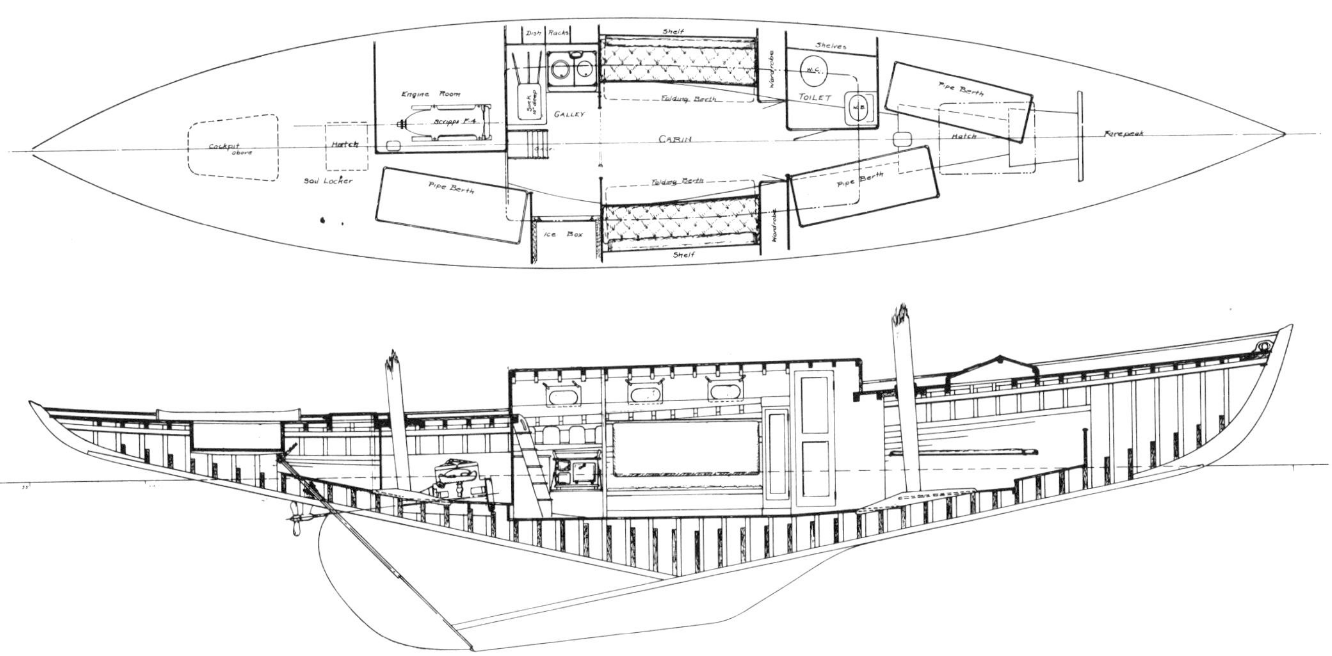

The 1,000-square-footer's interior arrangement. (Sensible Cruising Designs *by L. Francis Herreshoff, International Marine Publishing Company)*

thus, taken with her mainsail of 495 square feet and her mizzen of 221 square feet, her sail area is actually 1,016 square feet with the slightly overlapping headsail.

Under his own rule, Mr. Herreshoff's cruiser takes a slight penalty for too narrow a beam. The editor of *Yachting* at the time, Herbert L. Stone, thought that a loophole in Mr. Herreshoff's rule was the lack of reference to displacement, and that boats too light to make comfortable cruisers might be its unhealthy product. He also commented that Mr. Herreshoff's design had too little accommodation for her length to become a popular type.

The vessel is, at any rate, a sort of huge canoe yawl. There are many similarities between her and the *Rozinante,* a real canoe yawl designed by Mr. Herreshoff 25 years later. The big ketch has a very easily driven hull. Long and narrow, she would be fast and weatherly.

Her bow is certainly more rugged than her drawn-out, dainty stern, yet her profile looks in fine balance. She is quite cut away forward, her rudder is quite far forward and its post well raked, so there would probably be times when she'd be a bit hard to steer.

Look at her lovely, long, flat run. Is there enough lift in her stern to cope with a nasty, steep, following sea? Yes, for her waterlines are quite full aft. She has a sharp entrance. Her hull lines exude speed.

She has easy bilges, considerable flare above the waterline, and deep-slung ballast; she'd have low initial stability, but it would be hard to get her rail under. She'd have a relatively easy motion for such a deep, narrow boat.

The ketch rig of this vessel divides her 1,000 square feet of sail into easily managed parts, with her mainsail just under the 500-square-foot maximum decreed by Uffa Fox as the biggest sail one person can normally handle.

She could carry bigger jibs, but would seldom need them. Her running backstays could have an alternate forward lead for short tacking.

Francis Herreshoff said this boat would be very easy in a seaway and would be capable of being driven to windward with very little sail. Having sailed his *Rozinante,* I'd certainly agree. This big ketch would be some seaworthy. She'd stand a tremendous lot of breeze under jib-and-jigger and could work to windward under a storm jib and reefed mizzen in really frightful conditions.

The ketch's hull speed would be close to 10 knots; and she would turn in, I believe, a very high average lifetime speed, which is the kind of speed really wanted in a cruising boat.

The pram shown stowed athwartships across the sailroom hatch looks a bit awkward; perhaps she'd be better atop the house over the skylight. Such an arrangement would leave lots of deck space aft; between the after end of the house and the forward end of the cockpit you could spread around a few low deck chairs and chaise longues and things.

That separate sailroom would be a joy, as would the

separate engine room, which houses a Scripps F-4. This boat would be quite fast under power. Note the propeller coming out above the deeply buried rudder.

The ketch's accommodation plan is quite normal, with galley aft, saloon amidships, and head and bunks forward. Her five bunks are all slung on hinges, so you could sleep reasonably level however she was heeled. That quarter berth would be a nice place for the next person on watch, tucked back out of the way but still quite handy to the deck. There's 6 feet of headroom under the house.

Racing or cruising, this Herreshoff ketch would be a wonderful boat. Standing up to her wheel and just watching her beat her way to windward in a breeze would be quite an experience.

37/ The *Sauk III*

Length on deck: 53 feet
Length on waterline: 37 feet 6 inches
Beam: 12 feet 4 inches
Draft: 6 feet 5 inches
Sail area: 1,115 square feet
Displacement: 39,000 pounds
Designer: Norman H. Boettcher

The arrival of the plans for a ketch designed in 1980 by Norman H. Boettcher made my day. Most cruising boats designed as recently as 1980 were unduly influenced by fads resulting from a racing rating rule that rewards light displacement, fat bellies, short ends, and tiny mainsails. Mr. Boettcher's ketch, designed for shorthanded offshore cruising, was clearly not under the influence.

Mr. Boettcher is from Lansing, Michigan. The boat is to be named the *Sauk III,* after the Indian tribe originally from that region.

The boat has a pretty hull, thanks to her pretty sheerline and her graceful overhangs. She has a well-formed run. Her topsides are nicely rounded. The diagonals are very fair. She has reasonably low wetted surface. The cornered rudder looks efficient.

And notice her handsome deck plan; after all, it is the shape of the deck and curve of the rail that are watched hour after hour by a vessel's people.

The *Sauk III* should have an easy motion and should be a dry boat, two key requisites of an ocean cruiser. She'll do all right to windward, being just fine enough forward to avoid being slowed much by a head sea and just deep enough to hang on reasonably well. The designer said he would have preferred a bit more draft — as would I — but he kept it moderate for gunkholing and ease of hauling out. She'll be no weather-going demon, what with her divided rig, fairly shoal draft, and lack of a knife-edge entrance.

The *Sauk III* is 53 feet long on deck, with a waterline length of 37 feet 6 inches, a beam of 12 feet 4 inches, and a draft of 6 feet 5 inches. Her displacement is about 39,000 pounds, and her working sail area is 1,115 square feet.

She is to be built of fiberglass over C-Flex. The topsides will be just under ½ inch thick; the bottom will be just over ½ inch. She'll have extra thickness in her ends and in way of the chainplates.

I wrote the designer: "I'd like to see a longer-based sailplan, with 200 or 300 square feet more sail, but that's just personal taste, and a lot depends on the intended use for the vessel." He wrote back: "The sail area has been kept rather modest because the shorthanded crew are in their late sixties." Fair enough.

She does have quite a lot of length of spar for her sail area. Her mizzen preventer would be needed only off the wind in a hard breeze or maybe in a nasty head sea.

She'd stand quite a bit of breeze before needing to shorten down from her working sail area, but when it did blow hard you'd have plenty of combinations to choose from. You might start, for instance, by reefing or double-reefing the mainsail. Then if it kept on breez-

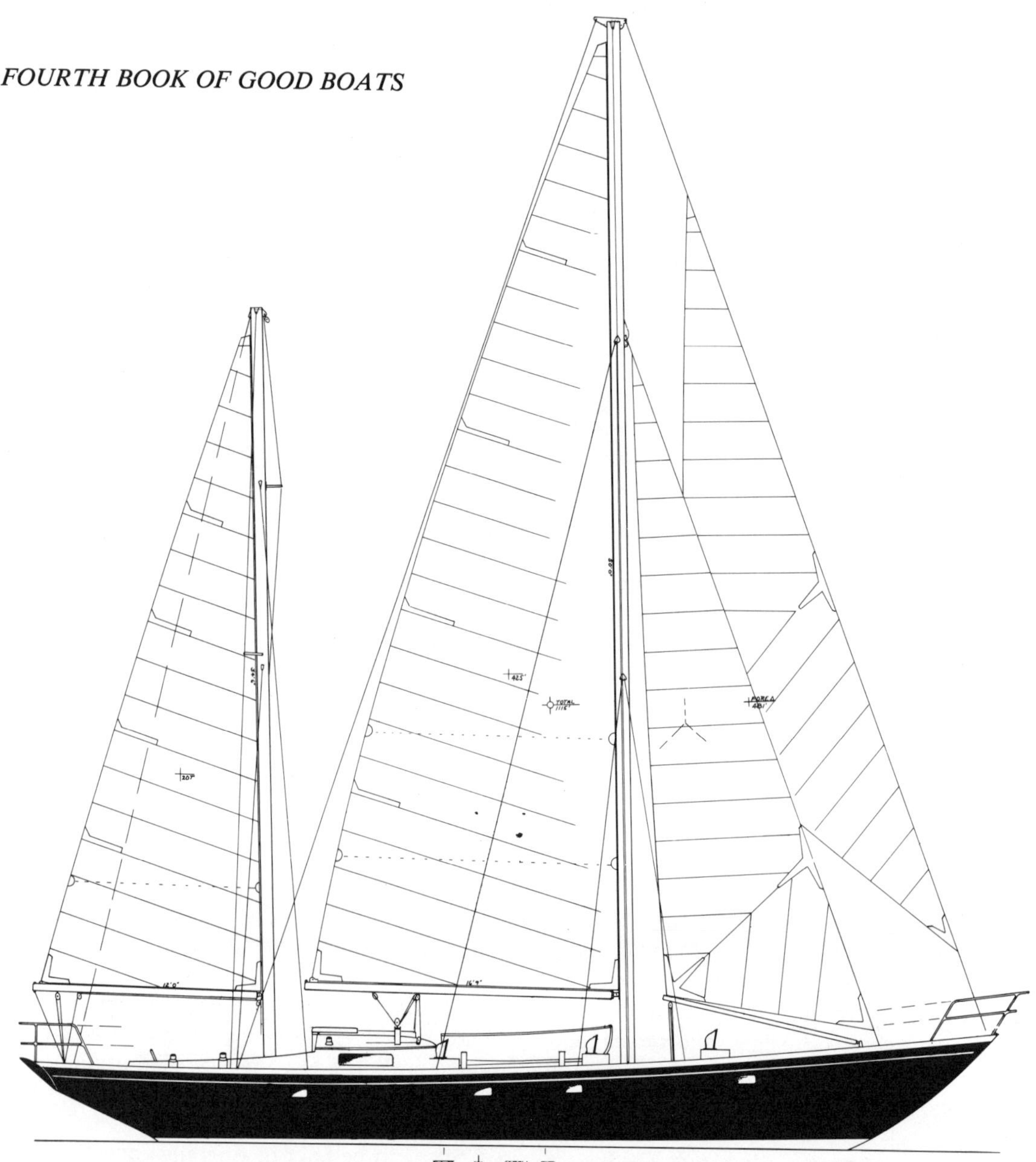

The sailplan of the Sauk III. *(Norman H. Boettcher)*

ing up, you could take the mainsail right off her. Next, reef the mizzen and run off to take in the jib. With her mizzen alone, she'd lie more or less head to wind, making sternboard.

There are, of course, a lot of jibs that could be set on this boat, but the one shown would be the workhorse when offshore shorthanded. A bigger headsail, one tacking to the deck, going almost to the masthead, and coming just abaft the mast with a high clew would be a tempting sail to get out on a nice day. You'd especially want a big jib to set on a broad reach when the mizzen will have to be dropped so it won't kill the mainsail.

The flush deck of this ketch preserves her good looks despite her fairly high freeboard. It also provides right-side-up stowage for a 9½-foot dinghy, to be hoisted out by the main halyard. This feature, and the ketch's small cockpit, are two more essential ingredients of the offshore cruiser.

She has four hatches, a pair on each side, placed so the dinghy fits between them. This arrangement is much better than the usual skylight on the centerline, which ends up being covered by an upside-down dinghy to the disappointment of those in the gloomy saloon below. I'd want higher coamings over those hatches, though; and why not make the low fo'c's'le hatch a booby hatch, which can be left open in a head sea for ventila-

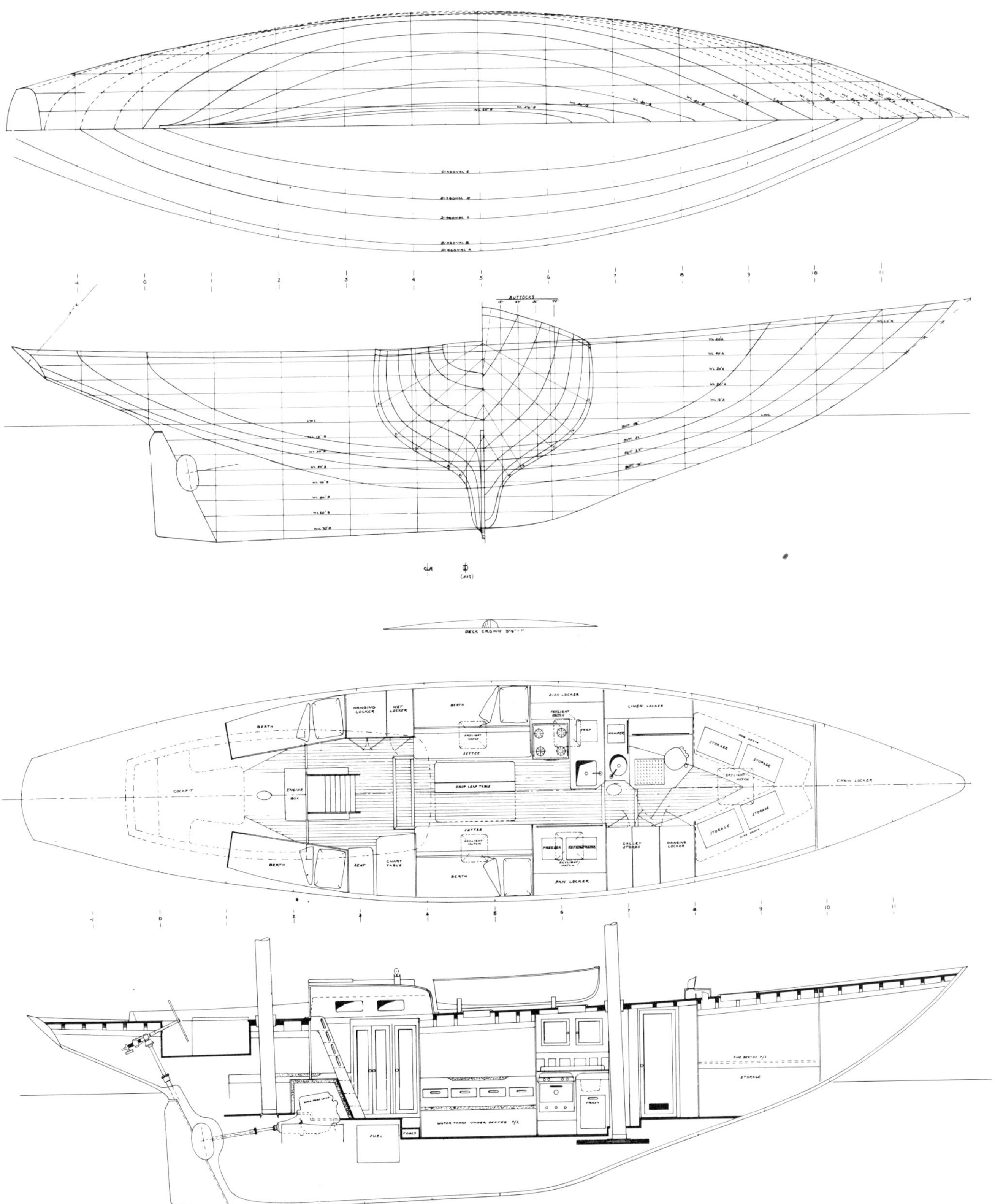

The Sauk*'s lines and interior arrangement plans. (Norman H. Boettcher)*

tion in most weather. Besides all these hatches, the *Sauk III* has five ventilators on deck.

The vessel's engine has plenty of room around it once the paneling is removed. Her fuel tank is in the bilge just forward of the engine. There's a water tank under each transom in the saloon.

Her layout below is sensible, straightforward, and symmetrical. The quarter berths are handy for the off-watch, yet placed just far enough aft so that people using the companionway won't disturb the sleepers too much.

She has a nice chart table to starboard of the companionway; the forward of the two hanging lockers opposite is a wet locker.

Her saloon berths would be good sea berths. How many boats designed in 1980 do you know with four good sea berths, and in addition, a good place to sit down or stretch out to leeward on either tack?

The cook is out of the cockpit-to-saloon traffic, yet is not isolated from the rest of the crew. The vessel's washroom is of generous size. The huge, double-doored locker opposite is for galley stores. Her big fo'c's'le will take plenty of sails and gear, or can accommodate two extra people if the vessel is cruising coastwise.

How do you measure the value of this cruising vessel of 1980? Well, a man who bought two sets of *Sauk III* plans from Mr. Boettcher sold his boat, the Alden schooner *Malabar IV*. Is there any other 1980 vintage boat that wouldn't be a come-down?

38/ A New York Thirty

Length on deck: 43 feet 6 inches
Length on waterline: 30 feet
Beam: 8 feet 9 inches
Draft: 6 feet 3½ inches
Sail area: 1,100 square feet
Designer: Nathanael G. Herreshoff

The gentlemen of the New York Yacht Club wanted a new racing class 30 feet long on the waterline. They liked Captain Nat Herreshoff's Newport Thirties, but they wanted the boats to have cruising accommodations so they would be "suited to accompany the squadron on a cruise." This was 1904.

A committee was appointed in October: W. Butler Duncan Jr., Addison G. Hanan, and Newbury D. Lawton. They acted swiftly and decisively. Nathanael Greene Herreshoff was contacted; he agreed to see what he could do. He produced a design and a cost estimate, which the committee met to consider on November 10. On November 15, contracts were signed for eight boats to be built to the design at $4,000 each. On December 6, contracts were signed for eight more boats. On January 5, 1905, the first New York Yacht Club 30-footer was launched, rigged, sailed to the satisfaction of Captain Nat and the head of the committee, stripped, and hauled out for the rest of the winter. Two more boats were added to the class, and all 18 were completed and ready for delivery by April 14, 1905.

W.P. Stephens, to whose book *Traditions and Memories of American Yachting* I am indebted for the early history of the New York Thirties, wrote that they came with 88 items of equipment. There were two 47-pound anchors; a leadline; two blankets, two pillows, and eight sheets; one butcher knife; three soup plates; and six dessert spoons among the equipment carefully stowed on board by the men of the Herreshoff Manufacturing Company at Bristol, Rhode Island.

Here are the original names of the 18 New York Thirties with the racing numbers they carried throughout their careers:

1. *Alera*
2. *Ibis*
3. *Atair*
4. *Maid of Meudon*
5. *Pintail*
6. *Dahinda*
7. *Tabasco*
8. *Carlita*
9. *Adelaide II*
10. *Linnet*
11. *Oriole*
12. *Neola II*
13. *Minx*
14. *Cara Mia*
15. *Banzai*
16. *Nautilus*
17. *Phryne*
18. *Anemone*

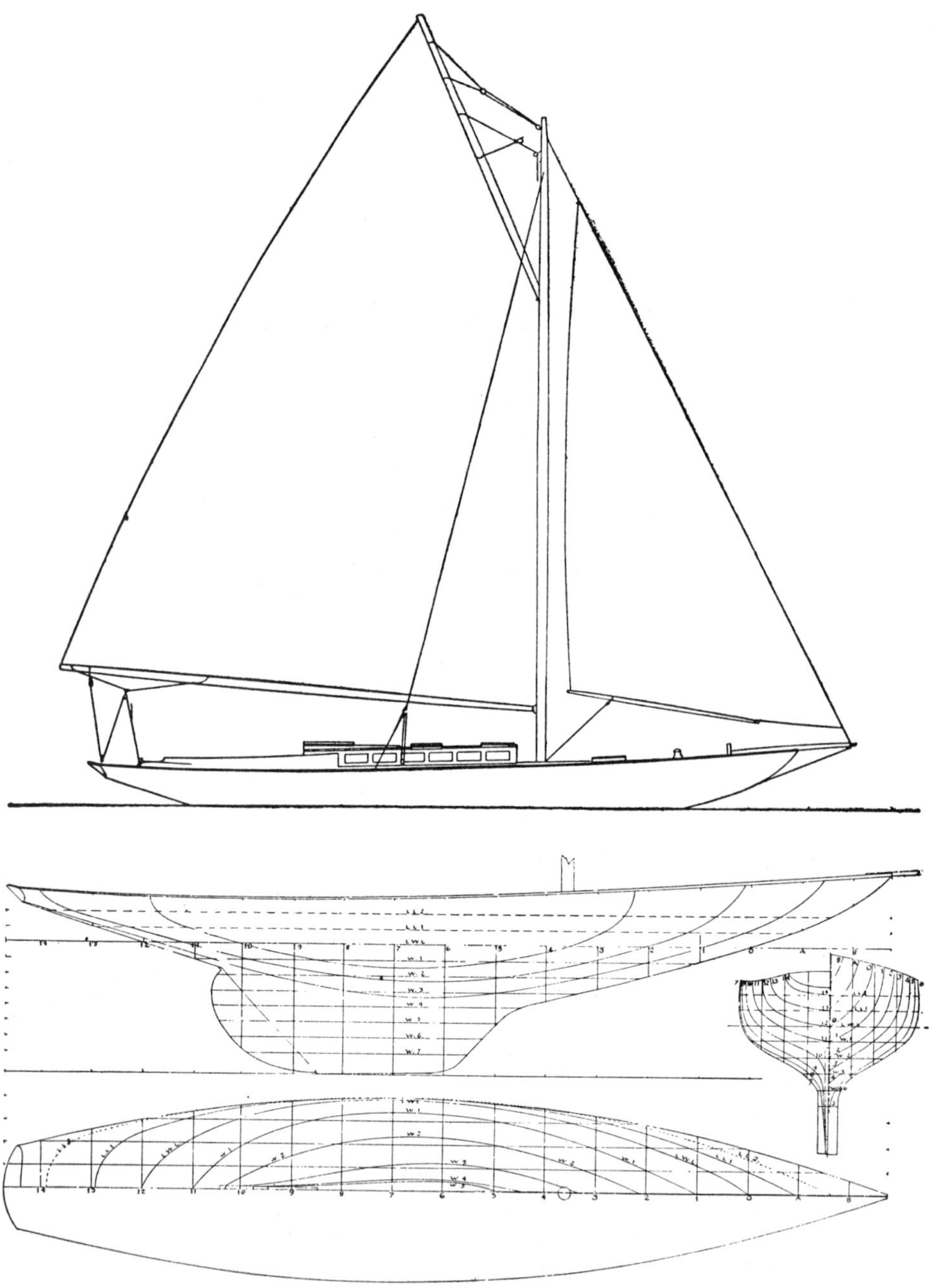

The sailplan and lines of the New York Thirty. (Traditions and Memories of American Yachting *by William P. Stephens, International Marine Publishing Company)*

The boats were raced hard and often. The class seems to have been a sort of intermediate training ground for highly competitive yachtsmen on their way to bigger boats. The longest an original owner kept his New York Thirty was nine years, and all 18 of the boats changed hands (and names) often. Morgans, Roosevelts, and Vanderbilts were among the owners.

The first year you could have only four people on board when racing, but in the second and subsequent seasons the crew limit was increased to five. No more than two professionals could be on board when racing. "Prize money to professionals shall not exceed the following schedule: $1.00 for start, $4.00 for first place, $3.00 for second place, $2.00 for third place."

Racing skippers in the New York Thirty class developed a great reputation for never reefing, though the

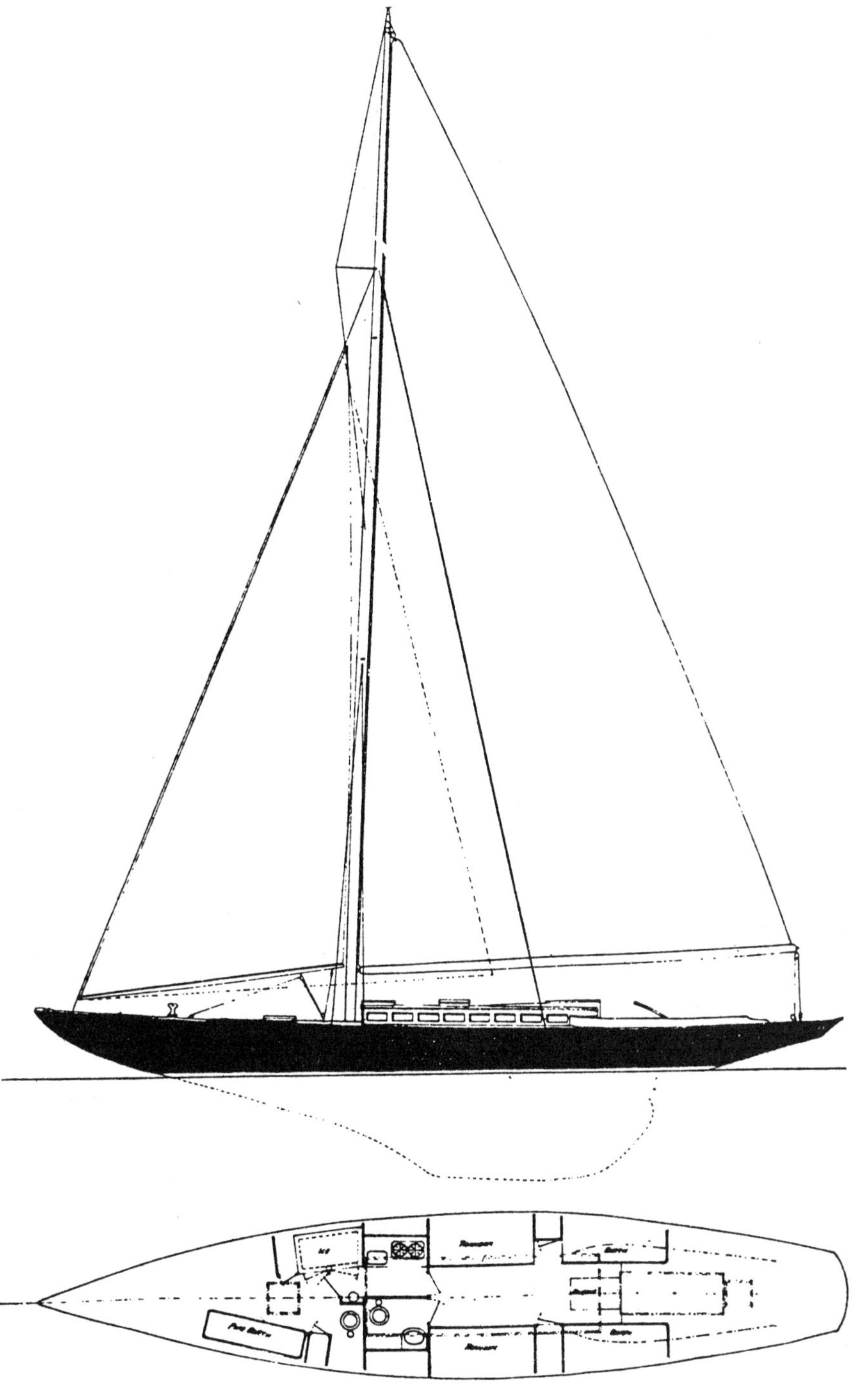

The Herreshoff Manufacturing Company's bid for a modern New York Yacht Club class in 1934. She is 50 feet long on deck, with a waterline length of 33 feet, a beam of 10 feet 6 inches, and a draft of 6 feet 10 inches. Her sail area is 1,120 square feet. (The Rudder, *December 1934)*

boats had rather generous rigs, so they sometimes sailed at great angles of heel. This didn't seem to slow them down much, but probably reefing wouldn't have slowed them down much either.

The class stayed popular. Seabury Lawrence wrote an article for *Yachting* about the Thirties' twentieth anniversary. He told of how two 20-year-old Thirties on a 37-mile squadron run raced from Newport to a finish line at the head of Buzzards Bay before an increasing sou'wester, and Number 4, then called *Countess,* beat Number 5, then the *Lena,* by three seconds. He added, "It will be remembered that Captain Ogden Reid's *Lena* this year [1924] accompanied the New York Yacht Club fleet on its annual cruise all the way to Bar Harbor. This was a trifle lengthy perhaps for a vessel of the size, unless accompanied by a good sized tender, but there are plentiful accommodations in a '30' for a cruise of short duration." On their twentieth birthday, 16 of the 18 New York Thirties were still racing. By the time *Yachting*'s William H. Taylor wrote of their silver jubilee five years later, a mere dozen were still active. The class kept going another 10 years before newer boats took over.

The Lena *sailing fast in smooth water.* (The Rudder, *August 1919)*

In 1934 Nat Herreshoff designed a 33-foot-waterline class quite similar to the New York Thirties but with a marconi rig; the gentlemen of the club finally wanted new boats. Instead of his design, however, the club later selected one from Olin Stephens, the New York 32.

A number of the New York Thirties continued racing and cruising long after the racing class disbanded. I used to see one of them as recently as 25 years ago sailing in Fishers Island Sound. She was that same Number 5, by then called *Cockatoo II* and owned by a friend of our family, Lloyd Bergeson. I remember being mightily impressed by her one day when Lloyd and his family got underway from East Harbor after lunch and with a single reef tucked into the big gaff mainsail strapped her down to a hard sou'wester coming right off the land of Fishers Island and went roaring up the shore like a hunting cheetah.

Lloyd asked me to go racing with him. We went up to the Pine Orchard Yacht Club and I was so excited to be on one of Nat Herreshoff's New York Thirties that all I can remember about it was a seemingly endless amount of deck space on the boat and the way, in a light air, she ate out to windward and went right away from whatever competition was trying to stay with her. I thought the *Cockatoo* was some big wonderful boat.

The New York Thirties are 43 feet 6 inches long on deck, have a beam of 8 feet 9 inches, and draw 6 feet 3½ inches. The sail area is 1,100 square feet.

The New York Yacht Club committee had specified that the boats were to have "short overhangs," so that's the way Captain Nat modeled them — by his standards. The bow and stern of this design are certainly handsome.

The buttock lines are quite shoal; the boats have a long, flat run. The waterlines are all convex forward, but I never recall the *Cockatoo* pounding much, because her forward sections had so much deadrise.

The Thirties have deep keels with a lot of outside lead making them stiff. They have great power to carry sail. One time I remember well in the *Cockatoo* is a sail back to Noank, Connecticut, from Dering Harbor on Shelter Island, after an Off Soundings race. The fall northwester had plenty of very hard gusts. At that time the *Cockatoo* had a marconi yawl rig. Coming in through The Race, we had to jam her right up on the wind so the strong ebb tide wouldn't set us down into a big tide rip to leeward. I was steering, and I'll never forget what happened when the first big blast of wind hit us after we hardened up. I braced myself to ease her through it, hoping to keep her staggering along all right until it let up again. Then I experienced an unbelievable feeling of a boat transforming all the power of the wind into forward motion. Instead of staggering, she accelerated. She wasn't about to be overpowered, and she certainly wanted no mollycoddling. She looked forward to those great blasts so she could show her stuff.

As I got to know this remarkable boat, I got to know her remarkable skipper. Lloyd is, among other things, an engineer with an engineer's drive to make his physical surroundings — especially when afloat — work better. He's a dissatisfied improver of things. This trait of his led to one of the great shocks of my life. We happened to be "cruising" in our home port of Camden, Maine, at the time, so my shock was recorded in the log for July 31, 1973: "Lloyd Bergeson sailed in in the *Cockatoo*. He has chopped her stern off!"

While I looked at his handiwork, speechless, Lloyd calmly explained the reason for his action. He reasoned that the last couple of feet of overhang didn't add anything to her sailing waterline length and that its weight added significantly to her pitching moment. So he cut her off, and gave her an upright, curved transom. *Cockatoo* pitched less, but she wasn't as pretty after her surgery.

Lloyd has had several rigs in the boat since he took the original gaff rig out: I think two different marconi yawl rigs and two different marconi sloop rigs. All of them seemed to work well, whether the boat was racing or cruising.

The New York Thirties are planked with yellow pine. They are single-planked below the turn of the bilge and double-planked above, with an added run of cypress inside the yellow pine. Lloyd rebuilt the *Cockatoo* extensively over the years, installing bronze floors and covering the hull with Dynel. He made a tremendous number of small changes to her construction, always seeking to make her stronger and more durable.

I was lucky enough to be able to sail in the *Cockatoo* a fair bit from time to time and gradually got to know what to expect on the boat. One thing to expect was apparent chaos at the start of a trip, a chaos that seldom bothered Lloyd and that never interfered with another of his strong traits, his managerial ability. Lloyd Bergeson has managed most of the major shipyards east of the Mississippi River. In any given situation he has a very clear sense of resources, time, and priorities. Orderliness for the sake of orderliness is rather low on his mental list.

I recall arriving at the appointed hour to leave Noank for New London for the start, next day, of an Off Soundings race. Lloyd was sawing a few inches off the main boom. Glancing below, I saw a great array of tools and raw materials. There was no bedding or food on board. We were going to race the next day, and the boat's rating came before housekeeping amenities, which came before departing at some arbitrary hour.

We went in an Annapolis-to-Newport race. An hour before the start, somebody wanted hot soup. There was no kerosene in the stove. A half-hour before the start it was concluded that there was no kerosene on board the vessel. We spotted a friendly spectator who would lend us some and maneuvered alongside his boat to get it. In the process, the spectator's main boom fouled our mizzen rigging and a mizzen spreader broke. Ten minutes before the start Lloyd went aloft with some tape and some fast-acting epoxy mixed up in a little can. Two minutes before the start he was back at the tiller concentrating 100 percent on beating the competition to the line. I think his repair held for the season. I know it held for the race.

When Lloyd's top priority is steering, he's the best helmsman I have seen. A New York Thirty is a lovely boat to steer, and Lloyd can get more out of one than anybody.

The man is a competitive racer. In that race to Newport we huddled on the stern when running, in response to his belief that the increased waterline aft would help her along. I have seen him prowl his foredeck for an hour, clew of his ultimate drifter in hand, seeking and finding every breath of air and giving the *Cockatoo* barely perceptible way through the dense fog of a Marblehead-Halifax race.

Lloyd is a compulsive cruiser. He was always sailing all over the place in the *Cockatoo,* shorthanded or singlehanded.

When I started getting gray hairs, Lloyd thought I was too old for the foredeck and made me navigator. This speeded up the process considerably, particularly because about that time Lloyd decided to sail mostly in northern waters so there would always be plenty of fog around. Why is it that the navigator's comeuppances in fog are always so basic? We were coming back to Northeast Harbor, Maine, from an Astor Cup race that a Frenchman's Bay fog bank had cancelled, and all the wrong islands began showing up. Just when we were supposed to get to a fat round island, we'd get to a long skinny one instead. It was all very confusing, and I wasn't enjoying my lunchtime sandwiches. My digestion improved when I took a hard look at the sandwich container. Lunch had been served in the dish drainer, a rubber-covered-wire affair. This light, airy, convenient lunchbox had been set down next to the compass. I smiled at its closely spaced parallel lines of wire-masquerading-as-rubber, moved it aside, and watched the compass swing a good 15 degrees.

One of the good things about sailing with Lloyd in the *Cockatoo* was that sometimes his friend Eric Olsen would come along. Talk about your competitive racers. He was with us in the Monhegan Race one time and simply talked the *Cockatoo* out of Hussey Sound ahead of all competitors. Light head wind, head tide. Tricky stuff. Eric stationed himself amidships where he could

Alera *and* Oriole *starting in the annual regatta of the Larchmont Yacht Club in a fresh breeze.* (The Rudder, *August 1920)*

talk to all of us more or less simultaneously, whether we were forward or aft, on sheet or tiller. Right from the start he told everybody what to do. "Head off a little, don't strap that boom down quite so much, there's a puff over there, keep your weight to leeward, we've got to tack, what's that guy doing, there's less tide in there, don't bring that jib across too quick," and on and on. And right in the middle of everything he looked at each one of us and said, "BS! BS! BS!" I, for one, was mystified. Nobody had gotten a word in edgewise, so what was *he* saying "BS" to *us* for? It turned out to be racing jargon for "Boat Speed." Evidently Eric thought that by fiercely saying "BS!" at all of us the boat's speed would somehow increase. I'll be damned if it didn't work. He got us out of Hussey Sound ahead of everybody.

The wind stayed light and we beat all the way to Cape Porpoise. The minute we got there the wind shifted 120 degrees and we beat all the way to Monhegan. That sail was some frustrating, but we finished first in the ocean cruising class and were also first on corrected time, beating the second boat by something over six hours.

The original rig Nat Herreshoff put in the New York Thirties was a big, handsome one. He gave the boats a generous mainsail with a high-peaked gaff set up parallel to the headstay. You can't do much better than this for a jib-and-mainsail boat for all-around sailing. The club rules said that maximum spar lengths were: boom, 32 feet; gaff, 19 feet; and spinnaker pole, 19 feet 6 inches.

After the boats came out, their bowsprits were lengthened 2 feet to reduce weather helm on a reach. Considerable weather helm is a standard characteristic of most Herreshoff boats. On the wind, the helm goes from a very light weather helm to a moderate weather helm as the breeze increases. On a reach in a real breeze, most Herreshoffs are a handful, or rather two hands full and feet well placed. The combination seems to work as far as speed is concerned. The boats are certainly fast to windward and they are not easily passed when reaching.

For the Thirties, the Herreshoff Manufacturing Company furnished a working mainsail and jib, a small jib, and a spinnaker. The spinnaker had to be sheeted inside the forestay when racing. Balloon jibs were banned except when racing outside the class.

J.P. Morgan tried a marconi rig on the *Phryne* in 1927. He gave her 75 square feet less sail than the gaff rig had. The experiment didn't seem to prove much in terms of performance, and, being done without the prior agreement of the other skippers, led to some hard feelings.

One of the best sails I ever had in the *Cockatoo* was

coming back to Maine after the 1975 Marblehead-Halifax Race. We saw no land from the inside of Halifax Harbor to the exposed ledges just outside Moore Harbor on Isle au Haut, where Lloyd has a summer place. My log for July 12th reads, "Weathered Cape Sable by noon. Thick fog, breeze increased to strong. Real smoky sou'wester, big sea. Set course for the whistle buoy off Isle au Haut, which gave her a beam reach. Boat roaring along at 8 knots. Changed to working jib before dark, getting thoroughly soaked in the process. Great sailing."

While we still had the genoa on her, I was sitting below on the weather transom watching the waves fly past to leeward through the *Cockatoo*'s long row of rectangular cabinhouse windows. Suddenly a trawler heaves into view, lying to her net, fairly close aboard. I go to the companionway and stick my head out to get a better look at her. To my horror I realize that Lloyd, steering, never saw her until that instant. We were lucky our track wasn't 100 feet farther to leeward. My view from below was out under the foot of the jib, but his from the helm was right into the sail. The things should either be high-cut or have a long row of rectangular windows.*

I was interested to note that the rectangular cabinhouse windows that Nat Herreshoff put in several of his designs of about the size of the New York Thirties were one of the few characteristics of the design specified ("glass transom lights" in the cabinhouse) by the New York Yacht Club committee charged with having the 30-footers built. They certainly provide plenty of light in the cabin; the Thirties have an airy feeling below because of them. This is good, for the boats are a bit cramped below for their length. Because of their low freeboard and low cabinhouses, they don't have full headroom.

The original arrangement had two quarter berths, a transom on each side in the cabin, head forward to port, galley forward to starboard, and a fo'c's'le under the foredeck with a couple of pipe berths. Lloyd gradually changed the *Cockatoo*'s cabin so that she had a galley and a good big chart table aft to starboard, quarter berth to port, "love-seat" to starboard in the cabin, and transom and narrow pilot berth to port. The forward arrangement remained unchanged except for the conversion of the former galley space into an area with big lockers.

There is grace to the way a New York Thirty moves through the water under any conditions. When it is blowing hard she roars along, the foam of her wake nearly up to her rail at the stern. Going to windward, she eats up through the seas with a minimum of fuss.

The Thirty does better in a light breeze close-hauled than any boat I have been on. And when it's light, she is not unduly bothered by a bobble of a sea — the nemesis of many an otherwise fast boat.

It doesn't take much breeze to get her really moving. She's not particularly quick at accelerating, but as the breeze builds, her speed keeps increasing imperceptibly until you suddenly notice that she's going a lot faster than she was.

From the helm you get a clear view all around the decks and rail of a Thirty, so you can enjoy to the fullest the way her long, slim hull works through the waves. Sitting at the tiller looking aft at her long, lean stern moving swiftly through the water, you get a sense of elegant power.

The helm of a Thirty feels heavy, as if everything about the boat has great momentum: her forward motion, her refusal to make leeway, her reluctance to yaw. You can sense that big, deep chunk of lead keeping everything going steadily as it should be. There's no doubt that the Thirty is a very fast boat; and with her low freeboard her speed is made to seem even greater than it is.

For the 75th birthday of the New York Thirties in 1980, Lloyd Bergeson's plan was to assemble a gang of us who had sailed with him over the years in the *Cockatoo* and do some racing against less historic vessels. He had, however, a higher priority for the *Cockatoo:* a voyage from Maine to Norway and an exploration of the coastline where his forebears put to sea. This cruise he made, crossing the Atlantic singlehanded in the summer of 1978, cruising in Norway that summer and part of the next, and setting off on the return crossing with his son Henry. Lloyd and Henry lost their vessel but not their lives to the hole behind an ultimate wave in mid-Atlantic. Lloyd told that story well in the January 1980 issue of *Cruising World.*

William H. Taylor called the New York Thirty "the most famous one-design class this country has ever seen." They are some fine boats, boats that deserve to be sailed and cared for by the best seamen around. The *Cockatoo,* for one, got just that.

---

*I mentioned this incident in connection with a motorsailer designed by Gordon Munro with similar windows in her cabinhouse in *More Good Boats*. I say this only so you won't think I'm so senile I don't know when I am repeating myself. Of course, I don't indicate every time I repeat myself.

39/ The *Scrimshaw*

Length on deck: 31 feet 2 inches
Beam: 18 feet 8 inches
Draft: 2 feet 9 inches
Sail area: 453 square feet
Displacement: 5,600 pounds
Designer: Jim Brown

On my office bulletin board is a cartoon, clipped out for me by one of my colleagues, showing a guy at a big desk absolutely covered with little bits of paper with notes on them. He is saying to the person across the desk, "Let me just make a little note of that. I never seem to get anything done around here unless I make little notes." My colleague gave me the cartoon because that's the way I am, always making little notes of things that I hope someday to get done.

Somewhere in the midst of working on Jim Brown's book *The Case for the Cruising Trimaran,* I pulled out an index card and made a little note on it: "Get a sail in a Searunner."

I kept that little note handy for over a year before I was able to crease the card and heave it one October day. It was the day Jim and Jo Anna Brown took a small group of us sailing in their Searunner 31, the *Scrimshaw.*

Jim's book was the first thing I had read on multihulls that made seamanlike sense to me. He designs trimarans for cruising, not for racing. He is attracted to the type for its high performance, among other things, but rather than go all out for speed he goes all out for safety and comfort, and then takes what speed is left over, which is considerable. His Searunners can carry a half-decent cruising payload, and he keeps that payload down in the middle of the center hull to give his vessels maximum stability. He tries to create safe, comfortable, fast vessels — not record-breakers — in which to keep the sea.

I was excited to be going sailing in a real multihull, my only previous experience with the type being a dismasting in a 17-foot catamaran in a flat calm. A cotter pin dropped out of the pin of the shackle holding the forestay to the mast, and the whole rig fell aft, neatly bisecting the craft. Fortunately, one of us was perched on each hull at the time, so the spar fell harmlessly between us. We left it right there and paddled home.

Jim Brown calls the Searunner 31 the "klutz" of the series. She is not the smallest; there is a 25-footer. Then there's a 34, a 37, and a 40.

Jim built the *Scrimshaw* eight years ago. He and his family use her as a way of traveling. Jim and Jo Anna had come to Camden, Maine, in her from their home in Virginia, via Nova Scotia. Their idea of cruising is to get somewhere that appeals to them and stay a while. To them the best part of cruising is getting to know people in different places. With their two sons they made a three-year odyssey from California to Virginia through the Panama Canal.

Soon after we were all on board, Jim pulled his little dinghy up alongside the port ama, politely waved

Left: *Jim Brown. (Jim Sollers).* **Below:** *The sailplan of the Searunner 31.* (Searunner Construction Manual *by Jim Brown)*

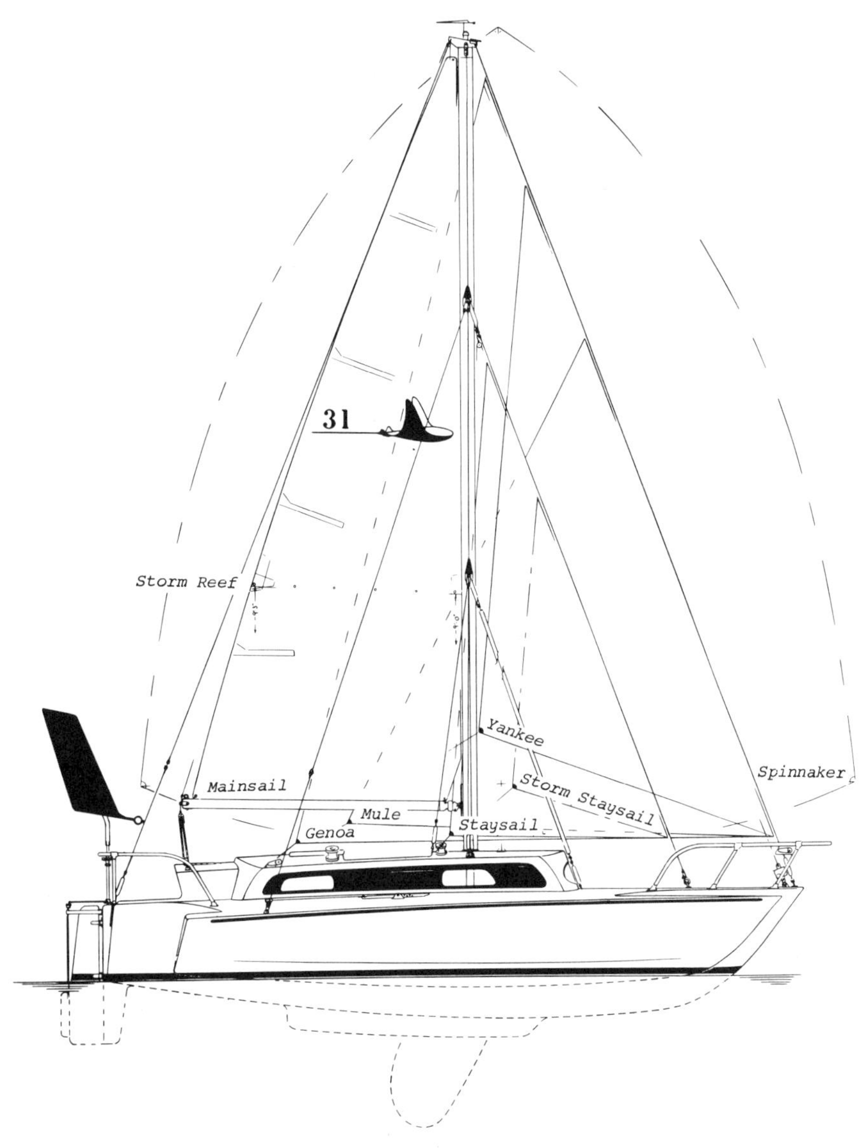

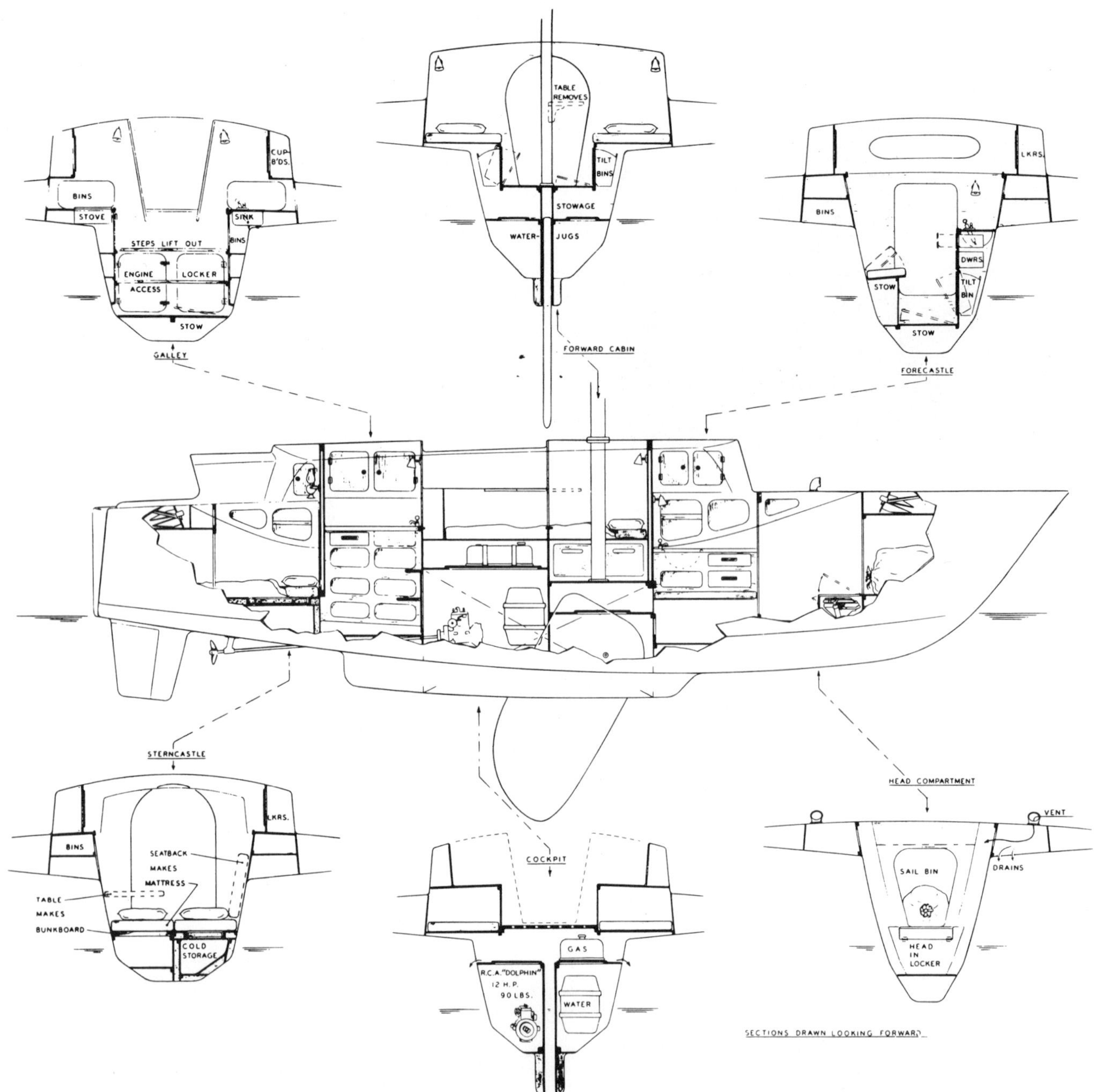

The interior arrangement drawings of the Searunner 31. (Searunner Construction Manual *by Jim Brown)*

would-be helpers out of the way, hauled the little boat easily up on board, and swiveled her fore and aft. It wasn't blowing much, so he didn't even need to lash her down. In three seconds he had brought her on board and she was all nestled in the netting between the main hull and the ama. When at sea, Jim stows her atop the house, back aft.

We were tied to the lee side of a moored float, wind abeam. Jim and Jo Anna cast her off, let her slide off sideways a few feet, ran up and trimmed a genoa jib, and then set the mainsail at their leisure. Off we went, as smoothly as you please.

The *Scrimshaw* consists of a lot of hulls. There are three of them, and the amas are nearly as long as the

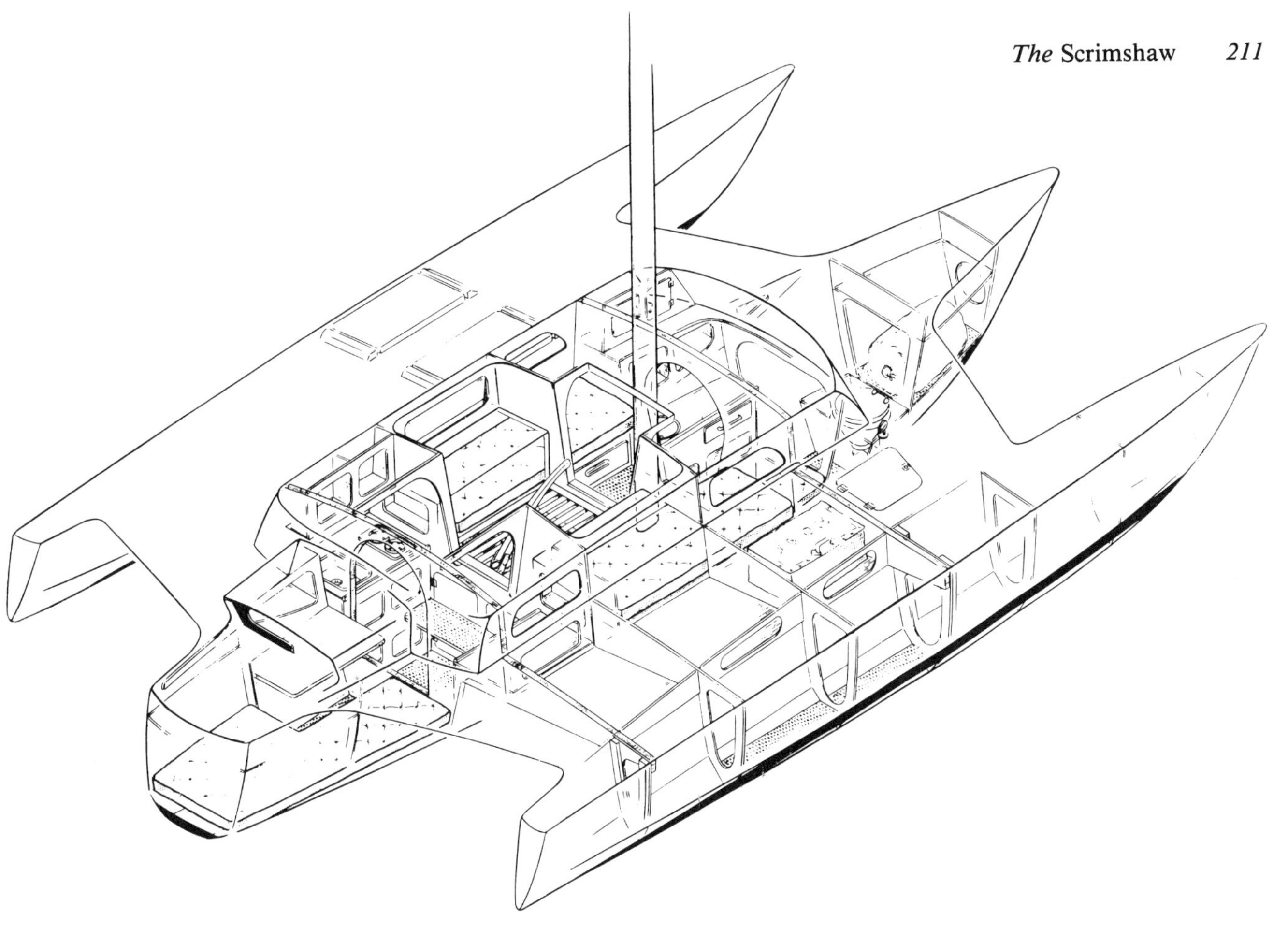

An interior perspective of the Searunner 31. (Searunner Construction Manual *by Jim Brown)*

main hull. It seems as if you are embarked in either a fairly sizable fleet of vessels, or at least in a large, complicated ship. Another first impression is that this fleet, or ship, sits high and very lightly on top of the water.

I might as well say right here that the *Scrimshaw* is not a pretty boat. Interesting-looking and businesslike, but not pretty. Why couldn't she have lovely whaleboat-like bows and sterns to all her hulls and at least a gentle, rather than absolutely flat, sheerline? The pretty ends would have to be higher and longer to achieve the same buoyancy in the hulls and so would increase windage and pitching moment, to be sure. It's a trade-off I'd gladly make.

Without my presumptuous modifications, the *Scrimshaw* measures 31 feet 2 inches long on deck, with a beam of 18 feet 8 inches and a draft of 2 feet 9 inches, board up. The main hull has a beam of 5 feet. The amas are 27 feet 2 inches long on deck with beams of 2 feet 5 inches. Provisioned for short-range cruising, she displaces 5,600 pounds. She can carry another 1,400 pounds of gear and stores for long cruises. Her sail area is 453 square feet.

The *Scrimshaw*'s hulls and superstructure are built of plywood covered with fiberglass on the outside and sealed with resin on the inside. Each ama is held to the main hull by two aluminum girders running athwartships.

We reached across Camden Harbor in the light breeze, sailing right away from a heavy-displacement cruising boat wallowing along in our wake. She looked a bit precarious back there, balancing along without any amas for support.

We sailed out past Sherman Point and hardened up on the starboard tack, heading across Penobscot Bay. Watching her go from the cockpit, the *Scrimshaw* appears rather clumsy. There's a lot of structure spread out in all directions; you're on a big raft. But then you look at the water rushing by and you realize that this great raft is sailing along very nicely, thank you.

Peering down through the netting on the weather side, you see that the windward ama is flying. Not touching the water at all. Just flying along over it. You climb out onto this flying platform to see what she looks like from there. Now this is fantastic, you've gotten

The Scrimshaw *in Penobscot Bay. (Jim Sollers)*

You can get "right off the boat" and watch her go from the weather ama. (Jim Sollers)

right off the boat and are looking back at her, watching her knife along through the water. Who says you never get to see your own boat sail? Anytime you want that thrill in a trimaran, you just walk out onto the weather ama and watch her go to your heart's content.

You can also watch the lee ama from the main hull. It's a very long skinny boat indeed, and is charging along through the waves under the pressing burden of the heeling force of the rig of a bigger hull locked to it to windward. You feel kind of sorry for the little ama thrashing along down there. "Hey, big shot. Try carrying your own rig for a while."

Stability there is plenty of. Jim Brown says that when the lee ama starts to dive through the seas it is time to reef. He says he actually shortens sail with the first dollop of spray. "We reef her a lot." This is conservative, high-speed sailing, not going for broke.

The *Scrimshaw* has a snug cutter rig. Her shrouds attach at the sides of the house, giving her rig what might be considered average monohull spread. This arrangement allows normal sheeting of a genoa jib on the wind. Preventer backstays can be set up to the amas, giving an enviable angle of pull.

The *Scrimshaw* has steps on her mast so you can climb up to clear a fouled halyard or whatever. (Of course, you have to watch out that the halyards don't foul on the steps themselves.) All her sheets are right in the cockpit.

Out in the middle of the bay we ran into a little lump of a head sea, and she seemed a bit pitchy. Do two or three skinny bows (the number depends on whether or not the head sea reaches the weather ama) pitch more than one fat one? (I'd still be willing to try my nicely curved bows and sterns.)

How fast does she go? Well, as a Dark Ages sailor who is used to sailing around in relatively heavy, fat craft without those slavish side helpers to keep the boat sailing relatively level, I must say her speed is impressive. The breeze increased to moderate for a while, so we saw her in light, gentle, and moderate conditions; and though I wouldn't describe her speed as phenomenal, it was certainly impressive. My 32-foot Herreshoff, the *Aria,* described in *More Good Boats,* couldn't have stayed with her. And, of course, off the wind in a breeze these trimarans move up onto a whole 'nother speed range.

The only direct comparison we had to the *Scrimshaw*'s sailing ability that day was the husky cruising sloop we outdistanced rapidly leaving the harbor. Of course, that vessel, of about the same length, was carrying around a lot more accommodations and could carry a much bigger payload.

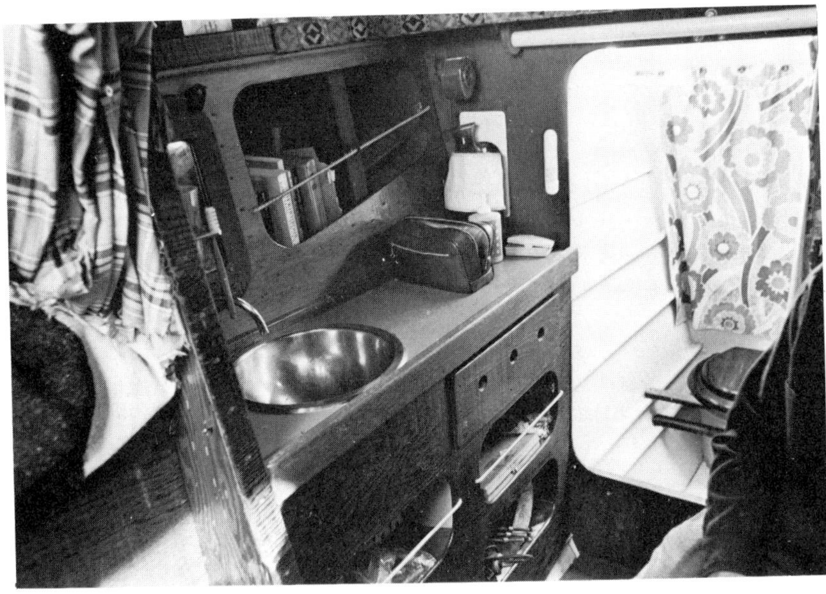

The washroom with the WC beyond. (Jim Sollers)

The main saloon (with table pushed back), movie playing. (Jim Sollers)

The *Scrimshaw* seemed sensitive to the vagaries of wind and wave, like any light-displacement boat. She accelerates like mad.

The *Scrimshaw* steers differently from any other boat I have sailed. In an overall sense, she is steady on her helm. She is nicely balanced and isn't trying to suddenly change course 45 degrees. She tacks majestically but surely. Yet on a small scale, she yaws around and has to be steered like a dinghy or an IOR boat. She has an outboard rudder, and Jim has a good wind-vane self-steerer on her.

After you have spent a bit of time in one of these trimaran contraptions, you begin to appreciate a few of the advantages of having three hulls sailing along side by side. You can handle the vessel entirely from the main hull, and if you should fall off it in so doing, you probably will fall into a nice netting or something instead of the ocean (a good reason to make these nettings very strong). There are even lifelines on the outboard sides of the amas to remind those with exceptionally strong wanderlust that there is, after all, some limit to the distance you can walk safely in a straight line.

Outboard of the house and cockpit structure, running fore and aft on each side is a heavy plank like a running board on an old-fashioned car. I found these contrivances a delightful contrast to the smooth, slick, modern-looking construction of the rest of the vessel. Climbing out of the cockpit for a stroll on one of those long heavy planks is like leaving the city for a visit to a farm.

And out there on the wings of the vessel you can lash down all sorts of ungainly stuff like spinnaker poles, boat hooks, and sounding poles. In the amas themselves there is plenty of space for light gear to be put away.

At the ends of the amas you can have fittings for great widespread bridles, a rigger's delight whether working with ground tackle at the forward end of the vessel or, say, a drogue at the after end.

When we got out near the islands in the bay, the idea was to put Jim Sollers, his cameras around his neck, out in the little dinghy to take pictures of the *Scrimshaw* as she circled around him and sailed by. We tacked her, left the genoa jib aback, hove-to, launched the dinghy, and sent Jim on his mission. He looked a bit lonely, even in the small sea. Discovered that a weather spreader had poked a hole in the poor old genoa, so we shifted to forestaysail and Yankee jib. The sail drill was performed by Jim and Jo Anna Brown, obviously a competent cruising team. We helped by staying out of the way. Then we steered various courses past the dinghy trying to look photogenic.

As a local, I was asked to explain the meaning of a massive dark cloud bank building up in the northwest. Since the breeze was steady from the southwest, I said not to worry. In fifteen minutes it was raining, and in thirty minutes it was a flat calm. We brought Jim Sollers back on board, followed by the dinghy. He was quite impressed with the difference between the small-boat feeling of the diminutive rowing boat and the big-ship feeling of the high, wide trimaran.

We all got out of the wet and let her drift. It was a benign little shower. Otherwise, Jim could have rigged his dodger over the forward end of the cockpit and even his canvas seat that goes into the forward companionway giving him a comfortable place from which to conn in comfort.

The breeze seemed to have taken off for good, so Jim lowered his 4-horsepower long-shaft outboard that was mounted on the stern and lighted her off. We headed back for Camden Harbor at a steady 4 knots. Jim says the Searunner 31 will do about six with his maximum recommended engine of 20 horsepower. Standard tankage for the design is not great: fuel, 20 gallons; water, 25 gallons.

It was a lovely evening as we plodded across a now-glassy bay. There was spectacular fall color on the Camden Hills. Well-defined, dense clouds slowly changed their immense sculptures overhead. All at once they left a long tunnel to the light of the low sun — it was just the right size for a giant to throw a medicine ball through — and the brightness from that cloudy shaft shone on the gray water like moonlight.

We tied up the *Scrimshaw* to her float just about dark, and then huddled out of the chill in the sterncastle. Jo Anna kept filling up mugs with hot cider. It's a tiny, snug little saloon back there with just room for four people to sit at the table playing kneesies. It may be a bit cramped physically, but never mentally, for your eyes are close to the wide stern window overlooking the harbor lights. You just can't keep from doing what one Searunner builder called "watching the movie."

The accommodations in the narrow main hull of the *Scrimshaw* are laid out in an exceedingly clever way to make use of what space there is. Away forward is stowage space. Next aft is the head compartment with sitting headroom. Then there is a stand-up washroom and wetroom. Next, in way of the mast, a sleeping area with two berths tucked away in the wings. Stowage for heavy gear is under this compartment and under the high center cockpit.

Go down the after companionway and you're in the stand-up galley. And right aft is the sterncastle with its narrow seats and table, or, when converted, a double berth and its free movie, playing continuously.

Since I disapprove of broadcasters telling you who won the election with less than two percent of the vote counted, I'm not going to pronounce any great conclusions with regard to trimarans. The *Scrimshaw* certainly captured my attention. I want to sail a lot more in these vessels, and the feeling is so strong I haven't even had to make a little note about it.

40/ The *Bionic Slug*

Length on deck: 24 feet
Length on waterline: 20 feet
Beam: 8 feet 11 inches
Draft: 4 feet
Sail area: 261 square feet
Displacement: 2,700 pounds
Designer: Rodney S. Johnstone

One year at the New York Boat Show we played a cruel trick on one of our cohorts, an editor at International Marine, the boating book publishers. Our book booth was right around the corner from where they were showing off the J-24, and our editor had spent most of his time at the show drooling over that fast-looking boat. We fed him this story about how the J-boat people were willing to sell him a boat at a discount with a couple dozen exotic sails thrown in. The poor fellow was some disappointed when he found we were pulling his leg.

I spent some time myself around the corner eyeballing this fancy machine. As an old dog who can easily visualize myself going to sea in something like Slocum's *Spray,* I didn't really think she was my type of vessel. Yet there was something purposeful in her look; she certainly had every appearance of being able to sail. So, months later, I jumped at the chance to try out my friend Del Babb's J-24, the *Bionic Slug.*

As is the fashion in these new-fangled sailing machines, her name is scrawled in huge letters all down each side. Approaching her in the launch, one of the passengers, probably on his way out to some saltily named vessel, asked Del where he'd ever come up with that name. Del looked at his J-24 for a second and then said, "Well, I couldn't call her the *American Eagle,* could I?"

A few minutes later we were underway in a rather nice northerly breeze that actually stayed steady for a few minutes at a time and varied over the next couple of hours from light to fresh, giving us a chance to try her out in quite a variety of breezes. Some fun!

The first J-24 was designed and built by Rodney S. Johnstone in his garage in Stonington, Connecticut, in 1976. He wanted a relatively small boat for his big family to sail, race, and cruise in. "She was just my idea of what a good sailing boat ought to be."

The Johnstones raced her in the spring Off Soundings race that year. She won the thing. At the cocktail party afterward on Block Island, Rod Johnstone was on the receiving end of a lot of congratulations about his new boat. One man who came up to Rod was Ed Raymond, a crusty old sea dog of a sailmaker who had seen and done it all when it comes to boats and sailing. "Good going, Rod," says Ed. *"That's a really nice-looking boat you've got there."* Rod Johnstone later told me, "It was when *Ed Raymond* said that to me that I first realized that I might really have something in this boat."

Rod and his brother Robert, a marketing expert from Alcort, the Sunfish makers, decided to see what they could do about having some boats built to the design and promoting the idea of racing, sailing, and cruising

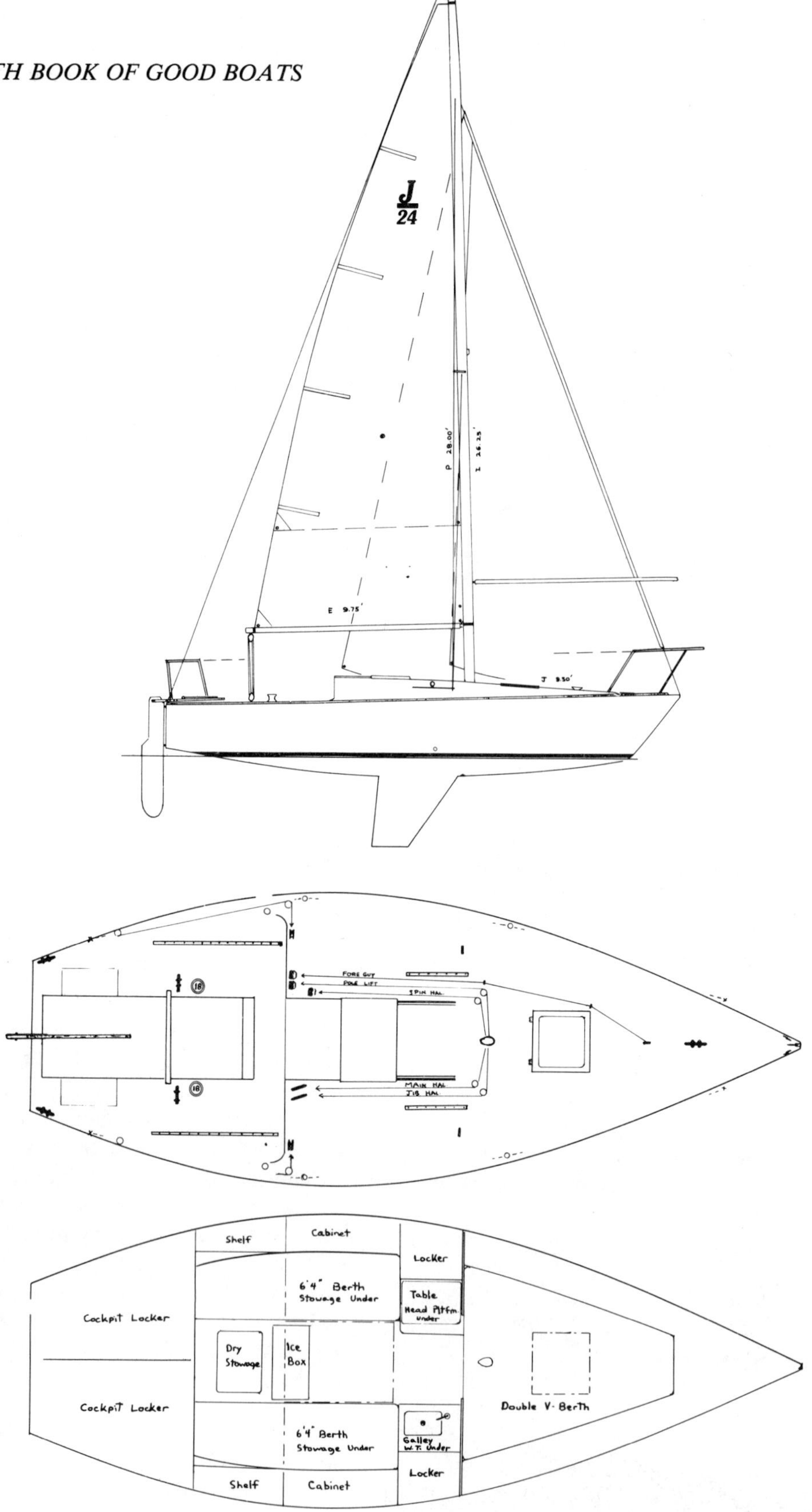

The sailplan and interior arrangement of the J-24. (J Boats)

Ballast to windward helps the J-24 stay on her feet. (Alex Brown)

The Bionic Slug *living up to her name? (Alex Brown)*

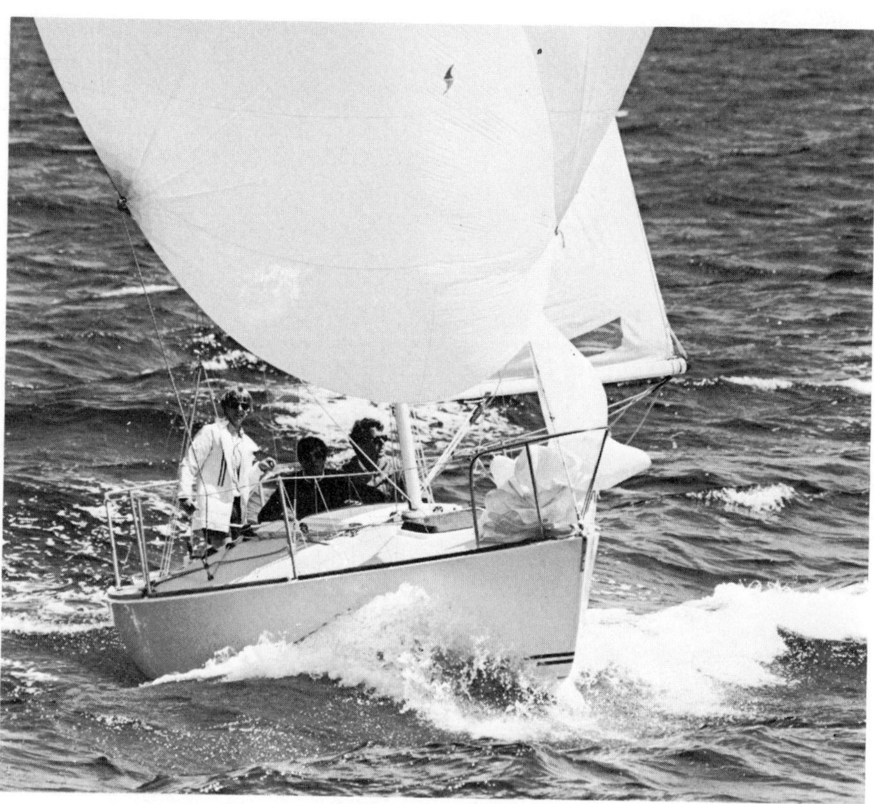

A J-24 is a lively creature with spinnaker set to a fresh breeze. (J Boats)

in them. They started advertising in 1977, telling you that the builder of this new J-24 thing was Tillotson-Pearson, "builders of the Etchells 22" (whatever that is).

A lot of people agreed that the J-24 idea made sense. There are now 3,000 of them sailing, of which some 2,000 are actively raced.

Rod Johnstone says that one of the reasons for the great success of the J-24 as a one-design racing class is that class officials are strict about not allowing modifications to the boat. If you get smart and tamper with rig or sails or add a little surface to this appendage or shave a little off that one, you find yourself putting your J-24 back exactly the way she was designed and built before that race, if that's when your changes are discovered; or, if they escape notice and you win races, you find yourself giving back the trophies during the inspection ceremony that follows the applause. The result is that as long as you race in the J-24 class, you know you can compete with other sailors on an equal footing, rather than having to try to sail faster than souped-up rule-beaters.

J-24 sailing has become a sort of movement. There's a 100-page slick J-24 magazine in which you can respond to advertisements for J-24 ties, J-24 sweaters, J-24 blazer emblems, J-24 half models, J-24 cocktail glasses, J-24 plaques, J-24 14-karat pendants, J-24 billfolds, J-24 blazer buttons, J-24 tool kits, J-24 carryalls, J-24 tote bags, and, of course, J-24 T-shirts. What do you think of that, Captain Slocum?

The balsa-core fiberglass hulls of J-24s are built in Fall River, Massachusetts, and they are also put together in such far-flung places as California, Brazil, Argentina, England, Japan, and Australia.

As soon as Del and I worked the *Bionic Slug* clear of her mooring under mainsail and Del ran up the jib, I could see that this boat sure is light 'n' lively. She just stepped right out in the gentle breeze and danced nimbly out through the anchored boats. Away we reached, out into the bay, where we found a bit more breeze. It might have been blowing 12 knots. We put her on a beam reach chasing after a big yawl. She climbed right up to 6.59 knots or so and chattered along up there within a dozen hundredths either side of that. The *Bionic Slug* has a digital speedometer that measures her speed to the nearest hundredth of a knot. Fascinating. We didn't catch our big yawl, but she didn't pull away from us much either.

Jamming her up on the wind, we found (Del didn't "find," because he knew it all along, but he was polite enough to share in my excitement) that she is very close-winded indeed. Fairly eats to windward. Now our target was a big marconi cutter. We tacked after her, inside 90 degrees if anything, despite the fact that the breeze was

These quick little boats do throw a bit of spray, to be sure. (Alex Brown)

Del Babb spoiling himself at the helm of the Bionic Slug. *(Alex Brown)*

taking off and leaving a bit of a bobble. We gained rapidly on the big boat ahead under these conditions.

The J-24 is 24 feet long on deck, with a waterline length of 20 feet, a beam of 8 feet 11 inches, and a draft of 4 feet. Her working sail area is 261 square feet. She displaces a mere 2,700 pounds, with 935 pounds of that in outside ballast. What she is, is a fat 24-foot dinghy with a fin keel.

She ain't pretty, but there's something about her low freeboard, squared-off stern with its outboard rudder, and high-crowned flush deck that make her look — well, intriguing.

The flush deck crowns up fore and aft as well as athwartships. I never can get used to looking *down* along the deck to the bow; the thwartships crown gives you a level patch to walk on however she's heeled.

The J-24 has a definite but light weather helm. Like other light-displacement fin-keelers, she has to be steered every second, but she responds like a cat chasing a mouse. You can spin her round really fast. The first time I tacked her, I surprised Del by putting the helm right over. This is sort of like shoving the stick at the instrument panel in a Mach 2 jet — you just don't do it. Once I got my leg on the wrong side of the tiller and she whipped off 6 or 8 compass points before I could skip free. There's a hiking stick on the tiller, as on any good dinghy.

The sails go up in grooves; there's a headstay foil with two grooves in it so you don't have to take one jib down before putting another up. All aerodynamically efficient, I am sure, but when you lower the sails, they're all adrift.

She has internal halyards, an internal outhaul adjustable at the inner end of the boom, Cunningham, boom vang, traveling car for the mainsheet, and jiffy reefing. The backstay has a four-part tackle on a slide on its bridle to use for bending the mast all over the place. When tacking or jibing you have to look out for her head-high droopy boom.

I wondered how steadily she'd heave-to, so on one tack we left the jib aback, eventually got her slowed down, and put the helm down. She stayed put just fine, but it wasn't rough or blowing hard.

We ran her off and found she had a rather quick little roll with the bobble working in under her quarter. According to Del, she's exciting to sail off the wind in a real breeze, planing with spinnaker set. He's seen her speedometer say 11.00.

The vessel has no real cockpit; you sit on deck with your feet in a well. Presumably, this can get a little damp at times.

She is nicely laid out below. A double bunk forward, two quarter berths, and just sitting headroom on the forward ends of the latter. The galley is amidships. I am not sure I'd want to cruise far in her with four people on board, but somehow her four bunks don't seem as ridiculous as you might think in such a small boat.

Coming back into the harbor close-hauled again, it breezed up and we got some fresh, maybe even strong, gusts off the hulls. We luffed the main and she heeled well over and seemed to sort of skitter along in the blasts, yet she hung on fairly well and footed fast. I guess we needed more weight to keep her upright.

Or, maybe we should have taken the jib off and sailed her under mainsail alone. Her mainsail is big enough so that she doesn't die without a headsail. It's a beautiful airfoil. When we made the mooring with the jib off, she was certainly perfectly maneuverable under mainsail alone, which is more than you can say for a lot of the modern racing boats.

Del Babb is relatively new to this crazy business of sailing around in small boats. The *Bionic Slug* is the first boat he's owned and the first one he's sailed in a lot. I wasn't about to reveal to him how spoiled he is. Shucks, if Del goes out someday in some ordinary boat, he'll probably cry from boredom.

41/ The *Nimbus*

Length on deck: 25 feet 6 inches
Length on waterline: 20 feet
Beam: 6 feet 4 inches
Draft: 2 feet 10 inches
Sail area: 301 square feet
Displacement: 3,700 pounds
Designer: Peter Van Dine

Drew McManus, down on Cape Cod, used to have an interesting approach to boat ownership. He'd buy a new boat every spring, keep her in pristine shape while sailing her all summer, put her on the market in the fall, sell her in the winter, and be ready to repeat the cycle. Once he'd swallowed the initial capital investment, he didn't spend much of anything on boating, he had the enjoyment of boats in near-perfect condition without having to do a lot of maintenance work, and he got to try out a lot of different boats over a period of years.

I was Drew's customer for a 25-foot Tancook whaler designed and built by Peter Van Dine of Annapolis, Maryland, which enabled him to buy one of Phil Bolger's Dovekies (see *Still More Good Boats)* built by Edey & Duff.

Thus began what was for me a three-year affair with a lissome lady with whom I had no right to be hooked up. It's only now that we've been separated for a couple of years that I can bear to tell you about her.

The *Nimbus* is one of 12 sisters, all built by Peter Van Dine. He also designed and built a big 35-foot version of the type. These are rather close replicas of the Tancook whaler, the local fishing and fetch-and-carry boats of Tancook Island, Nova Scotia, well known for their beauty, speed, and seaworthiness. Peter researched the type carefully, came up with a hull shape that a Tancook Islander would have been proud of, molded his hulls in fiberglass and built everything else in the boats of wood.

I thought *Nimbus* ("a rain cloud," but also "an atmosphere, as of romance, about a person or a thing") was a fine name for the little vessel, for more than one smallish fishing schooner has carried it honorably and, besides, the word was nicely painted on a pair of handsome oak quarterboards well secured to her topsides near the stern.

Of course I fell in love with her very fine, very pretty, slippery-looking hull. She has a perfect sheerline, a perfect hollow to her after waterlines, and a perfect curvature in her topsides. Her stem profile is just a little too straight to my eye; I always wished her clipper bow was more accentuated. She has quite a bit of drag to her keel, but enough depth of forefoot so a head sea didn't shove her bow off. She has very easy bow and buttock lines. Her entry is not as hollow as I expected for a Tancook whaler, yet she never stopped when hitting a sea and is just full enough forward not to root at all off the wind. She has lovely wineglass sections and flare in the topsides all around her waterline, which is important to the stability of a narrow, shoal hull. This flare all around the waterline also gives her a light and airy appearance in the water.

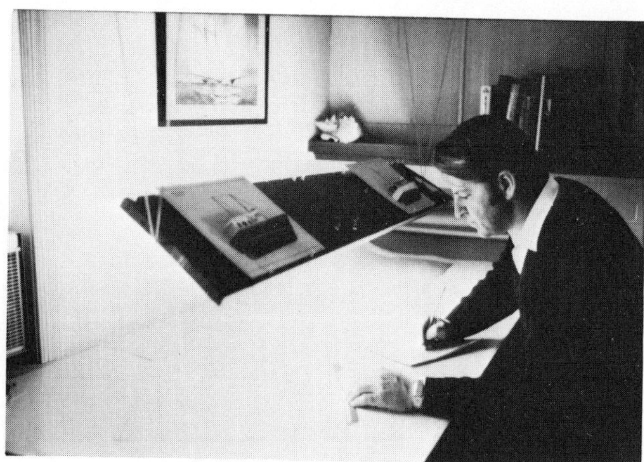

Peter D. Van Dine. (Robert de Gast)

The *Nimbus* is 25 feet 6 inches long on deck, with a waterline length of 20 feet, a beam of only 6 feet 4 inches, and a draft of only 2 feet 10 inches, with the centerboard up. She displaces 3,700 pounds, of which 1,600 pounds is ballast. Her sail area is 301 square feet in three working sails, plus another 100 square feet in the fisherman staysail.

Her ballast consists of steel punchings set in cement. The hull is all of a piece above this ballast, so she could pound on the bottom a bit without leaking.

Her outboard rudder is wood and its pintle-and-gudgeon arrangement — just a pin through two adjacent eyes; one lagged into the sternpost, the other into the rudder — is the only crude thing on the boat. It is just a little sloppy and lets the rudder stand out from the sternpost a little too far for really good looks. I was interested that one of her many admirers picked up on this minor flaw in her otherwise-perfect appearance and commented on it right away.

Her centerboard is asbestos cement covered with fiberglass; it is very light and easy to handle.

The little vessel was built by Peter Van Dine to a very high standard. Her molded fiberglass hull is extremely fair. Her deck is white cedar, strip-planked and painted; her cabin sides and coaming are white cedar finished natural. She has a nice oak toerail and a fairly heavy oak rubbing strake. Her cabintop is foam-sandwich fiberglass, well crowned and plenty strong.

The bulkhead between cabin and cockpit is vertical tongue-and-groove stuff. We never did succeed in getting this bulkhead fully watertight, which it certainly should have been.

Taking care of the *Nimbus* was a cinch. I'd have her plucked out of the water by a harborside crane in the fall and dropped onto her trailer. She'd come home to the backyard for an immediate bottom scrub. Get her all cleaned up and trundle her off to a boatyard shed for the winter. As soon as the snow had melted, back she'd roll into the driveway for the spring "fitting out." This consisted of wiping off her bottom with a rag and giving her two coats of the cheapest red antifouling I could find; auto-polishing the topsides; painting the deck (one tablespoon of pumice per quart for a perfect nonskid surface, formula courtesy of Peter Van Dine); touching up the cockpit paintwork; and scraping and giving two coats of varnish to the rail and rubbing strake.

The rig would have been given a going-over during the winter. Her nice, hollow, varnished spruce masts were slid into the cellar through the usual tiny ground-level window, and the rest of her wooden spars, blocks, deadeyes, and belaying pins were lugged downstairs too, so the cellar became a rigging loft, and the smell of varnish gave a lift to more than one January thaw.

There were seven spars to varnish, counting the tiller, but not counting the foresail, jib, and fisherman clubs, which never needed attention during my ownership, for they seem to be protected from weathering by their respective sails. Of course, the fisherman was stowed below when it wasn't set. The gaffs were two diminutive, interchangeable sticks. The masts were beautifully made; I was always going to stuff a bunch of tinfoil up the hollow of the mainmast for a radar reflector but never got around to it.

Her mainmast is not quite as tall as a Tancook Islander might have made it, which hurts her looks a little and kills a little of the advantage of the fisherman, but I must say the slightly shorter spar made putting up her rig just that much easier. I could just do it alone.

The foremast could simply be manhandled into a vertical position and lowered through the deck into its step on the vessel's backbone. Then set up the forestay and the foremast's single shrouds.

Now came the tricky part, for the mainmast steps on top of the centerboard trunk and has no bury to hold it up while you set up the rigging.

I'd lay the mast in the cockpit with the masthead out over the stern. Reeve off the deadeyes and lanyards on the shrouds so they'd be slack while the mast was going up, but would hold it aft and athwartships once it got up. The most convenient line leading from the foremast head to haul the mainmast up to a vertical position was the fisherman staysail throat halyard. Make one end of it fast to the eye in the free end of the springstay, the eye that was to go over the head of the foremast. Stand back in the cockpit where I could steady the mast, and heave away, raising it up, steadying it from swinging outboard, and, when above 45 degrees or so, lifting its heel

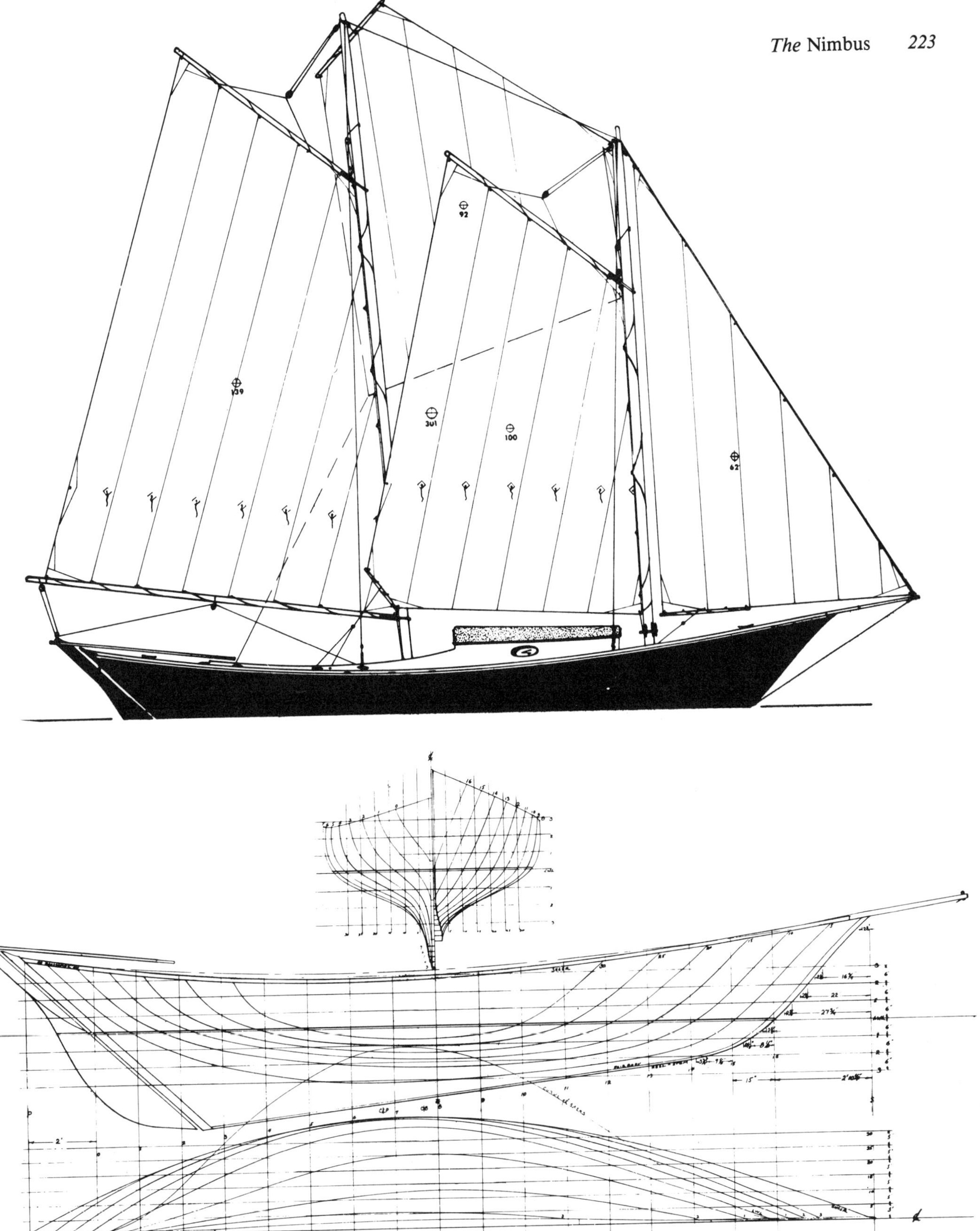

The sailplan and lines of the Tancook whaler Nimbus. *(Peter D. Van Dine)*

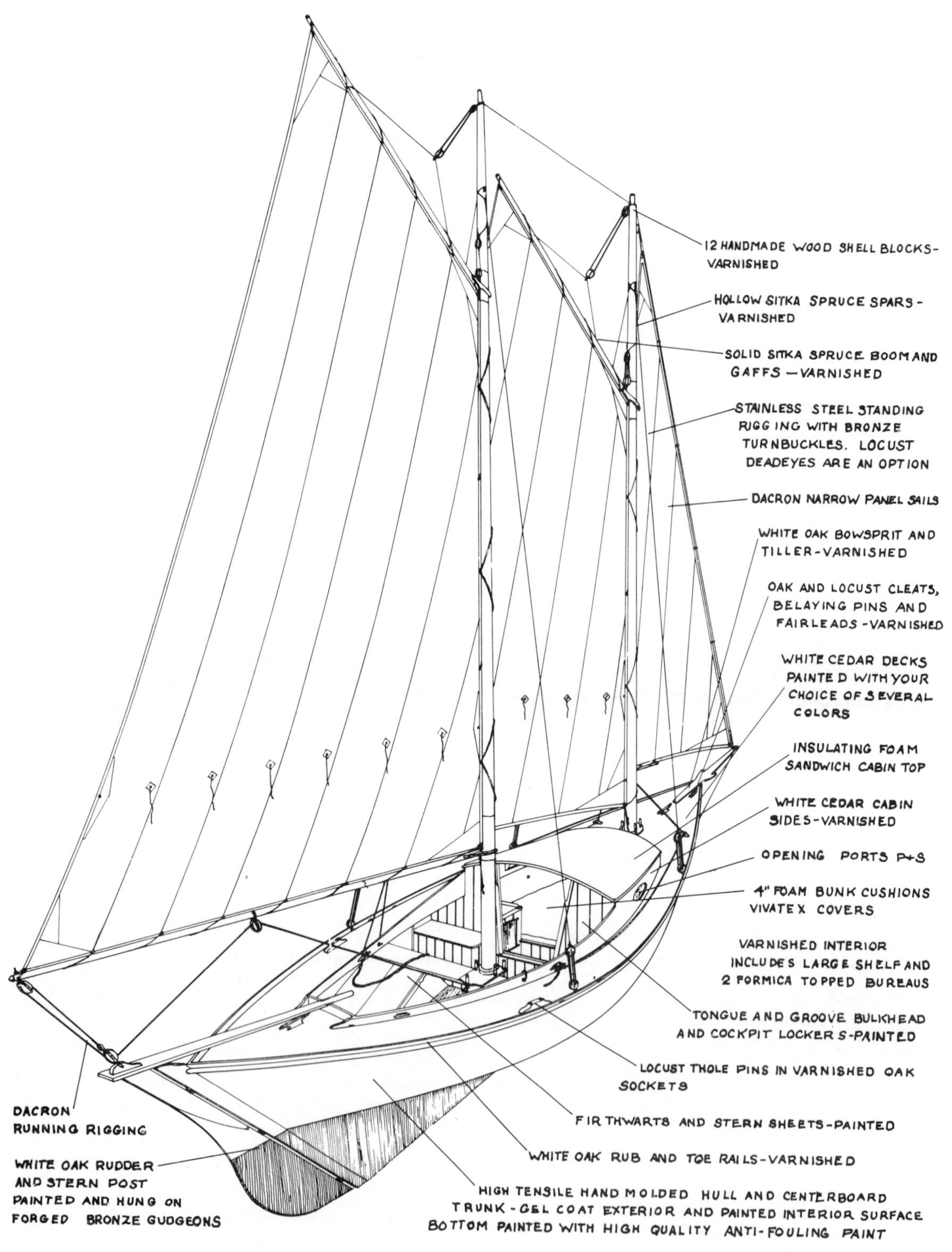

A perspective drawing showing her interior arrangement. (Peter D. Van Dine)

into the mast step on the centerboard trunk, then continuing to heave right up until the springstay was up against the foremast head and the main shrouds came tight. Then all that remained was to get to the foremast head to slip the eye of the springstay over the masthead. I cheated on this in Camden Harbor, for there was a little staging coming off the harbor wall to take a gangway down to a float, and at low tide from this staging, my foremast head was right in front of my eyes.

When I was trying to make up my mind whether or not to buy the *Nimbus,* I used to worry about the mainmast being stepped on top of the centerboard trunk. What a crazy scheme, I thought. So I decided to call up Peter Van Dine to try to get him to agree that such an arrangement didn't make any sense. "I was wondering about the mainmast being stepped on the centerboard trunk," I said to Peter on the phone to open the discussion.

"Yes, wasn't that lucky?" Peter said. "It just happened to work out that way." In the conversation that followed, it dawned on me that with fiberglass construction, the centerboard trunk is a strong girder rather than a source of leaks. All you have to do to convert it to a mast step is give the top of it some support athwartships, which Peter did with a thwart right across the boat in way of the mast step.

The standing and running rigging on the *Nimbus* is all too small, in my opinion. Oh, it's plenty strong — at least no *rigging* carried away on her in my experience — but it's so tiny it hurts your fingers to catch hold of a shroud to steady yourself when she's jumping a bit, or give that last little swig on the foresail sheet to flatten it in. A little more diameter all around wouldn't do her any harm.

When I started sailing her, I found myself once again worrying about that mainmast stepped on top of the centerboard trunk. All in the world that was holding the spar aloft was the springstay and two shrouds, a triangle of single wires. If any one of the three should carry away, the mast would suddenly be swinging around by the other two. So I doubled up, by rigging a second springstay right alongside the first and by rigging a pair of preventer backstays, making down to eyebolts in the deck with lanyards, about 18 inches aft of the shrouds.

The shrouds made down to eyebolts in the deck, the lower deadeyes being secured to the eyebolts simply with a none-too-hefty bolt through the eye, which thus took a bending strain. Peter Van Dine warned me about this arrangement, saying that on second thought it ought to be beefed up with bigger eyebolts. Good idea, I thought, and I think I'll change those crossbolts that take the bending strain from bronze to stainless steel for greater strength while I'm at it. But I didn't get around to doing this simple job.

She has a nice little flat bowsprit that is really too small to work out on. I put a downhaul on the jib.

Her sails are vertical-cut without battens and are made of heavy Dacron. They set beautifully.

The loose-footed foresail with club is hard to furl until you learn to lower the gaff right down onto the housetop, which you can then use as a table to help you get the thing under control. Yes, the foresail club bangs the mainmast a couple of times when you go about, and it would bang your head too, so you just have to stand from under.

The sheet arrangement on a loose-footed foresail — even one of only 100 square feet, as in this tiny schooner — is a dilemma. You want it simple, so that there won't be a whole lot of blocks and ropes thrashing around the mainmast when you tack; but then you want it powerful, so you can flatten the sail right in on the wind in a breeze without breaking your back.

The two-part sheeting arrangement that Peter Van Dine came up with is so absurdly simple that at first I couldn't see how it worked (and so, of course, was sure it *wouldn't* work), and I must say it took me and everybody else who came aboard the boat quite a few tacks before we could operate the sheet without thinking hard about just what to pull on.

The foresail sheet on the *Nimbus* is a single line, the ends of which are made fast to the cockpit coaming, one on each side. The line runs through a bull's-eye on the club at the sail's clew. That won't work, will it? There's no hauling part. Ah, but there *is* a hauling part. It's the slack weather bight of the sheet, which is brought round to leeward of the mainmast, hauled aft, and belayed. The rig is so utterly simple it's mystifying, but once you work with it enough to see through the mysterious simplicity, it works like magic.

No vangs are needed on this vessel's short gaffs, for the leeches of both mainsail and foresail lead aft far enough to keep most of the twist out of the sails. Too bad. I love vangs.

The fisherman staysail is a great sail. On any kind of a reach from a light air to a gentle breeze, it gave her an exciting extra bit of speed. Camden's my kind of place to sail out of, because no matter which way the wind is blowing, as soon as you get out into Penobscot Bay you can steer anywhere from northeast around through southeast to southwest, and pick yourself out a nice reach out and back. One day, doing just this, we found ourselves sailing fast in a gentle breeze under all plain sail in company with a modern 32-foot sloop, also under working sail. We were going just about even. Down comes his working jib, and up goes a big overlapping reacher. Oh no you don't, we said, and up went the fisherman to pull her rail down and make her fly just that much more. Thanks to that beauty, we didn't have to watch that guy's stern. (And they talk about the excitement of the America's Cup.)

With all this gear and rigging on the little vessel, it was tempting to add more. Up went a main topsail with both jackyard and club, and here again we could have used a bit more mainmast, for even with a fairly long jackyard extending the head of the sail past the masthead, we could only eke out 30 square feet in the thing. This sail is a good deal more trouble than it's worth, and I must admit we never fussed with it enough to get it just right. Still, it gave us something to occupy our minds on a calm day.

The *Nimbus* has a set of tholepins back in the middle of the cockpit out near the rail on each side. She also has a nicely carved sculling notch fastened to the side of the sternpost just above the rail. Shaw & Tenney made me a fine pair of 12-foot oars for her. There's room for only one person at a time on the oars. You can stand up and push, rowing with both oars, but it seems like an awful lot of work for the progress you make. Better to row with just one oar and compensate for the turning moment with the rudder. With one oar you can stand up and push, or sit on the thwart in way of the mainmast on the side opposite the tholepins you are using and pull. Rowing with one oar gives a bit more speed than sculling, but sculling was far superior for maneuverability. We'd always scull in or out of Camden's inner harbor if there was no breeze.

The best way to move her in a calm was to tow her with a dinghy. Now you have rowing comfort, maneuverability, and the easy power of two light oars. You could tow her up to twice as fast as you could move her with an oar from on board.

Peter Van Dine has put small electric motors in some of his boats, but the *Nimbus* didn't have one, for which I was grateful. It's as much work carrying batteries around as it is to scull, row, or tow, and not nearly so satisfying.

The cockpit of the *Nimbus* is divided in half by the thwart at the mainmast. This thwart gives her a nice small-boat look, somehow. The forward half of the cockpit is sort of a standing room with a locker built into each forward corner, so you get two individual seats. We protected this area with a simple white canvas dodger, so these seats stayed dry in rain or spray underway or at anchor.

With the dodger struck you could stand in this forward part of the cockpit leaning your back against the mainmast, or move right out and plant your thighs against the coaming. From this latter position you could easily reach right over the side into the water without any fear of falling overboard, which always gave me a feeling of security in case somebody *did* fall overboard. Most boats have no such secure place from which you can reach the water in a stance from which you can apply lifting power.

My wife, Priscilla, complained that there were too many strings and things in the cockpit. She was right, of course. Right in the middle of the best part of the place were centerboard trunk, thwart, and mainmast, and there were plenty of halyards round the foot of the mast. Then there was the foresail to be trimmed through, around, and in what little space remained. I made a minor concession by leading the inboard end of the hauling part of the main sheet up through a snap hook on the main boom to at least get *that* out of the way a little. If this rig caused too much bend in her skinny main boom in a hard breeze, we'd just take the sheet back out of the hook and let it be in the way.

I reasoned that if you have no engine in a boat, you ought to have plenty of ground tackle. I wheedled a nice 15-pound yachtsman's anchor out of Drew McManus (part of his scheme was to transfer his own collection of gear from boat to boat), added a 25-pound, three-piece yachtsman's anchor made by Paul Luke, and gave each a 200-foot rode. When not in use, the anchors stowed in the big locker under the cockpit seat way aft and the rodes stowed under the side benches in the cockpit.

I tracked down a handsome and accurate box compass that mounted just beautifully on the center of the thwart just abaft the mainmast. It could easily be seen from the whole after part of the cockpit and was up out of the way where nobody kicked it.

I succumbed to a plastic jerry can for a water tank. This practical but ugly device I hid away in the big locker under the cockpit seat aft. Above this seat, still farther aft under the very stern deck was another locker with an open front. In there went the tholepins, foghorn, spare line and small stuff, and the chart in use at the moment, all immediately to hand from the helm. In there, too, I hid the key to the padlock on the cuddy boards. As a test, I told our youngest son that the key was somewhere on the boat outside the cuddy and asked him to see if he could find it. It took him about 30 seconds.

The little schooner has a small sump running down into her "deadwood," with the suction hose of her bilge pump running down to its bottom. The pump is a diaphragm affair permanently installed in the bilge right under the cockpit floorboards. The discharge hose runs

Peter Van Dine's boat making the most of a light breeze on Mill Creek, just off Chesapeake Bay. (Peter D. Van Dine)

into the top of the centerboard trunk well above the waterline. So to pump the bilge you lift a floorboard, reach back into that same open locker in the stern for the handle of the pump, stick it in, and start pumping. No pump to get out, no hose to lead overboard, no hull valves to open. Of course, I also had a big horse bucket on board in case she ever shipped a sea.

There's a little lanyard on the tiller that lets it swing out just about to the rail and no farther. I could tell at a glance it was too short and would restrict maneuverability. The first time I got her underway, I made sure it was let go; I wasn't about to ram somebody in the inner harbor just because I couldn't put the helm over as far as I wanted to. Of course, it didn't take long to realize that she never could use any more helm than the lanyard allowed anyway, so I put it back the way Peter Van Dine intended in the first place and was perfectly happy with it forever after. She turned majestically for such a little boat, even with the board down, but once you got used to her she was very easy to maneuver.

She has two basic steering positions: down on the big after seat when she's not heeling too much, and up on the side deck with your feet on this seat when she is. The latter position seemed a tiny bit precarious if she was jumping, but my preventer backstays came just right to hang onto.

Probably the best seat in the boat is on the lee forward locker, back up against the house, leaning against the lee coaming too, feet down on the cockpit floor or up on the thwart, or knees out under the lee deck. Sitting here with the boat heeled and sailing fast, you are really close to the water hissing by. Great stuff. And she is a fine self-steerer, so even alone I used to take this seat and look aft just watching her go. Of course I had to jump up and look ahead every other minute to keep from hitting anything.

The entry to the cuddy was through a small doorway that could be closed off with three vertical sliding boards. She has no companionway hatch. I'd like to have had one so I could have stood in the hatchway to watch her go, but I was also grateful for the simplicity of the arrangement and for the fact that it is really watertight. She has a lovely oval porthole in each side of the house, closed by Ralph Wiley-type, clear plastic rectangles on the inside. Somehow, they always leaked a little.

At the after end of the cuddy is a nice flat on each side with locker under. The starboard one I took over for a bookshelf, office, and stowage for the compass in harbor. The port one I left clear for cooking or a chart table as the occasion demanded. I thought seriously of putting one of those tiny solid-fuel stoves on the port flat, but then realized that if I got a good mantle lantern it would heat the tiny cabin and provide a bright light for reading in the bargain. This worked fine.

After considerable research, I combined a backpacker's canned butane stove with a sturdy Sea Swing gimbaled potholder. I could mount this on the cockpit coaming in time of peace, or down in the cuddy in time of war. Most of the cooking seemed to get done in the cockpit under the dodger.

Forward of the flats she has a double berth. It's tight quarters, and you play kneesies with the foremast. There was always plenty of light stuff to be stowed forward on the bunk: fisherman staysail, dodger, bedding. Quarter-folded charts went under the mattress.

I put a low camp chair on board. The place for it was on the big stern seat, right aft in the cockpit. With the little vessel anchored at the end of a day's sail, I'd put up the dodger to keep out most of the cool breeze, unfold that baby and set it up right at the after end of the cockpit, put something on the stove ready to light off, unroll a sleeping bag on the bunk and get the lamp going down below, set the riding light even though the sun hadn't quite set, and then settle back in the canvas chair to watch the harbor against the backdrop of all these little niceties on board. There's a snugness about a boat this size. Some evenings I'd get so carried away with it all that I'd forget to break out the demon rum.

For a 25-foot boat the *Nimbus* is mighty cramped, for she is narrow and shoal of hull. She makes a wonderful singlehanded cruising boat and a fine daysailer for two. Two can go cruising and four daysailing, but it's crowded.

And my goodness, won't she sail! This is a fast and able little vessel. She is extremely well behaved and docile, very steady on her helm, and just always seems to want to do the right thing by you, even reaching off when it's rough and blowing hard, a time when many fore-and-afters get rambunctious.

Peter Van Dine had mentioned to me that he trimmed the jib in for close-hauled and left it right there whether he was on the wind or off the wind. I knew better. Yet I found that off the wind, the close-trimmed sail holds her head off so beautifully that she will steer herself on a broad reach, and I couldn't see that easing the jibsheet and holding her off with the tiller made her go any faster. I never trimmed the jib the last two years I owned her.

For maneuvering in close quarters, the rig was jib and mainsail. With this rig you could tack without touching a thing but the tiller (the jib is self-tending), and, if things got really tight you could turn her sharply by backing one or both of the sails at the ends of her.

She would lie-to nicely with just the mainsail set and strapped in tight and the tiller snugged amidships by its lanyard, the boat making way dead astern.

She'd carry full working sail up through a moderate breeze. When you start getting some fresh gusts, slack the foresail sheet a bit to put some belly in the luff of the sail. This eases her without changing her balance at all. She'll still steer herself if you want. When there are more fresh gusts than anything else and it looks like breezing on, take in the foresail. If it keeps breezing up, take in the jib, reset the foresail, and let her jog under foresail while you ease the mainsail right off and reef it. Might as well put the second reef in and be done with it. Then away she goes with foresail overlapping what's now a smaller sail aft.

This is the basic rig of this type of boat. When it's blowing hard and rough, she just loves to get back to the ancestral rig of the Chebacco boat: overlapping sail forward, smaller balancing driver aft, no headsail. She'll go through a lot this way, and if things get even worse, you can reef away some of the foresail. Or, if you need a breather, hand the mainsail and lash the helm hard down, leaving her to jog along under foresail alone, looking after herself, making a bit of headway and a bit of leeway, rudder keeping her head up and foresail keeping her easing along on the same tack.

We had her lee rail well under a few times when we were too lazy to shorten down promptly, but she would heel so far and then stop with the wind spilling out of her sails. Thanks to her fairly wide side decks, I never had the feeling she'd ship water over the lee coaming when driving hard, unless in a seaway. And of course, you shouldn't be out driving hard in an open ballasted boat in a seaway.

She had a fine, easy motion for such a light boat, though she could be a bit lively going to windward if there was a steep, nasty chop. It was always fun to watch her high, skinny bow lift to a sea, and of course, there's just nothing like the refinement of watching a pointed stern slip through the water.

It was fun to watch her go on any point of sailing in any conditions of wind and sea, but probably the best was close-hauled under jib, foresail, and mainsail in a moderate breeze, rail down, lifting and settling to an easy sea. You'd sit on the weather deck, balanced between backstay and the lightest of tillers, watching her parallel schooner's masts, sails laced close to them, send her prancing along. Oh, my goodness.

Three of us took her out racing on Penobscot Bay on a crystal-clear northwest day. Never trust a northwester.

We were up against a trio of J-24 types, one of which was actually a J-24 (see Chapter 40). We didn't expect to

The Nimbus *working up through the fleet in Camden Harbor at the end of a cruise. (David P. Jackson)*

stay with these hotshots, with their spinnakers and hiking sticks, but we figured the day would be instructive. We weren't disappointed.

It was blowing fresh at the start, and the first leg put the wind abaft the beam. The speed demons went off with genoa jibs, and we went off with full working sail, no fisherman staysail. We held one of them, but the other two set spinnakers halfway down the leg and took off.

The second leg was a dead run, and the breeze eased to moderate. The spinnaker boys were long gone, but we wung out the foresail, pulled up the centerboard, and worked out ahead of our nearby competitor, with his poled-out genoa.

The last leg was a long beat home. No sooner did we harden up than it breezed back up to fresh, then strong, then more. Very quickly a short, steep sea built up, and things began to happen on board the *Nimbus.* The first thing that happened on board was that we watched our rival sail by to windward, outpointing and outfooting us. Schooners are reaching fools.

The next thing that happened was that one of those little bronze crossbolts that I had failed to replace gave up the ghost with a loud ping. We had just tacked and the new weather shroud on the mainmast disappeared. At the time, I was just in the process of setting up the new weather preventer, and had rove the lanyard and put on a half hitch. There was just time to clamp down on the thing and put on a couple more hitches. Thank goodness for preventers. We tacked again to bring the mess to leeward, retrieved the main shroud, and lashed it back onto its eyebolt.

Then we set about shortening down in earnest, for the nor'wester was starting to blow viciously right out of a clear sky. I suppose it would wreck the environment or something, but I really wouldn't care if it never blew out of the northwest again. On board the *Nimbus,* we had no leisure for such philosophy. We were busy jogging along under foresail with jib and main sheets eased, getting the jib down and half furled (a wet and lively job), and putting the second reef in the mainsail. That finally done, we got underway again under foresail and double-reefed mainsail. All the competition was way the heck up to windward someplace. And still she was a bit overpowered in the gusts. The hell with it, let's reef the foresail. That stopped her for another little while, and then we proceeded on our deliberate way, battering into just the wrong size sea for her.

I didn't like the jib furl and made the mistake of going out on the bowsprit to do something about it. Just as I finished, there was a bigger lurch than usual, another ping, and no more forestay. So we eased her up again, everything thrashing. Set up the jib halyard to the stemhead, proceeded on our way, and cleared away the jib below. The fitting at the bowsprit end had let go thanks to my weight on the bowsprit coming down as she dove and fetched up, the force being a good deal sideways, since she was well heeled over.

So we limped toward the finish, the breeze finally easing gradually so we shook the reef out of the foresail. Later that same day, we crossed the finish line, not bothering to take our own time. Within 48 hours, she had heavier eyebolts all around for the shrouds and stainless steel crossbolts to hold the lower deadeyes to them. I replaced the bowsprit end fitting without changing its size and henceforth stayed off the bowsprit when it was rough. No part of the rig gave any more trouble.

If the *Nimbus* left a little to be desired on her one round-the-buoys race, she proved to be a superlative vessel on her one "big" cruise. I went off for nine days singlehanded.

Thinking about this trip beforehand, I dreamed of two or three days of smoky sou'westers to take me Down East, say to Cutler, and then a week of working her back up to the westward. Yes, sir, I was really going to take her out and drive her. Far horizons.

Then, as the time to start drew nigh, I smartened up. It ain't really distance I'm after; I just want some time to enjoy the little vessel and have a good look round. Maybe I'll see where she goes without beating, like a gentleman. Well, that's what I did, and she went all the way to Swan's Island and back, sailing a circuitous route of about 100 miles.

The funny thing was that after shifting from a hectic plan to a serene one, it took me three days to calm down on the boat. You should have seen me thrashing around out there, losing my temper at every little thing. But by the end of the third day, the solitude had me standing back looking at myself. It was an absurd picture that I saw: *Homo sapiens* with the rare opportunity to go off cruising singlehanded in a lovely little vessel, roaring around the deck kicking stuff and swearing. Kind of silly. I stopped.

Slowed right down, took things one at a time, and gained a level of confidence in handling the vessel that was new to me.

It was just as well. The next day brought a moderate gale from the northwest. I got underway from my snug, deserted cove and headed southeast. Started under foresail and double-reefed mainsail. Before leaving the shelter of the last island and heading out into Jericho Bay, I rounded up in the lee and took the mainsail off her. Then away she flew, under just foresail. The seas began to build a bit as we got out from under the weather shore, and she loved it. Not so the tin canoe (see Chapter 3) I was towing. I was just about to shorten up her towline drastically when she took a sheer up to windward, realized she'd gone wrong, and tried to get back astern. In the process she built up a huge bow wave on the towrope side, and, all in slow motion, this bow wave rose up over her side and filled her. She capsized and then dragged disconsolately along, apparently not caring which side was up.

No matter. I had my new-found Peace of Mind. I rounded up and got her jogging along under the foresail with the helm down. Put over two big red plastic fishing floats on the lee side for fenders. Brought the slowly revolving canoe alongside to leeward, got her upright, and lashed her alongside. Took my station at the lee side of the standing room just forward of the mainmast, horse bucket in hand. Bailed out the canoe, being grateful for all her flotation taking up space that thus couldn't be filled with water. Let her aft again, but snubbed her painter right up to the sculling notch, lifting her bow up out of the water a bit and giving her to understand that as long as it was at all rough she'd be bound in that ignominious position so she couldn't go a-wandering. Then filled away and let the little schooner romp some more.

At the end of that day we came smoking into Burnt Coat Harbor on Swan's Island. The breeze had eased to fresh, and we beat into the harbor under the somewhat unlikely rig of foresail and full mainsail, jib furled. She certainly carried plenty of weather helm, but was traveling fast withal.

I picked my berth where there'd be plenty of swinging room and shot her into the wind. Let the foresail sheet go so that sail couldn't fill with wind any more. Strapped the mainsail right in tight and lashed the tiller amidships. Now she might go ahead or she might go astern, but there was no way she could fill away and sail. I went forward while she had plenty of headway, untied the anchor from its cruising position on the bow, and let it dangle off the bowsprit. Waited for her to stop, and just when she started astern let go the anchor. Watched her get good sternboard, and when she had drawn out plenty of scope, snubbed her hard. The hook held. Dropped the foresail right down onto the cabinhouse. Veered some more scope right out, the boat again going straight astern and the anchor again holding hard when she was snubbed, the rode showing a nice flat angle with the water. There she lay, mainsail still set.

Then something made me look up at a certain point ashore. I was being stared at by a row of a half-dozen Swan's Island lobster fishermen. One of them waved, and I waved back. I never once got the *Nimbus* underway in the three years I had her without receiving at least one verbal compliment on what a fine-looking little vessel she was, but this silent noticing by a bunch of pros was the finest tribute she got.

Index

EASTERN MASS. REGIONAL
LIBRARY SYSTEM
- REAR
02780